LEMON BELLY

A MEMOIR OF RESILIENCE AND CROHN'S DISEASE

BRAD HARRIS

For Cooper and Redding

CONTENTS

AUTHOR'S NOTE

This is a work of nonfiction. The events and experiences detailed herein are all true and have been faithfully rendered as the author remembers them, to the best of his ability. Some names and descriptions of people have been changed to protect their privacy.

"The world breaks every one and afterward many are strong at the broken places."

—Ernest Hemingway, *A Farewell To Arms*

PROLOGUE

BY LATE JANUARY THE FROZEN GROUND WAS AS HARD AS the pavement we played on. It was recess at Wheelock Elementary School, and the entire third grade class ran around outside. We had to move constantly to stay warm against the bitter wind that swept over the sprawl of soccer fields surrounding us. That gray New England landscape would have camouflaged the galvanized steel playground if not for the kids climbing, swinging and running around it in colorful coats, hats, and mittens. My friend Nate and I hung on a silver structure that the kids called The Spider: two cold steel ladders that arched like rainbows and connected in the center like an X. We started a race to the top, climbing the ladders on the outside. In a struggle at the finish line, he pushed me in an awkward way and I lost my balance.

The fall was fast. When my thin nine-year-old body collided with that frozen January ground, I had one of those moments. A second of uncertainty before the nerves can carry the message of pain. It might be okay or it might kill. It was just long enough for my face to contort into a wince, and then the searing pain erupted into my left side, which had taken the brunt of the impact.

Thumping. Pounding. I un-scrunched my eyes to a sideways view of the playground as the shrieks and shouts of my classmates at recess receded around me. I righted myself and began to cry. Then a warning in my head, "Don't you start crying." My grandfather's stern voice. "Come on now, walk it off," said the voice of my father in his attaboy tone.

I stumbled to my feet and began to walk away, and I could hear my friend pleading, "Hey! Are you okay? I'm sorry Brad, are you okay? Sorry!"

I couldn't think about anything except walking. Cradling my arm and forcing myself to settle down. With my nose running, I wiped tears and snot on the sleeve of my coat. Through the blur, I searched for the teacher on duty and soon spotted her.

If I kept my arm still it didn't hurt as much. Hold back the tears. Take a deep breath. Be brave. I made my way over to the teacher.

"Um, Mrs. Flynn? I hurt my arm. Can I go inside?"

Distractedly scanning the playground for mischief, she glanced down at me briefly. "No Brad, I'm sorry. Recess will be over soon. You can wait."

I knew this was wrong, but what choice did I have? We lived in a world where grown-ups and kids were entirely different species, and grown-ups were superior. My eyes narrowed and I turned away. I wandered alone on the salt-stained pavement, over to a colorfully painted puzzle-piece map of the United States. The map was brand new that year, along with the school itself. I made cloud shapes with my frozen breath as my sneakers stepped from state to state, avoiding the fractured lines of their borders. Step on a crack, break your mother's back.

Finally the bell rang, and it was time to line up. I was able to duck inside the heavy metal door without touching it as I thundered up the stairs with my classmates. Ms. Mills, my teacher, was waiting for us in the rich warmth of the classroom. She was pretty with dark brown hair parted perfectly down the middle, swept back on each side with twin barrettes. While the other kids were busy hanging their coats on their designated hooks, I kept mine on as I approached her. I couldn't hold it any longer, and I started to cry.

"I hurt my arm," I stuttered, "can I go to the nurse?"

Her kind face split with a mix of recognition and compassion. "Oh, of course Brad!"

Seconds later I was walking fast down the hallway with my friend Josh, who Ms. Mills had assigned to escort me down to the nurse.

"Do you think it's busted?" he said as he caught up to me.

"I don't know. It just hurts a lot," I said.

Turning the corner into the nurse's office, I saw Mrs. Baker. She was both the school nurse and our minister's wife, which was one of those small town connections that happened in a place like Medfield. Mrs. Baker's snow-white hair and kind blue eyes matched her conservative denim dress and white turtleneck. Her high and gentle voice relaxed me instantly.

"Have a seat over here, dear," she said "and let's have a look at that arm of yours. Now tell me what happened."

I relayed the tale of Nate and The Spider as her cold hands gently examined my arm, focusing on my wrist. She made some assessments and announced that it would probably be sprained or possibly fractured, so she would call my mother to come and get me. I sat on the big brown vinyl bed sipping water out of a Styrofoam cup as she phoned my mother.

"Yes hi Sally, it's Carol Baker. I have Brad here…"

It turned out that I had broken my wrist, and in return for my pain they awarded me a forearm cast for six weeks. I raised it above my head in triumph for my younger brother Steve as he came through our front door from the neighbor's house. As I relayed my war story to him, my mother talked on the phone in the kitchen with the recess duty teacher, Mrs. Flynn, who had called to apologize for not letting me go to the nurse. She felt terrible. There were just so many kids who faked being sick to go inside that it was hard to tell. Plus, she said, I didn't look hurt.

I had one person left to show, my father, who would be home soon. Today was a big day for him too, the first day in his new office. For as long as I could remember, he rode the train into the city alongside countless other suburban fathers working in the tall buildings of the Boston skyline. I imagined him on that train in his camel-colored overcoat, still smelling like aftershave and Vitalis, reading his National Geographic magazine. The briefcase at his feet held only one other item: his brown-bagged lunch.

That day, however, he traded that relaxing ride for a harrowing 1-hour commute to an office park in Peabody, which was north of the city. He was a slow and obedient driver making his way up the fast-moving, cutthroat highway of Route 128 that arched around the city. This would give my mother something to worry about for the next fifteen years. Her description made the highway sound like a demolition derby with cars whizzing past my father's blue Chevy Celebrity like rockets.

A previous version of my father would have loved it though. Two decades earlier and thirty miles west, he drove his blue 1964 Pontiac GTO down the newly paved Route 495 at night. With his best friend and wingman Johnny Sullivan beside him, boilermakers in their bloodstream, and the speedometer approaching 100 mph, I wonder if he knew the tame life he was driving toward, or if he could picture the measured man he would later become.

The sky outside had darkened, and I knew he would be home soon. My brother and I were upstairs in our family room watching cartoons when I heard the mechanics of the garage door spring to life. Lying comfortably on the family room couch, I tossed our zig-zag-patterned afghan over my body in preparation for the magic trick I was about to perform. I told my mother I was going to surprise him. She just didn't have the heart to tell me that surprising him today probably wasn't the best idea.

We all knew my father's routine. He would come in through the back door, kiss my mother, drop his briefcase in its designated spot on the low shelf of the fireplace, hang up his coat, change out of his suit and into a pair of dungarees and crack open the single can of Busch beer our mother would allow. The family room closet housed his suits and dress shirts, a full rack of them. I lay silently next to them on the couch, or the divan, as he would call it.

He ascended the stairs, and as soon as I could see him I whipped off the afghan, exposing the bright cast. The response I got couldn't have been further from what I expected.

"Ah jeez, what happened! What happened to your arm?"

"I broke my wrist!" I said, the excitement of my big reveal dimming with each word.

"Jesus, that's all we need today!"

Instead of undressing, he followed my mother's beckoning voice back down to the kitchen where she would explain the day's events to him in a way that would calm him down.

It would take me years to understand his anxiety toward any kind of medical issues, and his low tolerance for ripples in day-to-day life. He was a man of routines and robust health. I can't remember a single day when he was sick enough to miss work.

Something else seemed to happen that day, something I could never have imagined as I warmed underneath the covers of my bed that night with my hard-earned cast. A transfer had been made. When my body hit that frozen January ground it not only broke my wrist, but a coldness entered my body. Like a car never quite right again after an accident, that collision set something sinister into motion.

I didn't know it then, but something was different.

PART I

1

DISAPPOINTMENTS

"He's too thin."

As I sat on the exam room table in my underwear, goosebumps broke out like a rash all over me. I was freezing. I clenched my jaw to stop my teeth from chattering.

Everything in this doctor's office was new. New carpet smell filled the waiting room where bins brimmed with bright Fisher-Price toys that hadn't been played with yet. The doctor, my pediatrician, was also new. He was the complete opposite of my old pediatrician Dr. Wagner, who had retired that spring looking like a slightly younger version of Santa Claus in a white coat. Dr. Klein was young, fit, clean-shaven, and had short, curly, dark hair. He had just finished examining me with his cold, damp hands. He took a step back as if to take in a full view of me.

"He's too thin," he said again. "You can get dressed, Bradley," he said to me as an aside.

Relieved, I reached for my faux Adidas racing-striped shorts and matching striped collared shirt. My mother sat next to the exam table in a wooden chair, wearing a pastel pinstripe shirt and white shorts. Her permed hair frizzed from the humidity outside. Her eyes narrowed behind her large-framed glasses and I could sense an argument coming. My mother went through life on the defensive. At every turn in the road, she was being slighted or someone was trying to rip her off. She was confident and commanding because she used to be an elementary school teacher before my brother and I came along. She was old school, literally. She talked, you listened.

Steve and I endured this as part of our childhood. Every couple of months we would make a trip to my namesake department store, Bradlee's. They carried just about everything we needed, from clothes to toys. My mother would become instantly lured to the women's section, located strategically at the front of the store to entice mothers into buying popular '80s fashions. My brother and I would then take the opportunity to break away and visit the toy department in the back of the store, to sort through the Star Wars action figures they had for sale. After a while, we would meet back up with our mother to finish the clothes shopping and then head for the registers. Here again my brother and I would split from my mother as she shifted into battle mode with the unassuming clerk at the register about what coupons were valid and which items were on sale. We would sit on the small ledges carved out by the narrow windows near the exit, waiting upwards of twenty minutes while she argued with them. Triumphantly, she would finally emerge with bags full of correctly priced purchases and we would exit the store together. The customer, and Sally Harris, was always right.

"He's always been this thin," my mother said defensively to Dr. Klein, "you just don't know Brad. Dr. Wagner never said his weight was an issue. He's lost a little bit of weight, but it's not even that noticeable."

"Well, we're on week three with this virus. Fevers and weight loss, five pounds that he didn't have to lose in the first place." He paused to look up at me, my bony hands folded over my knobby knees. "This might end up still just being a virus. But," he counted off with his fingers, "headaches, stomach aches, mouth sores, and so much diarrhea he's developed a fissure on his anus. I'd like to do a series of test here. Bloodwork, urine. Stool when we can get it. But most likely I'm going to be recommending sending him to a specialist. A gastroenterologist."

As he explained to me that it was a long fancy word that meant stomach doctor, my mother sat without words. I guess when he listed everything out like that, it didn't look so great. My main complaint was that I was always cold.

The coldness started back in April when we were in Disney World, our family's first trip on a plane. I sat ecstatically in the window seat, while my mother passed out gum to me and my brother as a remedy for ear popping. After the exhilaration of take-off, I kept my face pressed to the plastic window in awe of the view.

"I definitely want to go skydiving someday!" I said to my mother.

My father, who had a paralyzing fear of heights, sat silently in the aisle seat facing forward as my mother laughed.

The trip captured the magic of Disney in almost every way. We stayed at the tropical Polynesian Resort right in the park. This made the monorail our primary mode of transportation, a futuristic train that seemed to be right out of the Jetsons cartoon that Steve and I watched on a regular basis after school. We went to the Magic Kingdom most days, exploring the four quadrants of the park as we cultivated my obsession with roller coasters.

The major ride was Space Mountain, a domed indoor roller coaster that zipped through the dark. Its legend preceded itself through my friends at home that had been to Disney as The Best Ride Ever, though you have to survive the hour-long wait first. It was closed for unexplained reasons the first few times we tried to go on it. But finally, on our last day, it was up and running. My father waited patiently and probably nervously outside as Steve, Mom, and I entered the cone-shaped dome and took our places at the end of the line.

As we waited in the dark maze of people, we could hear screams emanating from the ride directly above us. This, my friends told me, was what made it cool: you couldn't see where you were going. Quick flashes of light gave glimpses of what was to come, and our eyes widened. But then, about halfway through the line, the ride stopped. The house lights came on and maintenance crews began walking the tracks above. The mysterious invisible monster that had been swirling above us was no longer invisible nor mysterious. It was just a regular roller coaster. The lights turned off again and we were enveloped with darkness and disappointment. We did make it through the line, but all of our excitement and enthusiasm had vanished when those lights turned on.

After five days in the park, we went to Epcot for a day, which was as boring as school for Steve and me. On the last day, we went to a water park called Wet 'n Wild.

It was my first time at a water park where I struggled to have fun. The water felt too cold for me to stay in for very long. We spent the first part of the day going down the waterslides, then we headed to the giant wave pool. Without the swirling excitement of the waterslides, the wave pool just made me cold. After ten minutes I got out, leaving my family in search of my towel.

Wrapped in my towel and shivering in the warm Florida sun, I realized something: the other swimmers weren't cold like me. Families of all ages were having the time of their lives in the water as I stood warming my feet on the hot concrete. It felt like my body had been isolated in an entirely different climate than everyone else.

The cold feeling continued for the next few months, as spring turned to summer. Air-conditioning practically froze me, but I shrugged it off as nothing until the viral symptoms brought me into the doctor's office.

. . .

The next day Dr. Cohn called after receiving the test results, and referred us to a specialist at Boston Children's. My mother finally came around to the idea that sending me to a specialist was the right thing to do. For as strong as she was in arguing her position, she was also a chronic worrier. What if he was right, and I needed the expertise of the doctors in Boston? She reasoned that this new doctor was just out of medical school and didn't carry the complacency of old Dr. Wagner. Plus, it couldn't hurt to get some fresh eyes on what was going on, and at the very least it would put her worried mind at ease to know that a specialist had written this off as nothing. Just a virus.

It was weird to sit down to breakfast in the summer and have both of my parents there. Normally, my dad left for work at 6:30. But here he was, sitting in his chair, quietly eating his bowl of Quaker Oats. He had actually taken the day off to accompany us to this appointment with the gastroenterologist.

"Do you have any questions about the doctor we're going to see today, hon?" my mom asked.

"Um, no, not really."

"Well. This will be good to get a second opinion at least," she reasoned. This concept of getting a second medical opinion, because sometimes even doctors could be wrong, would become her modus operandi for the rest of her life.

After breakfast, we got into my mom's car, a white, mid-1980s Chevy station wagon. Steve and I considered this car to be a Transformer because the way-back could be converted to two extra rear-facing seats. We always jumped at the opportunity to sit there and make faces at the driver of the car behind us.

We dropped off my brother at a neighbor's house for the morning, and soon it was just my parents and me traveling through the center of Medfield. We made our way through the town center's three traffic lights, the first one next to a Friendly's restaurant, the fanciest eatery the town had to offer. Fast-food establishments like McDonald's and Burger King were outlawed there because its stodgy residents wanted to stay true to Medfield's colonial New England heritage. The second light was next to Royal Pizza, where we would get take-out on Friday nights, and the third was by Lord's, the town's five-and-dime store, with its name spelled out in red neon script letters that literally lorded above the entrance. Past the town center, dozens of restored historical houses from as far back as the 1600s lined the streets, and all the others tried to emulate them with their painted trims and conservative colonial looks. The sole reason we moved to Medfield was that it had a reputation for good schools, which my mother valued above all else.

The forty-five-minute drive into Boston was also a new experience. Both of my parents preferred backroads to highways, and up until then, Boston was only accessed by taking the T.

We made our way down Route 109 through Westwood and got to an intersection that I had never been through.

"Hey Dad, what's this road?" I asked.

"The VFW Parkway," he replied through his heavy Boston accent.

It was a divided two-lane road lined with huge oak trees, their canopies providing shade to the cars driving underneath. As we drove, I stared out the window at the apartment buildings that grew denser the farther we went. Unlike Medfield, this was new and exciting.

Soon we entered the Longwood area of the city, Boston's medical district. We passed an enormous square-blocked building that looked like a concrete Hershey bar. Later I would find out it was only a parking garage. My mom said that we were going to the part of the city where a lot of the big hospitals were.

"But don't worry," she assured me, "we aren't going to the hospital. That's just where the doctor's office is."

After we parked, we walked into a small six-story office building that sat right across the street from Children's Hospital. The building itself was dwarfed by larger buildings that surrounded it.

The entryway had a black letter board that listed the different practices and what floors they were on.

"There," my mother said, pointing to the words Flores/Katz listed on the board.

"Sixth floor, all the way to the top," my father said.

We turned and entered the lobby where a blast of arctic air-conditioning hit me, and I broke out in goosebumps. We took the elevator up to the top floor and entered the office across the hallway.

My mom, always the leader in our family, checked me in at the front desk and the three of us sat in the small waiting room. It was littered with toys for younger kids, and the muffled words of a man with a very loud voice could be heard from down the hallway. I just sat there shivering, rubbing my upper arms with my hands, my striped tube socks pulled up to my knees. I asked my mom if I could go back downstairs and go outside because I was so cold. She said sure, but be back in five minutes, and sent my father with me.

Back in the lobby, I pushed the heavy glass door open and felt the humid August heat wash over me. I stretch my arms out and breathed a sigh of relief as I soaked in the sun.

"Do you remember being in there," my father asked, both of us standing with the hulking entryway of Children's Hospital on the opposite side of the street.

"Yeah," I answered shortly.

Four years earlier, after countless bouts of strep throat, I had my tonsils removed at Children's. I stayed in a ward with six other boys; three beds on one side of the room, three on the other. After the operation I sat up in my bed, nursing my sore throat by eating ice cream, wide-eyed and watching the boy lying in the bed to the left of me. He was much bigger than me, probably a teenager, and his whole body was wrapped in a cast. One of his legs was elevated and held up by a chain that went all the way up to the ceiling. Underneath him, a plastic pan was positioned for him to go to the bathroom in. I stayed there for a couple of nights and never found out what had happened to him.

After a few minutes of glory in the hot sun, my dad began sweating through his button-down shirt. "It's time to go back upstairs," he said, looking at his black digital Casio watch. Reluctantly I went with him, back into the frigid air-conditioning.

A rush of panic swelled inside me back in the waiting room as a woman announced my full name. We were led down a narrow hallway and into an office that had the feel of an old library.

"Hello!" the doctor on the other side of the large wooden desk said as he rose from his chair. I instantly knew this man owned the muffled voice I'd heard in the waiting room. He was a young, short man with dark hair, olive skin and a ton of energy.

He shook my parents' hands and said "Alex Flores" each time.

"And you must be Mr. Harris," he boomed, and now I could hear that his voice also had a distinct accent. His hand was soft and warm. He pulled up a third chair for me, so I could be part of the conversation we were about to have at his giant brown desk. As he bent over to lift the chair, he revealed colorful, intricately patterned socks that I would later learn were called argyles. As the grown-ups began to talk, I focused on a photo he had sitting on his desk. It was a posed shot of him, his wife, and their baby.

After making small talk we began reviewing my symptoms, which my mother had outlined on the first page of a small spiral-bound notebook. Dr. Flores listened intently and then invited us into his exam room, which adjoined his office. The exam room was cold and clinical, and I hopped up on the table as the paper crinkled loudly underneath my floral Jam shorts. He went through the same kinds of familiar examinations I knew, like listening to my heart and taking my blood pressure.

Then he asked me to lie down on the table and pull up my shirt. His warm hands examined my cold belly as he explained that he was from Guatemala. I wondered about the country's location on the giant world map that Ms. Mills would pull down like a window shade. Probably somewhere in Asia. He began to poke and press on my belly in a methodical manner. I giggled and jerked.

"Does that hurt?" he asked with raised eyebrows.

"No," I said smiling, "I'm just ticklish."

He paired his index and middle fingers together and began to tap on my lower stomach. Two quick taps in an area, then he moved to a different part. Tap tap. Tap tap. They were both gentle and strong, sending seismic waves through my torso. He had me sit up and we returned to his office to discuss a plan of action.

"Okay," he said, "I know this will seem like a lot, but I want to admit him." He turned to me. "We're going to have you stay in the hospital while we run tests to determine why you're not feeling so good, okay?"

The three of us took this news entirely differently. The nerves I'd had about this appointment instantly turned into excitement, because the last time I was in the hospital to get my tonsils out it meant unlimited ice cream. My father's face turned white, and his eyes glazed over in a faraway stare. My mother sat studiously with her small blue notebook in her lap, asking questions. Why does he need to be in the hospital? Can't we do this as an outpatient? What does he think is wrong with me? How long will he be in the hospital?

If Dr. Flores had any ideas as to what was wrong with me, he didn't give any clues at that point. He said that he would be able to walk over to the hospital with us. As we left his office to make plans with the woman at the front desk, I saw him lift a handheld recorder off of his desk. He spun his chair around and start to speak. "August 8. 1986. The patient's name is Bradley Harris. Age 10. The patient was at his baseline state of health until…" His words lost their clarity as we walked down the hallway, and his voice transformed back into the muffled tone we heard earlier.

After getting information and making arrangements at the front desk, my mother decided that she and I would go across the street to get things going and my father would wait for Dr. Flores, and walk over with him.

I can't begin to imagine what my father said to the doctor on that walk, but he made quite an impression on him. In every single appointment my mother and I would have in the future with Dr. Flores, he would always ask about my father. Every appointment, "How is your husband?" he would ask my mother. I marveled at how someone could be so enamored with my father, because to me he seemed as two-dimensional as the men's room symbol.

My father and his whole side of the family had a very turbulent relationship with doctors, surgeons, and modern medicine in general. He had lost his mother the year before to heart disease. His father, blind and mostly deaf, now resided in a nursing home where he would drink beer and listen to the Red Sox on his clock radio. When his mother was hospitalized, I remember him hanging up our kitchen phone after getting the news that she would need some kind of surgery, exclaiming, "She's going under the knife!" to my mother, who spent most of that time trying to calm everyone down. My mother had a much more pragmatic approach to dealing with doctors and illness. She aimed to understand by asking questions, taking notes, and focusing on the problem at hand.

I was happy to learn that this time my hospital room only had one other patient, and I had my own TV. I put on the Red Sox, who were playing the Detroit Tigers. Baseball was my life, and the Red Sox were in first place. They were having a strong season, and I had most of their baseball cards. The Tigers were a big deal because Dwight Evans had set a Major League record for hitting a home run on the first pitch of the season against the Tigers back in April. Little did I know the upset that season would turn into.

My mother stayed with me overnight, while my father went home to take care of Steve. They didn't allow me to eat anything because of the tests they were going to do the next day.

In the morning, a nurse led Mom and me out into the hallway and into a small alcove, which had probably been a broom closet earlier in its career at Children's. I sat down in the chair and my mother stood nearby. They were going to draw blood from my arm for tests. I immediately became stressed. I hated needles. Up to this point I usually just had to have a finger-prick during my annual physicals. But this was a major-league blood test with a needle and several empty vials for my blood. She tied a thick rubber band to my upper arm, took out the needle, and I tensed up. She told me to relax, and that there would be a little pinch. The needle went in as I moaned in pain, but the blood didn't come out. I inhaled with a hiss as she redirected the needle that was still in my arm, trying to hit the vein. She missed.

"Sorry," she said as she slid out the needle, "let's try the other arm."

I nodded. My mother said that it shouldn't be hard to get blood from me because I had good veins, and I was thin.

"They always have trouble with my veins," she said, sighing. "I have very thin veins that are hard to find."

The second needle was another miss. Strike two. My mother was done being diplomatic, now she was mad. I knew this nurse was in trouble when my mother shifted into full-on Bradlee's mode.

"You have one more chance," she said sternly, "and then we're done here. Three strikes and you're out."

I couldn't believe it, but my mother had turned into an umpire. The nurse cracked under the pressure, missing a third time. She was out. My mother had me get up and we marched my sore, bandaged arms back down the hall to my room. I don't remember if they came back and actually had a successful blood draw that morning. I just remember feeling relieved and proud to have my mom there, and that she would do anything to fight for me. And that whatever this new thing was, we were on the same team.

By lunchtime, I was starving. I still couldn't eat, but they assured me that the test would be underway soon. Eventually, my mother and I were taken down to the radiology department where they were going to do a special X-ray called an upper-GI.

I was handed a flowery paper cup with a thick, white, milkshake-like drink. It didn't taste like a milkshake; it tasted like liquid chalk. They told me that this was the first of several cups I needed to drink, one every half hour. So much for ice cream. I raised the cup to my lips and began to choke down the chalk drink.

After the one-hour mark, they came for me. Time for my first set of X-rays. They brought me into the dark radiology room where a man in a white coat introduced himself and helped me up onto this big metal table. I lay down on it and couldn't believe how cold and uncomfortable a flat table could be. I was freezing lying there, and the technician in the white coat positioned a circular device over my stomach. He put a heavy blanket over my waist, went behind a wall with a glass window, and told me not to move. I heard a buzz as the X-ray snapped a picture. He came back to me, and this time he held another flowery cup filled with more of the white drink and a bendy straw.

"Okay, great," he said, "this time we're going to have you drink the barium as we do the X-ray."

"Okay," I responded obediently.

After that, I was taken back out to the waiting area where my mother and my original cup of barium were waiting for me. Someone had filled it up to the top again.

"Aw come on," I said sadly.

My mother didn't miss a beat. "Brad. You need to drink this. If you don't drink all of it, they'll make you do it all over again."

I made a face and started drinking again. When I reached the point where I couldn't drink any more of it, they brought me into the X-ray room. By then the drink had dried and caked on my lips. The cycle of drinking and X-rays continued for the next couple of hours.

Finally, I was done. They wheeled me back up to my room, which was unnecessary but also exciting. I treated it as a victory lap, something I really needed at that point. The test was over. I made it through.

Dinner would arrive soon, and my mom left me to watch the end of the Red Sox game so she could go down to the cafeteria to get something to eat herself. She made it a point not to eat in front of me because I hadn't eaten yet. Once I was alone, my gaze shifted from the wall-mounted television to the window. Instead of a nice view of the Boston skyline, I could only see the brick wall of a neighboring building. I daydreamed as the weight of what was going on finally caught up with me. I was still sick and even the doctors at this hospital didn't know what was wrong with me. Even worse than that, they thought it was something serious. How long would I be here? What other tests was I going to have to endure? I swallowed the small lump in my throat that was beginning to form, following the boys-don't-cry script that had been bestowed upon me over my short life. Better to just watch the game and try to not think about it.

The next day was Monday, my third day in the hospital. I watched a run of Hanna-Barbera cartoons while my mother sat in the chair next to my bed when Dr. Flores can into the room. He announced that I would be going home because they had a diagnosis and a plan.

"Based on both the lab work and the upper-GI series we can see that there is quite a bit of inflammation going on in the belly. This is what's been causing you to feel so bad. Now we know you have a chronic condition called Crohn's disease. Chronic meaning we don't have a cure for this disease. Crohn's is inflammation in the lining of the intestines, in your case the affected area is limited, which is good. It's Ileocolitis which means it's the end of the small intestine, beginning of the large intestine. Some patients are able to achieve remission, but even so, the Crohn's eventually comes back. We've had success managing the symptoms with drugs. Right now you're experiencing a flare, but once we start this treatment you will start to feel better. Okay? We want to put weight on this guy. Ten to fifteen pounds. So a very high calorie diet."

He and my mother continued to talk about this new condition, Crohn's. It was a disease that usually occurred in people in their 20s and 30s, but pediatric cases like mine were on the rise. He said it would be something I would have for the rest of my life. The most effective medication was a steroid called prednisone, and he was going to start me off on a high dose, 40 milligrams a day for my sixty-pound body, to get everything under control. Overall, I was being told that my life would be different from here on out.

Somewhere along the way, I pictured what was explained to me in terms of plumbing. My intestines were like a series of pipes in my belly, and one of those pipes was bad, or in Dr. Flores' terms, inflamed. The prednisone would bring down this inflammation, or at least try to control it.

The nurse brought in my first dose of prednisone, two white 20 mg pills. As I swallowed them, they scraped the roof of my mouth, leaving a bitter taste. As the nurse and my mother worked through the discharge paperwork, I got dressed. My Friday clothes felt foreign on

Monday, like putting on long pants for the first time in the fall after wearing shorts all summer.

Soon we were back in the car. While my mother drove, I thought about my new diagnosis. I didn't like the idea of being chronically sick. Dr. Flores had said that most people with Crohn's lead normal lives, and I was going to do that. I didn't know what I would tell my friends. Surely, by now, the word would have spread that I was in the hospital. One thing I knew, I didn't want this disease to interfere with my life, and I really didn't want people to treat me differently. I didn't want people to be extra nice to me or pity me. When school started in a few weeks, I didn't want any special treatment. Kids at school would certainly make fun of me if they knew I had an illness.

Aside from picking up the prescriptions at the pharmacy in downtown Medfield that afternoon, my mother followed through on one final request from Dr. Flores. As she dug through the drawer of the hutch in our living room, I stripped down to my white underwear, which hung loose on my bony hips. She pulled out our old Polaroid camera and loaded it with film. There I stood, my emaciated body on our fire-orange living room rug. I stood in front of the wall where Steve and I had always posed with our Halloween costumes, Cub Scout uniforms, and other dress-up occasions. She aimed the camera at me, and with my arms at my side, I smiled. It was the only thing I ever did in front of a camera. As my mother fanned the picture in front of us, she explained that this was my "before" photo and we would give it to Dr. Flores for my medical file.

The picture that appeared revealed nothing new. Just the same thin boy I had always known smiling back at me. But, if this was "before," what would I look like "after"?

2

NAME CALLING

"Dude, our new teacher looks like the Goodyear blimp!"

My friend Ian had found me at the double doors that led to our fourth-grade classroom. It was only early October, but for the past two weeks we'd had a steady rotation of substitute teachers. This was fine with me because I fiercely hated our original teacher, Mrs. Greer. She was old, she was mean, and she was allergic to chalk. Even at ten, I thought it was strange for someone to choose a profession where their body physically repelled the main tool of their craft. In a lucky and ironic twist of fate she had fallen ill, and as we were about to learn, had elected to retire. There was no goodbye party, we didn't make her any get-well cards. She just never came back, and that was fine with me.

Walking into class, I realized Ian wasn't kidding, this woman was enormous. And to top it off, her name was Ms. Little. A hilarious contrast in the eyes of immature nine-and ten-year-olds. But she was young and seemed pretty nice from the start. Maybe bad things didn't last forever, after all.

As much as I wasn't willing to admit it, Crohn's had certainly changed things for me. I had added ten pounds to my sixty-pound frame because a major side effect of prednisone caused me to be hungry all the time. This was a welcome change. I was eating larger portions at meals and constantly snacking. My mother filled the cabinets with a steady rotation of high-calorie snacks and desserts like Hostess CupCakes, Twinkies, Doritos, and every kind of cookie that was sold at the store. Caloric intake was the goal, and nutritional value fell by the wayside.

My mother had also purchased a digital bathroom scale, so I could weigh myself every day. Every morning when I got up, I would walk across the cold, tiled bathroom floor, tap the plastic lever on the front of the scale with my toe, which lit up the two red numbers to "00," and stepped on. Taped to the wall in front of me was a lined piece of paper. The days of the month were written down the left side of the page in my mother's script, followed by a space for me to record my weight with a blue Bic pen sitting on the shelf above me.

Both the increased food consumption and the daily weigh-ins were the beginnings of two bad relationships for me: food and weight. In the mid-1980s, no one knew the root cause of Crohn's. They knew it was an autoimmune disease, which means the body was attacking itself, but the cause and the reason behind why this happened was unknown. All they could do was control the inflammation with steroids. Because one of the main symptoms was weight loss, I was strongly encouraged to eat everything in sight regardless of how full I felt. I needed to constantly obsess over my weight on a day-to-day basis because if my weight dropped it most likely was an indicator of my Crohn's acting up.

I snacked throughout the day, whether I was hungry or not. Many nights after everyone else had finished eating, I sat slumped at the dinner table alone pushing the final bites of cold food around on my plate. Standing on the bathroom scale in the morning, I noticed that if I bounced up and down on the scale, it would nudge the number up. A 67 that became a 68 was an early morning win for me.

It wasn't just the weight number that was talked about, especially with my mother. She would regularly assess my appearance, and make offhand comments like, "you look thin today." Frequent judgments like this cut through me as I struggled to maintain my weight by eating everything I could. Couldn't she see that these comments hurt my feelings beyond anything she could imagine? Didn't she realize I was trying my hardest to eat, and that I was up against an unbeatable opponent? It was as hard for me to put on weight as it was for most people to lose it. I certainly didn't have the knowledge or mental ability to know how to express these feelings to her back then, so I buried everything inside. It was the beginning of the turbulent relationship she and I would have in the years ahead. She made those kinds of remarks when I was well into adulthood. "You look thin," she would say with raised eyebrows and a definitive tone. She wasn't being mean, she was just extremely opinionated. To her, she was being informative and helpful. Being a classically mom-sized, mom-jean-wearing mom, her running joke was always, "I wish I could give some of my fat to him." For her and everyone else, putting on weight was easy. So, to criticize me for being underweight was okay, no matter how helpless or hurt it made me feel.

Another major side effect of the prednisone, and the most physical, was the face swelling, or "moon face." The high dose made my bony face turn plump and round because the steroid caused fat deposits in my cheeks to increase in size. It looked like I was retaining the entire ten pounds I had gained in my cheeks.

But the biggest change was the stomachaches, which started after I left the hospital. It was as if my body somehow swapped the constant cold feeling for intermittent stomach pain. The cold was gone, and the pain was here to stay. Three to four times a day from out of nowhere my body would transition into a state of pain caused by food passing through the diseased portion of intestine. Like a dark cloud passing in front of the bright sun, I would go from completely fine to doubled over in dull pain for four or five minutes. Then as suddenly as it came on, it would disappear. If I was at home, I would stop what I was doing and curl up into a ball on the couch until the pain passed. At school, I would put my head down on my desk. Anywhere in between, I would find some way to quietly take the pain until I could resume my life again.

Those four to five stomachaches translated to four to five bowel movements every day. Trips to the bathroom were constant interruptions, as my body seemed to relentlessly produce poop. I would have to come in from playing with my neighborhood friends to use the bathroom. Stop watching the climactic part of a TV show to use the bathroom. Have my parents pull the car into a gas station to use the bathroom. Strategically, I always had a map in my head as to where the nearest bathroom was at all times, just in case.

My mother had talked to my school to make sure that I would be permitted to use the bathroom anytime I needed it. This was one privilege that I agreed with, even though I still wanted Ms. Little to keep quiet about it. She had two laminated bathroom passes that hung on the wall by the door. One for boys, and one for girls. With the boys' room right across from our classroom, I could get up and go when I needed to, though I had to still endure the immature behavior of fourth-grade boys. They would joke about the smell and try to identify the owner of the white high-top sneakers by peeking through the crack in the door or popping their entire head below the stall.

I also became a champion pill taker. Every morning at the breakfast table I had a small scalloped Tupperware container with four pills. Prednisone was circular, white and bitter, for controlling inflammation. A dark green and triangular iron supplement was important for inflammatory bowel disease patients who might have intestinal bleeding. Sulfasalazine was a big yellow pill that was also in the Crohn's treatment canon but never seemed to do anything. And a multivitamin that looked like a giant red Tic Tac, for overall health and nourishment. I started taking them one by one with a big gulp of water for each pill. Soon I learned to toss the whole handful of pills into my mouth and wash them down with just a small swig of water.

The other daily supplement I took to increase my caloric intake was a nutritional drink called Ensure. It packed about 200 calories into an 8 ounce pull-tab metal can of nutty chocolate grossness. I'm sure the original goal was to have several cans per day or as many of these as I could, but one was all I could ever stomach. I put this daily ritual off as long as possible, taking it at night before bed. I would take a chilled can out of the fridge, shake it quickly in a clockwise/counter-clockwise fashion for ten seconds, open the pull-tab which made a loud *crack*, pour it into a cup, and chug it as fast as I could.

My original plan for sharing the news of my new condition was to tell people on a case-by-case basis. But I was afflicted by disease embarrassment and toileting shame, so I told exactly no one. Gradually, a feeling of toughness grew inside me and I resolved to hide Crohn's from the world as best as I could. My family knew. My mother's close friends knew, and I'm sure some of that knowledge trickled down to some of my neighborhood and school friends, but I was determined early to make them rethink that information. I wasn't going to be some sick kid. I was going to be a normal kid and keep Crohn's a secret. So what if I had an unusually round face? Every time I had a chance to tell a friend about my stomachaches and why I seemed to always be in the bathroom, I decided not to. It was mind over matter, and an ignored problem was a nonexistent problem.

Having a disease in the 1980s was very much a negative thing.

Wearing your disease on your sleeve would certainly lead to swift social punishment, because concepts like disease awareness wouldn't rise into the mainstream for years to come. If you were sick, you had one of three things: cancer, heart disease, or AIDS. Medical textbooks were as thick as they were long, filled with all kinds of conditions and disorders, but no one knew about chronic illness or anything that wasn't a death sentence. I didn't want to be marked as having something as serious and terrible as The Big Three.

I carried toileting shame around with me wherever I went, and boy did I go. Four or five times a day. But, no one wants to talk about bowel movements, feces, excrement, stool, poo, poop, caca, crap, turd, dung, deuce, number two, or taking a shit. To have a disease that turned my body into a shit-making machine wasn't exactly good dinner conversation or any conversation at all. My mother was one of the most modest people I would ever know. My brother and I learned at a very young age that "bathroom talk" would not be tolerated, and bodily functions were not to be discussed. As we grew older we learned that anything about sex would also fit into this category. No birds-and-the-bees talk for us. Questions about puberty were to be answered by a glossy book that mysteriously appeared one day on the faux wooden bookshelf in the family room called *Growing and Changing*. I often wondered if my Crohn's, which dealt so intimately with undesirable bodily functions, was some kind of curse from God for her.

At some point in everyone's childhood, they fake being sick to stay home. I faked being healthy every day to go to school. Because my mother was a former teacher, education was paramount in our house. A major rule stated that if you were sick enough to stay home from school, then you were sick enough to go to the doctor. This was fine for being regular-sick, like having a bad cold or cough. But this meant there was no way I would stay home because of Crohn's. An unscheduled trip to Dr. Flores would surely result in a trip to the lab for bloodwork, and that didn't jibe with my debilitating childhood fear of needles. Getting stuck a few times every year at my regular appointments was enough for me. So no, I wouldn't be missing school for Crohn's.

I didn't know it then, but learning to be tough would become the greatest lesson I would learn from this diagnosis. Sticks and stones can break my bones, but Crohn's can never hurt me. Popular culture of the day centered around being an underdog, and I attached myself to those ideas. There was Luke Skywalker, a young farm boy, who rose up to defeat Darth Vader and the Galactic Empire. Daniel LaRusso, the new kid bullied at school, learned karate from an old maintenance man and triumphs over the Cobra Kai villains. A group of outsider kids find an old map that leads them to a pirate ship filled with treasure that saves their town. My life seemed surrounded by endless stories of outsiders overcoming massive obstacles. Even the Boston Red Sox, who never won, were in first place.

I aspired to join the ranks of the underdogs. And being in fourth grade with a moon face and a strong tendency to make a run for the bathroom, I was going to need it.

"Boom-babba boom-babba boom-babba boom," my whole lunch table would chant whenever a fat kid walked by. By Ms. Little's first day, about a month into the school year, I had acquired the nickname Chubby Cheeks by the masses. Though sometimes it was Chipmunk Cheeks, and sometimes it was just Fat Face. I sat with my friends at the lunch table, making my way through the calorie-packed, carbohydrate-laden brown-bag lunch my mother had packed.

"Up for grabs!" My friend Matt tossed his bag of Doritos in the middle of the table. It was quickly snatched up by Garrett, who pumped his fist in celebration. Up For Grabs was a lunchtime ritual we came up with to discard items our mothers packed that we didn't like. It was win-win because you weren't going to eat that apple or that bag of chips anyway. But today, a new twist arose.

"Up for grabs!" yelled the kid next to me, another Matt, who grabbed my Twinkie and threw it into the center of the table to be quickly snatched by someone else.

"Hey!" I said. The others laughed.

The boy on my other side, Gabe, grabbed another item from my lunch, a bag of Lay's potato chips, and tossed it in. "Up for grabs!"

At this point the joke became relentless and everyone had taken the rest of my food. I was fuming. Everything that I had been keeping inside me bubbled to the surface. I couldn't help what was happening. I had passed the point of no return and the tears started coming. My wall of toughness cracked like an egg shell. Pure emotion began to pour out of me as I stood up.

"I need to eat!" I choked out each word between sobs.

The other kids froze, staring at me wide-eyed.

"You guys cut it out!"

This got the attention of one of the teachers who came to my rescue and defused the situation. My smirking friends returned my food and lunch commenced in silence. I stuffed a few more bites in my mouth and the bell rang. I dropped the rest in the trash. I was embarrassed and sad that I had let their joke get to me like that, though it felt good to let it out. I needed to do a better job of keeping my cool about all of this.

I wiped my face and got in line, ready to walk out to recess. I could only hear the muffled sounds of the other kids: "Did you see Chubby Cheeks crying?" I steeled myself and pushed through the heavy double doors into the chill of the crisp October air.

Later that month, huddled around our TV set in pajamas, my family watched the Red Sox as they battled the Mets in the World Series. It seemed that the weight of the world hung on them winning because they hadn't won since 1918. My neighborhood friends and I had followed them the entire season, from that first pitch when Dwight Evans hit a home run to now. Victory seemed inevitable, and with everything that had changed for me health-wise over the course of this baseball season, I really could use a win.

They got down to needing just one more out in Game 5 when a slow ground ball rolled through the legs of the first baseman, Bill Buckner.

It was a classic error, baseball 101, and they ended up losing the game. In Little League, we were taught to get down on one knee to prevent the ball from passing us. From then on, a ball-through-the-legs play would be followed by a chorus of "Buckner" chants. Even our heroes were taunted. My mother, always with her own opinion, had a different take. She said that Bill Buckner shouldn't have been playing due to a bad back, and it was the manager's fault for having the man play injured.

For the Red Sox, it was another losing year and it was a losing year for me, too. For now, I was going to do the only thing that came naturally to me. I was going to tough it out.

3

CHARLESDALE

FOR THE MAJORITY OF MY CHILDHOOD, I WOULD BE BETTER friends with the kids on my street than I was with the kids in my grade at school. Charlesdale Road was a world all its own. It was suburbia and it was the Wild West. Steve and I were part of a tribe of roughly a dozen boys, about five years between the oldest and youngest, who were friends simply because we all lived close to one another. We stormed the sidewalks on our black Huffy BMX bikes and we knew every crack in the pavement and break in the sidewalk. Fights and quarrels broke out and broke up as fast as they were started. But mostly we all got along.

There were never any arrangements made to play with one kid or the other. We would simply go outside and find everyone else, or knock on someone's door to see if they were around to play. If the phone was used, a typical phone conversation went like this.

"Hello?"

"Hi, is Seth there?"

Parent hands phone to Seth.

"Hi, can you play?"

"Yes, okay bye."

"Okay bye."

On Charlesdale Road it didn't matter that the rest of the town aspired to be a puritanical upper-class town. The houses on our street were capes, ranches, small colonials, and hybrid split-levels like my house: three different-sized yellow blocks. It's a style that I have yet to see replicated. While our parents were a mix of middle-class workers, blue and white collared, the neighborhood was dominated by boys. The running joke was that there must be something in the water because the boy- to-girl ratio ran about 4:1. Even the occasional family that moved there from out of town brought more boys to the neighborhood.

The town cemetery lay at one end of Charlesdale Road, which to us wasn't a resting place for the dead, but a labyrinth of paved roads for us to explore on our bikes. It also possessed the best sledding hill around. After snowstorms, we would trudge out with our toboggans and Sno-Tubes to a big sloping hill not yet covered by headstones.

For the boys of Charlesdale Road, baseball had become our religion. It felt like surviving the 1986 Red Sox season had been some kind of baptism for us, and now baseball was a year-round sport. Our stadium was a cul-de-sac road at the elbow of Charlesdale that we called The Circle. It was a central location in the neighborhood and a perfect place for us. A round infield of pavement, a grassy warning track, and a canopy of trees for home run territory. We christened this new sport T-ball, short for the tennis ball we played with.

I loved playing baseball, but I was somewhere between terrible and godawful at all sports. My younger brother Steve, on the other hand, was a born athlete. Given that we were only thirteen months apart in age, we were endlessly competitive. Steve was a natural at every sport and all things physical. He even learned to ride a bike before me.

So, I needed a different way of standing out, and I needed something to deflect the insults that were coming my way due to my big round face. I slowly realized that making others laugh came naturally to me, and more and more I was able to use humor as armor. I found comedy to be an underdog's craft. My jokes were mainly at the expense of others, but in those days kids were kids. We all dished it out, and we all took it. Hurt feelings or not, we all remained friends.

Day in and day out we would play T-ball in The Circle. We mimicked the odd batting stances of Dwight Evans, Rickey Henderson, Eric Davis, and Chuck Knoblauch. We would rest the bat on our shoulder and point to the trees like Babe Ruth calling his shot. As mediocre as I was, I loved playing. I didn't want to miss out, so I endured those stomachaches, and ran home to the bathroom when I needed to go, all along acting like this was totally normal.

At some point during those years, one of the Crohn's and colitis charities decided to make a commercial about inflammatory bowel disease. One afternoon after school as I lay on the couch watching TV by myself, I saw it.

A dark set with a single spotlight on an unbranded bottle of pink liquid that was obviously meant to portray a bottle of Pepto Bismol, which I actually had never even tasted before. A deep, ominous voice chimed in. "For most people, a bottle of the pink stuff will solve their stomach troubles." The camera cut past the pink bottle, and through the darkness a new scene appeared. The announcer continued in a deeply ominous tone. "But for people with Crohn's disease or ulcerative colitis, it will take something more." The scene settled in on a metal table with shiny surgeon's tools laid out. The commercial ended with a sponsor message and the next commercial began.

I sat frozen and completely floored. My secret world of Crohn's was being flaunted across the network for all to see. "It's okay," I told myself, "no one knows that I have it." Just hearing the word "Crohn's" outside of the safety of Dr. Flores' office was enough to give me an internal sense of panic. In fact, this was the first time I had heard that word used out in the real world.

I never mentioned that commercial to anyone, and unlike the medical ads of today, it didn't run frequently. For me, once was enough.

Every few months I had to take a break from the after-school fun on Charlesdale Road to see Dr. Flores. After a short time seeing him in his office across from Children's, he moved out to a new suburban office at Newton-Wellesley Hospital, only about thirty minutes from home. His office was in the Ellison Building, a historic building on the campus. Walking through the heavy front doors, the smell of must filled our nostrils as the wood floor cracked and lurched under our feet. The lobby walls were filled with oil paintings of old doctors, like the kind that would have the eyes following you in a Scooby-Doo cartoon. We put my name in and sat in the chair-lined hallway that acted as the waiting area, occasionally hearing Dr. Flores' trademark voice through the walls as he finished up with another patient.

Soon I heard my name called. I followed the nurse into an adjacent room to go through the dreaded activity of getting my weight. On doctor's appointment days, I would intentionally wear jeans to give myself an additional pound. The chunky weight on the big metal scale would be moved to the left, followed by her painted fingernail nudging the smaller weight to the right. I had the math done in my head and she would confirm it by saying it out loud. I would return to the hallway and tell my mother, bracing for judgment. If it was lower than expected, I would be in for two things. Bloodwork and a higher dose of prednisone.

After my initial dose of 40 mg of prednisone, I was dropped to 20 mg. Soon after the dose was lowered to 10 mg. At that dose my moon face was barely noticeable. But by then my body had completely latched itself on to the addictive steroid, and I was unable to wean off of it completely. My comfort zone seemed to be between 10 mg and 5 mg, but whenever we shifted to 5 mg and 2.5 mg my body would revolt into weight loss and more stomachaches. I would then be brought back up to 15 mg and the cycle of trying to wean off the drug would continue.

"Hello, Mr. Harris!" Dr. Flores greeted me and we followed him into his office. He typically wore a light-colored suit that had wide shoulders, probably a couple of sizes too big for him.

We would leave my mother in the office and he would examine me in the room next door. He went through the same thumping and tapping and pressing on my belly that he normally did.

"Tell me how you're doing!" he said, now back in the office.

"Pretty much the same," I said.

"How many times a day are you having cramps?"

It was weird that he called them cramps. They felt nothing like the sharp knots I would get from running. Crohn's aches were a specific pain, dull and dead and overpowering. Nevertheless, we were talking about the same thing.

"Four or five a day," I replied.

"And bowel movements?"

"Four or five a day," I replied.

In the beginning, I asked him why my whole digestive system seemed to be affected by just one segment of diseased bowel.

"This is the case with everyone," he replied. "There's a lot we don't know about the disease."

We would return to his office, and I sat down next to my mother. She kept notes about the appointments in the same small spiral-bound notebook in her lap.

"How is your husband?" he would ask my mother before they soon turned the conversation back to me.

We would review everything and ultimately Dr. Flores would

either let me go without any changes, or he would elect to do blood-work. My entire day hinged on this decision. I didn't care that he wanted blood to examine, or about the outcome. I spent an unreasonable amount of time fearing that sharp metal needle.

The verdict came in. "We will check bloods today," he said offhandedly.

A swirl of panic and fear broke out inside me. Though, like everything else, I kept this to myself. I just put on a straight face and nodded.

He would finish up talking with my mother, and we would hear him making notes in his handheld recorder as she made another appointment with his administrative person in the next room.

Then it was time to head to the main hospital. We would walk the length of the Ellison Building and down a couple of flights of stairs. There we found the most exciting part of the visit, an old underground tunnel that connected us to the main hospital. I was always fascinated to travel through this arched, white-tiled hall like it was a secret passageway out of a movie. We never saw anyone down there, we just walked to the sound of our footsteps echoing off the walls as the late afternoon light beamed down through small skylights in the ceiling.

As we emerged into the main hospital, fear continued to grow inside me as we followed signs to the laboratory. Before I knew it, my name was being called and I would climb into the bucket seat with the padded armrests. With the rubber tourniquet tied tightly around my thin bicep, I hoped that they had butterfly needles. They were thinner and didn't hurt as much. Either way, I clenched my entire body when the lab tech unsheathed the steel needle out of the tangle of tubing. I would be told to relax, followed by an "are you ready?" followed by "a little pinch," as pain cut into my arm.

Soon it was over, and I was walking the halls back toward our car with my mom, white gauze taped to the needle-sized puncture in my arm. It was completely lost on me that the stomachaches I was enduring several times a day were far more painful than the pinch of a needle and that my suffering was self-inflicted from worried anticipation. Still, I had made it through the blood draw. I wouldn't have another one for a few more months. But there was always a next time.

My Charlesdale Road friends were all at home finishing up the fun, painless afternoon activities like playing T-ball, or Nintendo, or riding bikes. I would catch up on what I missed tomorrow without telling them where I'd been or what I had been through. Telling would risk having them view me as different or damaged or diseased when all I wanted was to be normal. Just a normal kid like everyone else. Perhaps I was envious of the other kids and their health. I fantasized about having a superpower to inflict Crohn's stomachaches on others so they could feel what I felt. Like Obi-Wan Kenobi giving a *these-aren't-the-droids-you're-looking-for* wave and having someone double over in stomach pain. Or what if everyone had Crohn's? How would other people live with these stomachaches? There certainly would be more bathrooms.

But life isn't fair and I learned that young. Somewhere along the way, I decided that whatever I do in my life, wherever I am, I can look at the people around me and know that I'm keeping up with them despite carrying this heavy invisible backpack of Crohn's. I would be seen as a kid with a normal childhood, like everyone else. I just had to work for it.

4

SHOOTING THE MOON

HAVING TO GO TO THE BATHROOM ALL THE TIME WAS AS much about holding it in as it was about going.

Every year on the Fourth of July week we would go to Cape Cod for two weeks with my extended family that lived nearby. There were ten of us. My family of four, my aunt and uncle and two cousins who were about the same age as Steve and me, and my grandparents. We stayed in Truro, the second town in from the very end of the Cape.

I was born with an insatiable optimism, and besides Christmas morning, our annual Truro vacation was the highlight of my year. The entire month of June I would be filled with excitement and anticipation as I counted down the days until we left. I would report this to anyone in my family that would listen, and my grandmother always got a good laugh about it when they would visit us on Wednesday nights for dinner, before they headed to square dancing at the Wheelock School gym.

Finally, the day would come. We'd pack the station wagon to the gills and head to the highway for the two-hour trek to Truro. With the windows down the front seatbelts slapped in the hot breeze. I always traveled with my Walkman on, listening to my tape collection as I stared out the window at the passing landscape. The Cars, Bryan Adams, and Michael Jackson would soon be replaced by the hair-metal bands of the 1980s. Steve always had his nose tucked into a book, reading. With my father's long commute, he quickly became a seasoned highway driver, though he still puttered along in the slow lane. My mother in the passenger seat acted like she was also driving, constantly checking the side-view mirror to warn my father of oncoming cars.

"Oh here comes one," my mother would say with alarm in her voice. "Jim. Watch Jim. Watch! Jim!"

"I see him," my father would respond casually, as a speeder zoomed by us.

The Gingerbread House was lettered on a white sign at the edge of the property that advertised both the vacancy status and *fishermen welcome.* Surely it was the latter that piqued my grandfather's interest in the mid 1970s when he inquired about staying there. The property was just a half-mile from Pamet Harbor where he would put his boat in every day in search of bluefish and flounder in Cape Cod Bay. He and my grandmother frequented the place in the summer months and became fast friends with the owners, Walter and Gertrude Bushey. By 1980 they had convinced my parents and my aunt and uncle to come down with the kids for a couple of weeks in July, and we've been going down ever since.

The tall white Gingerbread House sat perched at the top of a hill beyond the sign. It was a nineteenth-century steep-roofed house with ornate woodwork that ran along the gutters. Turning up the steep driveway that seemed to match the pitch of the roof itself, we soon emerged to a small campus of three houses at the top. A circular driveway united the structures, and a small island of grass and trees sat in the middle. The actual Gingerbread House was where the four of us stayed with my two cousins and my aunt and uncle. The gothic exterior couldn't have been more different from the décor inside, which was a charming museum of Cape Cod kitsch. Every item in our first-floor unit was an artifact from a bygone era, and not in a cool retro-chic kind of way. There was no stylistic plan, yet everything just kind of fit together, and over the years gave us all a sense of nostalgic comfort to come back to the same furniture year after year. Steve and I slept in twin four-poster beds with pineapples carved into their tall posts. Each room was adorned with colorfully peculiar lamps from decades past. The kitchen table where we played card games into the night had looping wooden legs and chairs with orange vinyl seat cushions. And a bookshelf with a random assortment of old books gave us kids vessels to leave notes and letters to each other for the next year.

The foursome of cousins were born within four years of each other. I was the oldest. Steve and our cousin Andy were a year younger than me, and our cousin Julie was a year younger than them. We were inseparable and reveled in the traditions of those two weeks. Fourth of July fireworks. Playing Pickle. Miniature golf. Seafood restaurants. The Wellfleet Drive-In theater. Morning bingo games with Gram for small sums of money. Hunting for treasures we could afford from our bingo winnings in the shops of Provincetown. And every night ended with ice cream.

We went to the beach every day. We had a ritual of applying suntan lotion as our moms packed lunches in matching red and white Playmate coolers. Most of us ate sandwiches with cold cuts, peanut butter and jelly, or tuna. Cans of soda and bags of chips and cookies were packed. My brother's one quirk was that he hated sandwiches and refused to eat them, so my mother laboriously made him a salad in a Tupperware container each day.

Then we would pile into two cars and drive to Ryder Beach, ten minutes away. Ryder was a lesser-known and less popular beach because it was out on the edge of town, near the Wellfleet border. A tall hill of hot sand stood between the parking lot and the beach, and each day we would conquer it with seared feet and burning leg muscles from the climb. Once we were over the hill, it was practically a private beach for us with maybe two or three other parties. It was on the bay side of the Cape, so the waves were smaller and the water was warmer. We could see clear across the arc of the bay to the tip, where the Pilgrim Monument stood like a stake marking the center of Provincetown. Boats dotted the horizon, surely one of them holding my dad and grandfather, who went fishing every day instead of going to the beach.

The kids spent the day running from the water to the sand, while the grown-ups read books and talked in their beach chairs. In the water, we snorkeled for hermit crabs and played in the surf. On the beach, we played Pickle, which was the perfect game for us. Two Frisbees served as bases about fifty feet apart. Two of us were the basemen, and two of us were the runners. The tennis ball was thrown back and forth between the basemen, trying to draw the runners off base. Back and forth the runners ran, trying not to get tagged out by the ball, and when we did we would swap. There was no score, and the game was never-ending.

Inevitably, though, I would have to go to the bathroom when we were at the beach. Public bathrooms were harder to come by back then. And by public bathroom, I don't mean a designated structure that housed bathrooms for the general public. When I had to go, I had to go. Any business, restaurant, or four-walled structure that had a toilet was fair game. As long as I walked in and acted like I knew what I was doing and where I was going, no one questioned me. I began to develop a sixth sense about where bathrooms were located based on the architectural layout of the building.

At one point, one of the Crohn's charities sent out a mailer with a wallet-sized blue card that said something like, *I can't wait! The bearer of this card must use the bathroom immediately! Due to a medical condition!* I laughed and tossed it into the trash, experience telling me that some official-looking card wasn't nearly as effective as good old confidence and urgency. I can't remember a time when I was denied access to a bathroom using my technique.

Seasonal port-a-potties at the beach only applied to much larger beaches, if at all. If you had to pee, you went in the ocean, and if you needed other facilities you had to hoof it home. So when the urge came on, which was just about every day at the beach, my mom and I would retreat up and down the huge hot hill, get into the station wagon, and she would drive me back to the Gingerbread House.

The journey and the wait were excruciating, and early on my mother gave me a simple strategy to make the time pass: counting. It occupied my mind and strengthened my ability to hold it in these types of situations. I would think, "If I can count to 100, we'll be there. I can do that." By the time I got to 100, we might not be there, but we'd be a lot closer. I would reset my mental clock to 20, even easier than 100, and soon we would arrive back at the Gingerbread House. She would pull up to the door when we finally arrived, and I would do a final countdown of 10. If I could count down from 10, I would be in the bathroom. On the toilet.

Ten, my mother turns off the car, hands me the keys. Nine, I open my door and exit the car. Eight, speed-walking down the curvy front walk, fast but not too fast. Seven, climb the concrete steps. Six, key in the door and turn. Five, open door and go inside. Four, move across living room. Three, round the corner. Two, enter bathroom. One, drop wet bathing suit and sit.

And exhale. Staring down at the bathroom floor I realize how much I'm sweating. But I made it across the finish line. I finally can relax for the first time since the urge to go came on, back at the beach. I'm all set until tomorrow's inevitable episode, when the trip will repeat.

After I finish, I would go out to the car where my mom was waiting. We drove back to the beach together, mostly in silence like coworkers in the groove of doing their usual work. My hair fluttered in the wind from the open car window as my eyes traced the passing landscape of scrub pines and occasional breaks of shoreline. Back at the beach, my mom sat back down in her beach chair with the adults and I rejoined the kids like nothing had happened.

Mid-afternoon the entire family would return home. All of us salty, sandy, sweaty, and greasy from sunscreen and ready for showers. The bathroom situation was difficult. We rented the lower floor and had one tiny bathroom for all eight of us. If it was occupied and I needed to go, I could run next door to my grandparents' small annex apartment, repeating my counting exercise all the way.

Once we were all showered and ready to go, we would head out to dinner. I was a hamburger-and-fries kind of kid at restaurants and wasn't interested in Cape Cod seafood until I was much older. Following dinner, we would explore some kind of lower-Cape activity like mini-golf or seeing the sunset or shopping in Provincetown. Then we'd get ice cream somewhere before returning home for cards.

Hearts was the house game. My mother, a seasoned card player who specialized in Bridge, taught us about skill, strategy, and luck. Each night, we played around the glossy kitchen table, the fluorescent light shining down from above, as a different person emerged each night as the winner.

Except for my father, who never won.

In Hearts, there's a reversal move called shooting the moon, where a player can risk it all to win it all. It was the ultimate trick for a player who'd been dealt a terrible hand to turn the tables and win. Rare to pull off, it might happen once a night. Unless my father was playing. He had a reputation for attempting this Hail Mary pass almost every hand.

I was never sure why he did this. It might have been that he just didn't like playing Hearts, and this was a way to end the game faster, or maybe he just had a swing-for-the-fences attitude in an area of life that mattered very little in the grand scheme of things.

Shooting the moon, I thought one night as I lay awake in my tall pineapple-carved four-poster bed, was exactly what I was doing with Crohn's. If I held my cards close enough to my chest, no one would know the bad fortune they told. I was then free to play my hand the way that I wanted. Winning meant living on my own terms, and not having the disease direct my life. It meant living a childhood that I could experience to the fullest extent. I was going to play the hell out of the shit hand I had been dealt because the life I had was the only game in town.

5

THREE-PART NIGHTMARE

ABOUT ONCE A YEAR, DR. FLORES SENT ME FOR ANOTHER upper-GI series so he could assess my intestines. When I was in seventh grade, he called for both an upper-GI and a new test that would assess my colon, a lower-GI.

Nightmare Part I: The Prep

Also known as the clean-out. There was a range of laxative options, but for digestive tests, the choice was always GoLYTELY. If ever there was an oxymoron for the name of a product, it was GoLYTELY. You did go, but there was nothing light about it. This wasn't my first run with this product. I had to do this every time I needed to have an upper GI, which was about once a year.

4:00 p.m.: time to start.

In the fridge sat the chilled tank of GoLYTELY, which dwarfed the gallon of milk next to it. At first, it's not bad. It's a clear solution like water, a little bit salty, but it seems somehow wetter than water, which is strange. At first, this is okay. I'm a little bit thirsty anyway, so bottoms up!

The torture of the prep is in the sheer volume of liquid you have to drink. Glass after glass after glass. Drinking on a full stomach. Burping to make space for the next one. Every thirty minutes.

Soon it starts to work and I'm going from the kitchen to the bathroom and back. All this until what's coming out of me looks like what's going into me: totally clear liquid. By now it's past my usual bedtime and the tank is mostly gone. The first few times my mother made me finish every drop of the GoLYTELY.

"You don't want to be sent home because you didn't do the full prep," she warned. "Then you'll have to do this all over again." I had heard this before.

The next morning, I slump my hungry, weary, and sleep-deprived body into the car, and Mom and I headed for Newton-Wellesley Hospital for the test. At least I didn't have to go to school. But what I was about to endure was much, much worse than seventh grade.

Nightmare Part II: The Test

This was going to be the opposite of the upper GI. So instead of drinking the chalk-flavored barium, they inserted a tube in my rear end and flooded my large intestine with it. This would give them a view of everything south of my ileum, the segment of my small intestine afflicted with Crohn's.

The thought of doing something so unnatural scared me. I didn't like the idea of a tube being shoved up my butt and being flooded with liquid. It sounded like something I wouldn't be able to tolerate.

I entered the X-ray room and met the radiologist who would be facilitating the test. I hopped up on the cold metal table in my johnnie, and the man told me to lie on my side facing the wall. My ribs and hips sat uncomfortably on the cold metal table while my heart pounded. I stared at random marks and smudges on the wall, waiting for what would come next. The cold, wet tube entered my body and I immediately started to moan and cry out. Then a massive urge that I had to use the bathroom as the barium began to flow into my bowels.

"Hold it in," said the radiologist from behind the glass.

"I can't!" I said, seemingly to no one.

This went on for a few minutes, and at some point, my mom entered. I felt better already. She coached me through the rest of this torturous experience. And finally, it was over. Once the tube was removed, I sprang off of the table, now completely naked, and into the bathroom that was connected to the X-ray room. I sat relieved on the toilet long after everything had passed through, totally wiped out. I could hear my mother talking with the radiologist in the other room, their muffled words indecipherable.

Nightmare Part III: The Reveal

I dressed and we headed for Dr. Flores' office, through the underground tunnel to the Ellison Building, for my post-test appointment.

We sat with Dr. Flores and discussed the results of the lower-GI. Everything looked good in my large intestine, so that was a relief. Hopefully, I'd never have to do that again.

Toward the end of the appointment, my mother asked me to wait outside. She had something she wanted to talk to Dr. Flores about alone. Skeptically, I stood up and exited the room into the chair-lined hallway waiting room. I stood quietly by the door, trying to hear their conversation.

"He has no... pubic hair?" said my mother's voice through the door, her sentence phrased in the form of a question.

I was mortified. In the throes of the lower-GI, she had certainly seen my naked 13-year-old body. Dr. Flores, whose loud voice carried easily to my ears, began to talk of puberty and the prolonged steroids I had been on. The never-ending cycle of small Crohn's flares and my body's addiction to prednisone was now taking a toll on my teenage body. With clothes on, it wasn't too obvious that my body wasn't changing. I had always been tall for my age, so the lack of a few growth spurts hadn't made me stand out.

Now, the only way to get me off of prednisone was to remove the segment of intestine that was causing the inflammation. And just like that, surgery was scheduled for April vacation, which would cut down on the school I would have to miss.

Happiness flickered inside me when I imagined not having stomachaches every day or having to go to the bathroom all the time. I spent so much time in bathrooms, alone. In our small downstairs bathroom, my focus would drift over the floor tiles, a lemon-yellow and black windmill pattern. In our upstairs bathroom, I would mentally trace the watercolor flowers on the wallpaper. Passing time. And thinking. Thinking about what I was doing right before I had to go. The TV show I was watching, or what was happening in the neighborhood game outside, or the homework problem I was stuck on.

I can't remember exactly what I told everyone. I might have told my friends that I was going into the hospital. I might have told them that I had a bad section of intestine that had to get taken out. I might have told them it was just for a minor procedure. I definitely told them that it wasn't a big deal, and not to worry. And that I'd be home soon.

6

THE LEAD PIPE

I WAS ADMITTED TO THE HOSPITAL THE DAY BEFORE surgery. At the same time I was admitted to my room, another boy was moving into the bed next to me. The boy had his mother with him too, and he was younger than me. He had the bed by the door, I had the one next to the window.

Soon, the doctors came in to talk to him, and I overheard his story. He was from the Midwest and also had Crohn's disease. He'd had several surgeries out there, so many that the doctors told him that he'd had probably more surgeries than he actually needed. At one point I caught a glimpse of his stomach, which looked like a roadmap of scars. He was there because he'd had so many surgeries that he needed to have a bag attached to his stomach to poop into. He would have this for the rest of his life.

That afternoon, they came in to do a procedure on him, right in the room. The dividing curtain was drawn. I don't know what they were doing to him, but it sounded like torture. I just sat in my bed, trying to watch whatever was on the TV over his cries of pain. Later, a nurse came in to show him the type of bag that he would have and how he would use it. She showed him how it would be attached to his stomach and that he would be able to empty it into the toilet when it was full. I didn't even know something like that was possible, and it sounded dreadful.

My mother commented to me that the hospitals where the boy was from weren't as good as the ones in Boston, and that's why he had so many surgeries.

"Be thankful that we live near Boston," she said. "These are some of the best hospitals in the world." Living a short distance from good health care would be one of my mother's essential beliefs throughout her life.

"Well, we have good news for you," the nurse announced. "You know how you have to drink all that liquid to get you cleaned out when you go for a test? Well, you're not going to have to drink it this time." The nurse went on to explain that for surgery they would have to insert a tube up my nose and down my throat. Normally they would do this after I was under anesthesia and sedated for the surgery, but seeing as I was in the hospital and needed to do a clean-out, they would put it in the day before so they could administer the GoLYTELY through the tube.

The boy and I were on the same schedule because we were going to have surgery on the same day. The nurse came and took him away for a little while, and when he returned he looked haggard behind a tube coming out of his nose, tape over his nostril to keep it secured in place.

It was my turn, and I walked past him with worry on my face. The nurse led me to a small exam room a few doors down. Another nurse soon joined us, and they were preparing the medical supplies in the room. My heart thumped in my chest as they explained what was about to happen.

"Okay, Brad. This tube is going to go in your nose." She showed me the clear plastic tube. I could see ointment glistening on the end of it. "I'm going to be pushing the tube in. It won't hurt, but it feels uncomfortable. Once it hits the back of your throat we're going to need to have you swallow as much as you can. Just keep swallowing."

The other nurse gave me her hand, "you can squeeze as hard as you want. It'll be over before you know it."

"Ready?" the nurse said.

"No," I said with a shaky voice, pulling my head away.

"It's okay, hon," the other nurse said, "just squeeze my hand."

"Okay, here we go."

An overwhelming pressure took over as the cold lubricated tube enter my nose. I started groaning and squirming. I squeezed the nurse's hand as hard as I could and dug my fingernails in. The next thing I knew they were both telling me to swallow. I made my throat swallow as if I was drinking air. I could feel the cold tube gradually slide down the back of my throat. Finally, it stopped.

I tried not to move. I sat in an awkward position like I was balancing a spoon on my nose, waiting for the nurse to apply the tape. Even when she did, it felt strange and slightly painful to move with a foreign object inside me.

Back in my room, the nurse hung a bag of GoLYTELY on an IV pole, and my stomach began to feel cold as the liquid began to flow in. I debated with myself whether it was worse to have the tube forced up my nose or having to physically drink all of the GoLYTELY. I began to feel full and could hear the liquid swishing around in my stomach. The clean-out had begun.

The next morning I was wheeled down to surgery. I don't remember the trip there, saying goodbye to my parents, or being put under anesthesia. I don't remember anything about the surgery or post-op. But when I made it back to my room, my nurse gave me a white joystick with a button on the end. I held it in my hand and realized it was just like the buzzer the Jeopardy contestants held.

"This is for your pain, it's called morphine. Every time you press the button, pain medicine will come through your IV, and you'll feel better." I pressed the button and heard the quiet churn of the machine. A few seconds later I felt numbed and a little woozy.

I pressed the button again and nothing happened.

"It's set so you can only get one dose for a certain time period," she said.

"Okay," I mumbled and drifted off to sleep.

The next morning my mother told me about her experience in the waiting room while I was having surgery. The whole thing took longer than she expected.

"I was in the waiting room, and finally after an hour, they sent word to me that the incision had been made. Can you believe that? An hour?"

Later we learned that the reason was that Children's was a teaching hospital. Somehow this validated the whole thing for my mom. Being a former teacher herself, she valued education.

That morning the surgeon, Dr. Cantrell, came in for a post-op visit. He was an older man with glasses and he had some of the other doctors with him that he announced were residents. Dr. Cantrell seemed like a grandfather compared to them.

He opened up my johnnie and examined my belly, which now had a weird plastic covering on my right side, at my waistline. The doctors explained that this was a new way of closing wounds.

"This way it won't require stitches to be removed," Dr. Cantrell explained. "The incision is horizontal, so once it heals, it'll be right at your waist, and it won't be so obvious that you have a scar."

He went on to explain that the surgery was very successful and that there was no evidence active Crohn's anywhere else in my stomach. He removed 12 inches of intestine from my ileum.

He turned to me. "But boy, that segment of intestine that we removed was quite diseased," he said. "It was hard as a lead pipe. I wasn't expecting that given that the reason we were operating was essentially to rid you of Crohn's so you can get off the prednisone and have Mother Nature take its course."

I listened intently and wondered if I was going to see the section of bowel he took out of me, or if he was going to show me a picture of it.

"I've been doing this for a long time, as you can imagine," he continued. "I've operated on kids with the severe level of disease you had, Bradley. But patients like that, kids like that, are much sicker than you appear to be. They're constantly in and out of the hospital, and..." he stopped. "When we met before the surgery you described your life as pretty normal, and that you haven't been in the hospital since you were diagnosed, is that right?"

I nodded.

"See, kids with this level of disease in their bellies aren't living a regular life like you. Like I said, that segment was as hard as a lead pipe. That's not Crohn's, that's scar tissue that makes it so hard. You must have a very high threshold for pain."

As he left, a feeling of pride filled my thirteen-year-old body. I felt like Dr. Cantrell had given me an award, like he had pinned an invisible badge to the chest of my patterned hospital johnnie. I was a little confused by the word "threshold." Wasn't that the piece of wood on the floor between two rooms? I guessed that threshold meant the same thing as tolerance. That I could take pain better than most people, even though I was just a kid.

I now had a new perspective on the past four years, a twist on the sickness I tried so hard to keep hidden. I had come to the end of a very hard game that I was playing with myself. I had succeeded in living a normal childhood from fourth grade to seventh grade.

• • •

The next days in the hospital were tough. My stomach muscles were cut during the surgery, and I was amazed at how incredibly difficult it was to move around without them.

Dr. Cantrell had mentioned that getting up to walk was one of the most important activities for me to do for two main reasons. The first was stamina.

"It's a 2:1 ratio," he explained. "For every day you're horizontal in bed, it takes two days to make up for it. The second reason is that it will help your body heal. It gets the blood flowing and your muscles moving."

This little speech gave my mother something to push me to do. Every day, several times per day, she made me get up and walk.

Just getting out of bed was a process. First, I would hit my buzzer for the pain meds, then I would adjust the mechanical bed to be as upright as possible. I learned to use the bars on the side of the hospital bed for leverage while pulling myself out of bed. Without working stomach muscles, pulling myself up with just my arms was a difficult task. Sharp abdominal pains struck me like a knife, despite the hit of the pain medicine I had just administered. Once upright, my mom would help me to my feet, holding one hand, and helping me grip the IV pole she had unplugged with the other. We then made our way across the room and out into the hall. By the time I made it out to the hallway enough time had passed so that I could activate the morphine buzzer again.

Each time I would get up to walk, Mom would push me to walk a bit farther. I can't remember which of us started it, but walking the halls soon became a competition with myself. One lap around the hallway turned into two, and so on. We walked past rooms full of other kids with their own problems and stories I would never know about.

By the time I returned to my room I was exhausted. I would lower myself into the bed, hit the Jeopardy morphine buzzer one more time, and drift off to sleep.

After a few days, I was eating and well enough to leave the hospital. The energy in my body already felt different even though the soreness of surgery still lingered. On one hand, it was luxurious to not have the repetitive stomachaches anymore. Yet without their constant interruption, they were soon forgotten, like how it's hard to remember the blustery cold of the winter in the hot heat of the summer. For now, I was healed.

The doctors told me that Crohn's would return at some point, but they didn't have any guess as to when. Maybe in a few years, and maybe not until I was a grown man. At any rate, hopefully it would be long enough for my body to go through as much of my adolescence as possible. I held a secret hope that for me it would be different. I would be the exception, and the doctors would point to my case and take note. "For him," they would say, "it never came back."

For me, remission would be forever.

7

HARD MILES

Long-distance running wasn't popular in high school. Running for the sake of running was an unorthodox idea. An undesired slice of other, more popular sports like football or field hockey or soccer. But the fall of my sophomore year, my friend Ray convinced me to join the cross-country team.

Every afternoon when school ended, a small band of kids would gather to stretch out on a patch of grass in front of the school by the parking lot. There were no tryouts or means to qualify anyone to be part of this team, which was largely made up of nerds, outcasts, and leftovers from other sports. It was co-ed, and all-welcoming, whether you ran as fast as a gazelle or as slow as a turtle. We would stretch out and then run through the streets of Medfield each day on a pre-determined route. We knew all the street names. Without them we'd be lost.

During that first cross-country season, I hit what would be my lifetime peak for my health. Crohn's-free and in top running condition, I could sprint as fast as I could for a hundred yards and not be out of breath, my heart rate barely increasing. Running had an effortlessness to it and a lightness. It was as if I weighed nothing and had wings. Speed, like athletics in general, was not my strong suit. I never placed in any of the cross-country meets, but still, it gave me a sense of endurance and accomplishment to run increasingly longer distances. Most days were practices. We ran through town, talking and laughing at jokes we made up along the way. If sports were intended to be serious, we'd found a major loophole.

Ray and I had become fast friends a year earlier at the beginning of freshman year when he sat behind me in English class. It was his first year in Medfield; he had just moved from Missouri. We bonded over music, reveling in the alternative scene that was emerging on MTV and the radio. Pearl Jam, Nirvana, and The Smashing Pumpkins fueled the airwaves and seemed to flow through our veins as we eked our way through Medfield High. Most of high school involved enduring subjects and things I didn't like. The one exception was art class.

At the art show at the end of eighth grade, each student had a piece of work mounted on colored construction paper for the school and parents to see. The piece I chose to enter was a drawing of my hand that had turned out really well. It was a lightly sketched pencil drawing of my closed fist, a pose that I had found to be the most simplistic way to model my hand. When I brought it home on the last day of school in June, my mother put it up on the refrigerator door. It remained there through the summer months for no other reason than that the cycle of refrigerator-worthy work had ceased until school started in September.

Every afternoon I would take a break from playing with my friends in the humid heat outside to get a drink of fruit punch or lemonade from the fridge. I would stand there, as if I were standing in a museum instead of our small kitchen surrounded by the summer heat, studying that drawing. The accuracy caught me by surprise every time and I would think, "Wow, I drew that." Every time. "I drew that."

By the end of the summer, I had decided to take art more seriously. From here on out, I was going to maximize how much art I could take, which at tiny Medfield High was one class per term. I disliked every other subject, but being able to lose myself for forty-five minutes in whatever project I was working on in art made the rest of my day a little more tolerable. Ray liked art too, and it became a great social space for us to hang out. We sat at the same table along with a couple of our other friends and passed the time talking about music, joking around, and making art. Ray had a comic that he drew called The 'Fros, and I mostly drew as realistically as I could. Pencil and pen and ink drawings from magazines, or pastel portraits from photos.

After having so much fun running cross-country that fall, I was easily convinced to continue with winter track. Where cross-country was light and fun, winter track was cold and grueling. The meets were indoors and occasional; most days were outdoor practices in the bleak New England winter. We would run a warm-up mile from the high school to Wheelock Elementary and run circles in the loop where the school buses picked up and dropped off the kids. Overlooking this loop was the old steel playground where I had fallen and broken my wrist years earlier.

My memory of that track season is spotty, but I persevered for two reasons. The first was that I didn't know any better, and was never one to speak up and change directions to try something that I actually would enjoy. I was stubborn and never permitted myself to change my mind. The other was that my mother was adamant that my brother and I were always involved in some sort of extracurricular activity because "colleges would be looking for that." This was extra important for me because of my unremarkable grades.

Over the years, I had learned to distance my poor performance in school from my mom as much as I could. At some point in middle school, I got tired of fighting with her. I realized that the cycle of showing her failed tests just so she could become furious and scream at me wasn't helping. By that point, just receiving a test with a low grade filled me with shameful remorse and the dread of knowing I would have to spend the rest of the term trying to bring up my average. I didn't need a fight with my mother on top of it. So, I stopped showing her my tests altogether. My report cards had to be signed, so those were the only grades she ever saw.

My brother, on the other hand, was as successful in school as he was at sports. He was in all of the top classes in each subject and a straight-A student. Everything just came naturally to him.

Every night, dinner went like this:

"How was your day at school, did you have any tests?" she asked both of us. My brother responded attentively by reporting what classes he had tests in, and willingly sharing the stellar grades he received, rarely anything less than an A-minus.

"What about you, Brad," she would turn to me and ask. "Did you have any tests today?"

"No tests today, Ma," I would respond in between bites, not looking up from my food.

Every night I would respond in the same oblivious tone, "No tests today, Ma."

I relied on myself to manage my grades so there wouldn't be a third World War when report cards showed up, and I began to develop an independence of my own. A small consolation for my mother was that I kept up with extracurriculars by running.

It's hard to say if winter track caused my health to falter, or if it was just my time to get sick again. It seemed like the coldness of those icy practices infected me. Once again, I found myself shivering even while I was indoors when everyone else was warm. I had lost my appetite and several pounds. Though I wasn't experiencing Crohn's-level stomach pain, my abdomen felt sluggish and sore most of the time.

"Are you feeling okay?" my mom asked one night. "You look thin. Have you lost weight?" Dinner had ended, and I still sat at the kitchen table pushing cold scalloped potatoes around on my plate.

I sighed. "Yeah, my weight's down. And I feel cold all the time again."

It was enough for my mom to make an appointment with Dr. Flores. After labs confirmed that my inflammatory markers were elevated, he admitted me to the hospital.

"We're going to give your belly a rest for a few days," he said in his loud, heavily accented voice.

"Back to Children's?" my mother asked.

"No, we can keep you here at Newton-Wellesley," he said.

I was saddened that the Crohn's had returned after only a few years. I didn't really believe that Crohn's was a chronic disease until then. Until it came back.

I started the hospital stay off with an upper-GI, and of course a diet of GoLYTELY until I was cleaned out for the test. After that, I could only ingest clear liquids and a new nutrition supplement drink called Boost, a high-calorie competitor to Ensure that tasted only slightly better. I couldn't eat food, but I could have as much Boost as I wanted.

The nurses served Boost in a Styrofoam cup with crushed ice and a straw. Apparently, they were under the impression that I would be enjoying bottle after bottle of this refreshment. That soon changed when I expressed my desire to drink only the minimal amount, with my nose pinched to avoid the taste as much as possible. It's hard to say if the taste was really that terrible, or if the fact that it was served with the news that I was truly sick again ruined any hope for flavor. I guess I didn't have the stomach for either.

The results from the upper-GI revealed that indeed the Crohn's had returned, but in a different location in my digestive tract.

"There are two inflammatory bowel diseases," Dr. Flores explained. "Crohn's and ulcerative colitis. They are similar in many ways, however, the main difference is that ulcerative colitis only manifests in the large intestine. But with Crohn's, it can appear anywhere in the digestive tract, from the mouth to the anus. When you had Crohn's before, it was in your ileum, which is the very end of the small intestine, before it enters your large intestine. Often, we find that when Crohn's returns, it's in the spot next to where we took out that diseased segment. But, this isn't the case for you. Your Crohn's has come back in your rectum. This isn't common, but as I said, it can happen. We'll start you off again on the steroids, which should get everything under control."

So it went. I spent the next week in the hospital, drinking chocolate Boost and watching TV. For someone who had been strongly encouraged and practically forced to eat, not eating was torture. I watched McDonald's commercials, with savory shots of Big Macs and fries in all of their luscious high-calorie glory. Years later when I would work in marketing, I would learn that the industry term for this was "food porn," and I would remember those days sitting in that hospital bed salivating over those seductive Big Macs and salty golden french fries while the melting ice shivered in the Styrofoam cup of Boost on the table in front of me. Someday I would eat again, and someday I would hold a Big Mac in my own two hands, ready to devour it.

Nurses would come by to take my vital signs and would joke with me about my low heart rate. "Are you alive? This says your heart rate is only forty-two beats per minute. Do you play sports?"

"Yep, I run cross-country."

"That explains it. Runners all have low BPMs."

Finally, after days of drinking nothing but Boost, I had put on some weight and my labs had normalized because they had started me up on prednisone again, which lowered the inflammation in my belly. I got the green light to advance my diet.

Hospital food usually tastes terrible, and to anyone else, the sad turkey sandwich delivered to me for lunch that day would be no exception. But to sink my teeth into something solid after a week of not eating felt incredible. White bread, dry turkey, and mayonnaise pinched out from the packet were the pinnacle of flavor in my mouth.

Before I had left the hospital, I started experiencing stomachaches again. Though now, because Crohn's inflamed my rectum, it wasn't at random times of the day. Now it hurt when I used the bathroom, and the new pain coincided with the start of the prednisone. It was strange that the pain returned now that I was getting medicine for the Crohn's. I distinctly did not have this kind of pain before I had been admitted to the hospital.

Dr. Flores was away when I was being discharged. A new doctor, the third one in his growing practice for pediatric inflammatory bowel disease, was there to discharge me: Dr. Burch. Alone with Dr. Burch, as he walked me through my discharge instructions, I ran a theory by him that I had been forming over the past few days.

"The stomach pain is back now. I think it might actually be the steroids, the prednisone, that's causing it. Because I didn't have pain like this before I was here in the hospital."

"That's impossible," he said curtly.

"Yeah, but I'm just starting to get them now."

"Well, the prednisone is there to bring down the inflammation. Inflamed intestines are what causes the pain."

I was a bit taken aback by his strong response, because after all, I was just reporting my symptoms. I didn't push it. Maybe I would ask Dr. Flores sometime. Regardless, what choice did I have? Prednisone was the only treatment, and the side effects were kicking in. Once again, I was hungry all the time.

When I was admitted to the hospital, I weighed 110 pounds. I had put on about eight pounds in my week in the hospital, and I returned home to kitchen cupboards stocked with all kinds of high-calorie snacks again. A big bonus was that my mom always had a batch of chocolate chip Rice Krispie squares on top of the stove in a baking pan, covered with aluminum foil. Her secret was to add extra marsh-mallows and extra butter and extra chocolate chips to pack on extra calories. They were famous among my friends because they weren't dried out like the other moms would make by sticking to the recipe on the side of the box. I would devour these, eating an entire row at a time.

It was now baseball season and I was on the junior varsity team. Baseball had been such a huge part of my childhood, but I found my interest dwindling. From T-ball to Little League, the Babe Ruth League to high school, I always played on a team in the springtime. And playing, for me, meant sitting on the bench every game until the last inning when the coach would inevitably give me and the handful of other weak players an at-bat. I got most of my playing in at practice, where I would be able to hit the pitches in batting practice because they were slower. I would miss fly balls in the outfield, while the other guys never seemed to have trouble predicting where the balls would land, an art I would never come close to mastering.

By mid-season I felt better. The weather was finally warmer and the onslaught of Crohn's seemed to diminish. The prednisone had rounded my face again, not quite as bad as when I was ten, because I was much bigger now, about six feet tall, so it was less noticeable. Astonishingly I had put on another twenty pounds since leaving the hospital because I was eating everything in sight. I now tipped the scales at 140, a high-water mark for my weight for years to come.

The pain had diminished and I was back to having somewhat normal bowel movements. I can distinctly remember taking a break from an afternoon baseball practice, walking into the empty locker room in cleats to use the bathroom. I was in there for only a couple of minutes, a normal amount of time, and I emerged from the stall to the flush of the toilet, feeling the mild euphoria of being completely evacuated, without pain. It was 1993, and this would be the last time in my life that I would experience a normal bowel movement.

With my upswing in weight and decrease in symptoms, Dr. Flores decided we could drop the dose of the prednisone. Unfortunately, this coincided with a drop in weight. Within a couple of weeks, I went from 140 pounds to 125. The weight loss happened so fast that a swipe of stretch marks appeared on my waistline on my lower back. I had no way of knowing that these would become permanent, the second scars my body would bear from Crohn's. If I had known, I would have mentioned this to my mother, who might have had a remedy for this common problem that women encounter after childbirth.

The pain returned as it had when I was in the hospital, this time to stay. I would spend the next several years suffering in private, behind bathroom doors and inside the confines of stall walls. The pain fluctuated from strong to massive. I would typically be in the bathroom for twenty to thirty minutes at a time, passing stool through an increasingly narrow and inflexible passageway due to scar tissue building up.

Once again I was alone in bathrooms, back amongst the mosaic tiles and imperfections in walls. Up until that point, I would have considered myself a pretty extroverted person, but I began to develop a rich inner life during all of that time by myself in the bathroom. I became good company for myself as my thoughts turned to dissecting whatever was going on in my life outside the bathroom door. Songs played in the stereo of my head while I thought about the art project I was currently working on, or what CD I wanted to buy next, or girls, or what cool music video I saw on MTV that week. I sat with my arms crossed on my knees, and I would lean forward and rest my head on my forearms as a way to comfort myself. Looking at my face in the mirror as I washed my hands, I would often notice a red mark across my forehead from sitting in this position for too long. Surely there were matching red marks on the backs of my legs, too.

And once again I cloaked my illness from everyone around me. I spent much more time in the bathroom than a normal person, but few people ever asked why. I didn't know anyone else with Crohn's or ulcerative colitis, or any other kind of chronic disease, nor was I interested in meeting someone else with a condition like mine. I preferred to keep my horse blinders on, and my focus straight ahead.

A few months later, I finished Boy Scouts by becoming an Eagle Scout. When I joined Scouts back in fifth grade, I had a choice between the two troops in Medfield, Troop 89 and Troop 10. Troop 89 was for what you would consider "regular" Boy Scouts, a lot of L.L. Bean clothing and rule-following. I joined Troop 10, which was the opposite. It was hard to believe such a thing existed. I loved hanging out with these rowdy teenage boys who were more like outsiders than Boy Scouts. They were hilariously funny, listened to Van Halen and Whitesnake, and used weekend camping trips as an excuse to get away from their parents for a few days. Our regular Tuesday night meetings were really just a bunch of kids screwing off while the scoutmasters smoked around a folding table in the next room. I'd found my tribe, and felt I belonged with them. Little by little the older kids either quit or became Eagle Scouts themselves. I pushed on, and eventually finished with an Eagle Scout badge of my own. And all the while, almost no one knew about my Crohn's. The only difference was that I had to go to the nurse's office during summer camp to get my medicine twice a day.

Dr. Flores loved this example of a Crohn's patient thriving in the world and taped up a newspaper clipping of me from the local paper on the wall in his office.

More and more I found the Crohn's was something to push against. I wanted to be successful despite having it. I did everything my peers did, yet I had this secret handicap they didn't have. I never wanted anything grandiose for my life. I didn't want to be rich or famous, I just wanted to be normal. To have a job I enjoyed and a family and a house. If I could do that with Crohn's, I would be a success.

My diet was still quantified in calories, but I still could eat just about anything. Onions were something I avoided, mainly due to an episode of food poisoning that summer on the Cape.

I had just acquired my driver's license, which meant the four cousins could finally go out by ourselves for the night. After many conversations as to where we should go on our maiden voyage, we left the Gingerbread House and headed toward Wellfleet. There was a mini-golf course in front of the Wellfleet Drive-In that we hadn't played yet that year, so we played a competitive round before dinner.

Overlooking the mini-golf course was a small building with an ornate sign: Famous Tang's, Chinese Restaurant. We had always wanted to try it, but our parents refused to take us. And rightfully so. Cape Cod is for seafood, not Chinese food. But to us, it was more about independence than a good meal. We sat in a booth in the nearly empty restaurant and ordered several dishes. A pu pu platter. Sweet and sour chicken. Fried rice. Vegetable chow mein. We didn't question the heaping bowl of onions and beige noodles when it arrived on the table with the rest of the food. We just doused everything in duck sauce and dove in.

I spent the next day in bed enduring razor-sharp stomach pains that came over me in tides. It was as if those onions were glass, cutting my insides to ribbons. I cat-napped, and each time I woke up the pain was slightly less. By late afternoon when everyone was back from the beach, the pain had subsided and eventually things went back to normal. From then on, I was cautious about eating anything with onions in it.

August brought on the start of cross-country training and a new problem. Sometimes I would get the strong urge to go to the bathroom when I was on a run. One time that happened, I was in the vicinity of The Frances Café, an old restaurant on a residential street, centered by a large awning that covered the walkway to the entrance. I made it there just in time. Breathing heavily and sweating from the run, I breezed past the hostess station with an I-know-where-I'm-going expression on my face as I avoided eye contact with everyone in the restaurant. I'd never been inside, but my instinct of knowing where bathrooms were in establishments was coming back to me.

I found the men's room flawlessly and inside was a typical one-stall, one-urinal set-up with an old man at the sink washing his hands. The stall door was closed and, to my shock, locked. I bent down and saw no feet underneath. I flashed a look of panic at the old man, my sense of urgency peaking. I was either going to have an accident or I was getting in there to use that toilet.

I slid headfirst under the stall door, Pete Rose style. A streak of sweat marked the tile floor from the chest of my T-shirt. A laugh and a hearty "atta boy!" came from the old man as he exited the bathroom. I sat on the throne, victorious. Initially, I feared that the toilet would be out of order in some way, but the water was clear and twenty minutes later when I was done, it flushed. I left the restaurant as unnoticed as I had arrived, and finished my run.

On other runs when I got the urge to go, I wouldn't be able to find a bathroom. Places like schools and churches were always unlocked, but sometimes I would get stuck outside of town where a public restroom was not an option. Usually I could slow down to a walk, and the urge would pass. On a few occasions, I found a wooded area to squat down and relieve myself. Boy Scouts had taught me how to identify poison ivy, so I never had any problem finding the right leaf to wipe myself. However, I would have a pretty bad rash forming on my rear end by the time I got home and could clean myself up properly. Fortunately, these situations never arose during a meet.

Senior year, Ray and I were elected team captains. This was a vote of popularity, not of talent. Ray was a pretty good runner, but I never once even placed in a meet. There was a group of juniors that were faster, better runners than us, but we were well-liked, funny, and fun to run with during practice. I joked that I ran in the back of the pack so I could keep an eye on everyone.

My body was in a slow but steady decline, barely noticeable to the naked eye that things were gradually getting worse. The scar tissue would build like thin onionskin layers in my rectum; the tissue was ever so slowly turning into another lead pipe. Like before, my dose of prednisone fluctuated, and once again my body became addicted. I was never able to get off the steroid completely.

Cross-country had become more of a chore for me by that point. I didn't want to run anymore. As the weather grew colder that fall, I decided that this would be the end for me as a runner. My last race, in November, was at the state park in Hopkinton, a beautiful wooded space beside a man-made reservoir. By then, the starkness of the next New England winter had started to settle in the landscape. My last hundred yards of that race was on a wide-open sloping road, and I could see the finish line. I began to run faster, my muscles screaming at me as I ran as fast as I could into retirement.

8

GROUP SIXERS

MY LIFE TOOK ON A PARADIGM SHIFT LIKE NO OTHER THE year that I started college. I was Dorothy in black and white, pulling back the door to the world of Oz, and suddenly my life turned to Technicolor. UMass Dartmouth was the only school I had applied to via early admission, and I had thankfully been accepted into their renowned art program despite my tragically low combined SAT score of an even 900. Actually, it's surprising that the test even counted, because I had to stop in the middle to use the bathroom. I was gone so long that my old algebra teacher who was monitoring the students during the test had to come to look for me in the boys' room.

I had no real concept of what it would mean to make a living through art, I only knew that I wanted to somehow get paid to draw. The only adults that I knew of in Medfield that were artists were the art teachers in the school system, and the portrait artists in Province-town who I could sit and watch for hours. Everyone else had "real" jobs. I guess my grandfather was considered an artist, carving intricate birds in his basement, but even he waited until retirement to take his craft seriously. The summer after ninth grade I went to work with my mom a few days a week to earn money helping with office tasks. She worked at a small computer programming company a few towns over in Natick. I remember thinking that my dream job would be working at a company like that, but instead of clacking away on a computer, I would draw things for people.

My saving grace was a neighbor's son who had gone to UMass Dartmouth for graphic design a decade or so earlier and worked at a metro-west newspaper, *The Middlesex News*. I didn't even know what graphic design was—probably just the art of laying out newspapers.

Evidence that employment could happen with an art degree made my parents, who were regular subscribers to *The Middlesex News*, open to the idea of going into an art program. The word *program* for them was the key word. I wasn't pigeonholing myself by going to an all-out art school. I would be getting a more rounded education at a state university. One where if I awoke from this dream of drawing for a living, I could switch majors and get a real job.

But to me, I was going to art school.

All of a sudden, I went from being one of a handful of kids in high school that had a flair for art to being completely surrounded by 18-year-old artists like me. We all rejoiced at the news that as art majors we would never have to take math again, and only needed two years of English classes for our degree. Cookouts on the quad and other activities allowed us to meet one another. We were all in the same boat: we knew no one. Art majors were easy to spot because we always looked the part. Flannel shirts, Doc Martin shoes, dyed hair, overalls. Many of us congregated in circles, kicking around hacky sacks, which was cutting-edge social networking in 1995. Because the art building was called Group Six, we were all called Group Sixers. This was both a badge of honor for those of us who were enlisted as art majors and a warning label for those that weren't. They usually viewed us as sideshow attractions.

The night before classes started, I went to dinner at the Res Caff, where the underclassmen ate all three meals. The building had an odd acidic smell to it, which had nothing to do with food. After making my way through the buffet line I spotted a guy I'd seen around that day in the hack circles but hadn't yet met. He was another easy-to-identify art major wearing a Phish shirt and a green UVM hat, which was a strange juxtaposition to all of the blue and gray UMD garb everyone else wore. I slid my tray of food onto the table and slumped into the empty chair, exhausted from a full day of asking the typical one-line openers. What's your name? What's your major? Where are you from?

"So, what's your deal?" I deadpanned.

"Hey man, I'm Gregg," he said and extended his bony hand over our trays of food.

Despite the mass getting-to-know-you scene that was happening across the entire freshman class, I knew instantly that Gregg and I were going to be friends. I don't remember what we talked about, but the conversation was fun and easy, and we bonded instantly.

The next day we discovered that we had identical class schedules along with about fifteen others. Now, almost every class was art class. Life drawing. 2D. 3D. And a once-a-week class, called Colloquium, which was a showcase of every major an art student could sign up for the following year. My classmates were a mix of kids who lived on campus and kids who commuted from nearby towns, or hubs like New Bedford and Fall River. Gregg and I were able to hitch a ride with a couple of commuter girls to a big art supply store they knew about in Somerset. It was a warm September weekday and I found myself riding down the highway to an art store with my new friend and two cute girls we had just met. It wasn't lost on me that any other year I would have been bored out of my mind and daydreaming through a high school class, waiting for the bell to ring.

Riverside Art wasn't just an art store, it was a mecca for every kind of art supply imaginable. It had several rooms full of everything we needed. Each of our classes had different requirements for materials.

Art pencils. Gummy erasers. Marker sets, pastels, colored pencils. charcoal, Conté crayons. Brushes. Huge pads of newsprint. And gouache, a required but barely affordable paint that came in tiny tubes. Everything fit into our fishermen's tackle boxes, which we bought at Walmart on our way back to campus.

Each day, Group Six became a buzzing hive of artists. Each of the three floors had small alcoves with low carpeted benches where students would hang out on breaks to talk. People commuted up and down the giant spiraling staircase in the middle of the building armed with their tackle boxes and carrying either an oversized pad of drawing paper or the beginnings of their 3D balsa wood creations. Outside the main door the smokers smoked, the hacky sackers hacked, and everyone else lounged on concrete benches.

In fact, everything was made of concrete. Monolithic gray buildings populated the wide-open landscape of the campus. It was an unusual world built in the 1960s from concrete and strange ideas. The architect used a block-like style called Brutalism to craft these futuristic structures. He felt that the world around him was speeding up too fast. To correct this on the campus, every outdoor staircase was designed to be a half-step longer than the average human gait. This caused you to stop and readjust your trajectory as you walked, slowing you down. He shielded the parking lots from the campus with manmade hills, and yet the rooftops were rumored to be equipped with landing pads because he felt jetpacks would surely be in common use soon. Some assumed he was a Satan worshiper because of three circular concrete benches that resembled the number 666 when viewed from above through a glass walkway. Inside and out, the campus impersonated a Jetsons cartoon on a black and white TV. A mysterious New England weather pattern made UMass Dartmouth a magnet for any storm system that came through the area, which doubled down on the gray gloom. We fought the wind walking to class with our drawing pads that acted as sails on the wide-open walkways, and sheltered our fragile balsa wood sculptures we made in 3D class.

A frequent challenge for me was being outside in between the buildings when the urge to use the bathroom struck. I quickly learned where all of the men's rooms were located and I was always able to make it in the nick of time, followed by a painful session in the bathroom passing stool through my diseased rectum. A consistently difficult part of my day was the bathroom-less ten-minute walk home to the dorms from dinner at the Res Caff. It didn't help that the food notoriously sent people with the healthiest of digestive systems to the latrines after eating there. That walk was always a struggle to hold it. Breathing. Counting. Almost there. I would rush into the bathroom in the lobby of my dorm, a hidden gem that almost no one used so it was always unoccupied. Often, I wouldn't even attempt the walk and just used the bathroom in the Res Caff building before venturing outside. My friends would be waiting for me when I eventually emerged from the bathroom, probably wondering if there was something wrong with me but somehow knowing not to ask. Even with my new life at college, I hadn't told anyone that I had Crohn's.

Almost every night, Gregg and I had a practice that we called Walking the Earth. It was a term lifted from Samuel L. Jackson's character in *Pulp Fiction*, the most heavily quoted movie of that year. For us, walking the earth meant visiting people, mostly girls, that we knew in the dorms. We'd just drop by their suite to see if they were around, and soon we knew entire suites of girls. In reality, we were just a couple of skinny dorky guys in oversized plaid shirts walking the halls and meeting as many people as we could.

The first few weekends were quiet. Most of the kids who lived on campus went home on the weekends. Not me. I loved being there, and my friends were mostly the kids who stayed and reveled in the freedom of being liberated from living under their parents' roofs. Gregg was one of those kids, too.

We were all poor, and again, none of us had cars to get off-campus, so we always jumped at the chance to get in on someone going to the liquor store to buy us alcohol. This was a new arena for me because I mostly avoided drinking in high school. I was always afraid of what mixing alcohol and the serious prescription drugs would do. I didn't even know what it was like to be drunk before Gregg and I went in on our first installment of beer: two 40s of malt liquor. One was called King Cobra, and the other Olde English. To us, they were two golden glowing tickets to intoxication for only $2 each. It only took about 20 of those 40 ounces for us to feel the effects. This was economical, we reasoned, because we'd keep the rest in our mini fridges for the following night. Malt liquor and ice beer became our drinks of choice that year due to their low costs and high alcohol percentages. We took our buzzes outside to Walk the Earth.

As we journeyed around the quad and through the halls of the dorms at night, I gradually realized something was different. My stomach relaxed along with the rest of my body, and I didn't have the urge to use the bathroom at all.

Learning to drink became my new hobby, and several drinking adventures later, I had my verdict. It turned out that having a good buzz from alcohol soothed my need to overuse the restroom. Mentally it gave me a break from the anxiety of always needing to be near a bathroom to be comfortable. And physically it seemed to slow down the peristalsis of my intestines so I wouldn't have to go all the time. Medical advice would say to avoid alcohol because it would worsen Crohn's symptoms, but for me, it alleviated them.

I also didn't suffer from hangovers like my friends did. My best guess for my no-hangover superpower was either that my incredibly fast metabolism flushed everything through my system, or it was that high pain threshold coupled with my persistent soldier-on attitude.

Or maybe Crohn's gave me a constant mild-hangover feeling as a daily baseline, and I'd forgotten what it felt like to feel normal.

Three hours of straight drawing was something that all of the freshman Group Sixers needed to build up stamina for. After a few weeks, we would all agree that the difference between a good day and a bad day depended on how well you succeeded in drawing class. After a month of still-life drawing, we moved on to drawing the nude figure, and I grew better and better at drawing the human form. Female models were rare, and most days we drew one of the three male models UMass Dartmouth employed for decades: Wayne, Gabe, and Henry. In Group Six, they were as legendary as any other trio, like the Three Stooges, the Three Musketeers, or the Three Amigos. The three men were a perfect set because they couldn't be more physically different. Wayne was short, fat, and hairy. Gabe made each pose a study in the skeletal system with his tall and thin frame. And Henry was ripped with muscles from head to toe. In my four years in Group Six, I took figure drawing every semester. It turned out to be one of my favorite classes.

Freshman year in art school was the first time in my life that I excelled at something. My work didn't feel like work, and it made me so happy. I knew I had found my direction in life, and my kind of friends. I reveled in my luck at being able to do what I loved day in and day out. All that time suffering through middle school and high school history and math and English and Spanish and science and sports over the years had led me to this. I was finally planted in fertile ground, and I was getting better every day. I wouldn't know it then, as a nineteen-year-old kid, but art saved me. With whatever terrible luck I had with my health, I would not be someone who slaved away at a job they hated. Work was not a four-letter word. My creative side was something special inside me that I would always have, and take comfort in.

One new treatment that I started in high school when the Crohn's returned, and that I brought with me to college, was a nightly cortisone enema before bed. This helped to keep things under control and wasn't too difficult to administer. I would just slip into my bed with the bulb syringe of cloudy white liquid gel. Insert, squeeze, remove, and wipe, followed by dropping the used syringe into the trash by my bed, all without anyone knowing, including my roommate.

That is, until the end of the year when we were all moving out of the dorms. I was one of the last to leave, truly saddened to say goodbye to my friends and trying to hold on for as long as I could before returning home to Medfield.

To help me move out, Steve showed up in the car that we shared when I was in high school, our parents' old blue 1987 Chevy Celebrity. He had full ownership of it for his whole senior year and would be packing up and leaving for UPenn at the end of the summer, so I would have the car for my sophomore year.

In between trips carrying the final boxes to the car, my RA came by to officially check me out. This meant inspecting my side of the room to make sure I hadn't missed anything. Sure enough, I had. When she slid open the bottom drawer of my wooden desk, staring back at us was my box of enemas.

"Oh! Sorry, those are mine," I said as smoothly as I could, trying to hide how completely mortified I was to have such a crucial secret out in plain sight.

"Um, okay," she said as I grabbed the white plastic medical-looking box. I stuffed them into a nearby brown paper bag while she was still wondering what they were.

Now red-faced and nervous, I quickly answered her remaining

questions and signed a shaky signature to her clipboard before bidding her a quick thank-you and goodbye.

Later that week I found myself back on Charlesdale Road in my bedroom laying my charcoal figure drawings out on my bed for my mother to see. I was excited and proud to show her my Waynes and my Gabes and my Henrys. But I forgot, or perhaps didn't yet know the extent of, my mother's modesty about anything sexual. For her, art was pastel beachscapes of Cape Cod and cute crafty knickknacks. She didn't have much to say about the sea of naked charcoal men spilling off my bed, and gave off a look that teetered between worry and regret that I was making this kind of artwork at school.

"This is, ummm," she said hesitantly, "this is fine."

"Don't worry, not all of my work is figure drawing," I backpedaled.

I showed her my 2D and 3D work, remembering that Group Six was a foreign world she was unfamiliar with. My parents weren't like me, I reminded myself. I was going to have to find my own way.

9

CRUMPLED

"AT THIS POINT, WE HAVE DONE WHAT WE CAN DO WITH drugs."

I sat in Dr. Flores' new office in Waltham with my mother. The practice that he started with one other gastroenterologist over a decade earlier had grown substantially. Now, several pediatric gastroenterologists worked with them. The waiting room alone was the size of their entire office in Boston where I had first gone as a patient. Everything was brand new. In 1986 I was considered an outlier to be diagnosed with Crohn's so young. The majority of people who develop inflammatory bowel disease do so in their 20s and 30s. But the size of this new office revealed the rapid growth of pediatric IBD in the past decade.

As Dr. Flores spoke and his booming accented voice bounced off the white walls, my focus drifted to two items in his office. One was the photo frame he always kept on his desk of his growing family, now consisting of several children along with him and his wife. The other was a yellowing newspaper photo that he still had taped to the wall behind him, that featured me getting my Eagle Scout badge pinned to my uniform. He told us that he would refer to it with other kids who were recently diagnosed with Crohn's as an example of how the disease doesn't have to hold you back.

That summer we had been in touch about another issue. I'd gone to an oral surgeon who revealed I had seven wisdom teeth instead of the usual four. This meant a trip to the operating room for outpatient surgery to have them all removed at once. While that plan was executed with minimal weight loss, I still suffered tremendously from Crohn's. Every bowel movement inflicted corporal punishment on my body. From the outside, I was a thin but normal college-age kid. On the inside and behind closed bathroom doors, I felt like a tortured soul.

"Unfortunately, the rectum is really scarred down," he continued with a serious tone, "and the next step will be to have surgery. Which will mean you have a colostomy bag."

He placed a closed palm over his pleated waistline to support what he was saying.

"You don't need it right away, but this will be something to happen in the future. I can give you the names of a couple of surgeons in the city for you to meet with, so that when the time comes, you'll have someone."

This news flooded me with dread. I had a very rough idea of what a colostomy bag was. After all, that's what my roommate in Children's needed to have when I had my first surgery. But really, colostomies were something for old people. I didn't realize this would be my inevitable future. I would be going back to school in a month to start my junior year. Always the optimist, I eventually reasoned that I probably wouldn't need that surgery for a long time.

Dr. Flores gave us his recommendation for a renowned colorectal surgeon at Deaconess Hospital. At my mother's request for a second opinion, he suggested we look into Boston University Medical Center.

My mother and I arrived at Deaconess to meet with the first

surgeon, Dr. Boyle. This was the guy that Dr. Flores favored and strongly recommended. After a brief hello in his office, he and I parted with my mother so he could examine me. He looked young for someone at the top of his field. My last surgeon at Children's, Dr. Cantrell, had probably been in his sixties, but here was Dr. Boyle, who had to have been twenty years younger with the same kind of established reputation.

He performed the usual manual exam of my abdomen with his hands, the same pressing and tapping that Dr. Flores always did, and my body reacted in its usual ticklish ways. As he talked, I noticed his crooked teeth, which to me was a sign of humble beginnings and made me like him more. He then advanced things rapidly by announcing that he was going to have to feel inside my rectum. My heart began to beat faster as my body filled with panic. Dr. Flores had rarely done this over the years, knowing the pain it caused me. I hadn't realized this would be part of the exam, but given the reason I was here, it made sense.

I clenched down and braced for impact as he inserted his lubricated, latex-gloved finger through my anus. I moaned through the excruciating pain even though I sensed that he was being as gentle as he could, slowly turning his finger to get an accurate assessment of things.

"All done," he said as he removed his finger. Relief was instant, and somehow this didn't trigger the urge to use the bathroom. I wiped myself as best I could with a brown paper towel and followed him into his office across the hall as we reunited with my mother.

"Well Bradley, you're definitely going to need to have an ostomy, it's just a matter of when. There actually isn't much Crohn's present in your rectum. It's almost all scar tissue, and there's nothing that can be done about that except to surgically remove it."

It took me a few seconds for my brain to register what he was saying. Ostomy. The shorthand for colostomy bag was ostomy. Like how "quake" could be used to describe an earthquake, or how a sea captain would refer to a shipwreck simply as a wreck.

"How that works is that we'll remove the anus and rectum and sew you up in the back. Then we take that end of your intestine and create what's called a stoma, which is where we'll bring the intestine to the outside of your skin." He made an upside-down "okay" sign with his hand and placed it over his lower stomach, just above his beltline.

"Seeing that you have Crohn's-colitis, what I would actually recommend doing is removing the entire large bowel. We've seen several patients with your type of inflammatory bowel disease, and by removing the whole large intestine we've found that it takes care of the need for surgery for them indefinitely."

My mother stopped him immediately. "No. He has Crohn's. The last time he had surgery was to remove a section of his small intestine. I would think we should be removing only the diseased section of bowel, leaving the healthy portion."

"Yes, but the odds of Crohn's returning in the bowel north of your last anastomosis would be highly unlikely seeing as you have Crohn's-colitis. The decision is up to you, of course. This is just my recommendation."

"Well, we'll be getting a second opinion on this whole thing, so we'll see," said my mother.

"That's great. And it's important that you're having these appointments now so these kinds of conversations can happen, and everything can be planned. This is a big decision, I know. But this surgery always goes better when the patient is on the healthier side. Some people wait until they're extremely sick and emaciated, and that comes with complications. I know it's a big decision, just don't wait so long that it's an emergency."

"Okay, I understand that," I said.

"One other thing you'll want to do," said Dr. Boyle, "is to visit a sperm bank and have your sperm frozen. Because of the area we're operating in, it is a risk, although an unlikely one, that nerves could get severed and you could become impotent. Again, highly unlikely, but it's a precautionary measure to take before we operate. I can give you the contact information for a few of them to look into."

We thanked him, and we exited his office. On the drive home, we talked about the appointment.

"I just don't think it makes sense to take out healthy intestines," my mom said.

"Right, if I had ulcerative colitis then it might make sense to remove healthy parts of my intestines," I said.

"Well, even if you did have ulcerative colitis we might not want to remove more than the essential diseased portion. At least we'll have a second opinion for this."

Our next appointment was at BU Medical Center the following week. Anxiety began to linger for the inevitability of another rectal exam with more painful probing.

If ever there was a time when I wished we didn't need a second opinion, it turned out to be that appointment. BU Medical was a teaching hospital, and the doctor I saw had two medical students with him. I was asked to change into a johnnie in a bathroom across from the exam room and join them when I was ready.

We went over my medical history and my symptoms as they took turns examining my belly. I knew what was coming. The doctor had his medical students put on latex gloves. There was no way all three of them were going to examine me.

"Okay," I said as confidently as I could, "only one of you is going to do that, so decide which of you gets to do the honors."

It was decided that we'd all assess how we felt after the first student examined me.

The pain was several times worse than with Dr. Boyle. The student's unexperienced finger felt rough and forceful as the doctor coached him through what he was feeling for. I groaned as I clenched and crinkled the paper on the table. I could feel that this provoked my urge to use the bathroom. When it finally ended, I jumped off the table and flew across the hall into the bathroom, collapsing on the toilet. In relief, I slowly undid the tie behind my neck, and the johnnie fell to the floor. I wouldn't be putting it back on.

As I endured my usual pain during a bowel movement, I turned to my left to see my reflection in a full-length mirror on the back of the bathroom door. For the first time probably ever, I could see myself slumped over on the toilet. My ribs visible, my legs bony. My mother's words to my pediatrician rang in my head: "he's always been thin." However, I could finally understand that this emaciated person languishing on the toilet was not the clean picture of health that I identified myself as. Underneath my bulky plaid shirts and my thrift-store fashions, I was sick. But, even with this knowledge, I wasn't ready for the body-altering surgery that would inevitably come.

I wiped my tender bottom and stood up. I turned to the sink and washed my hands. I put my clothes back on. I paused to look up at my red-faced reflection in the mirror on the back of the door. "One thing at a time," I whispered to myself. I picked up my crumpled johnnie from the floor and tossed it into the laundry bin as I emerged into the fluorescent light of the hallway.

10

LOSING MY RELIGION

Sometimes things that look awful from a distance really aren't as bad as they seem. One year later, the summer before my senior year in college, I lived with my aunt Jeanne on Cape Cod. Between the four cousins, we all agreed she was the cool aunt, and a stranger seeing us together would assume that she was my mother. We both inherited the same thin frame of my grandfather, her father. In reality, I looked more like her than either of my actual parents.

She lived alone in her house, a charming cape on a quiet street in Falmouth, which was on the opposite end of the Cape from Truro. She had an unfinished second floor, aka her attic, where I set up camp. The idea of living in a non-air-conditioned second-floor bedroom might have sounded sweltering, but my window fan did a nice job of cooling the place off. The army cot I slept on looked like the worst night's sleep you ever had. But it was so narrow that my body had no choice but to sink into the middle, wrapped in a sort of cocoon, resulting in a great night's sleep every time.

Our lives seemed to be in sync with each other that summer. We were both at relatively low points. She had gotten divorced a couple of years earlier and had just finished school to become a physical therapist, the cost of which was covered by her ex-husband. Though she graduated at the top of her class, she struggled weekly to find per-diem work in the handful of PT facilities on the Cape. My rent supplement of a few hundred dollars a month helped her out. We both took on a solitary existence. Cooking our own meals, shopping for our own food. I didn't know anyone on the Cape and failed to make friends at the internship where I was working.

Soft As A Grape, a T-shirt and apparel company based in Falmouth's town center, took me on as an intern that summer. Their main enterprise was screen printing, and I worked in the small art department in the basement of the store. My boss was a laid-back fisherman named Drew, who was never seen without a tightly curled baseball cap and goatee. I helped him with various art projects related to the screen-printing side of the business.

That was my life that summer. I drove to work each morning, passed three or four golf courses along the way, and worked with Drew doing little art and design projects. At night I went home, ate dinner, and watched TV. My only real pastime that summer was going to the bathroom. The Crohn's in my body welcomed that summer's solitude by acting up. Sessions on the toilet clocked in at upwards of an hour and a half, several times a day, and the pain was becoming increasingly intolerable. I suffered that summer in my aunt's downstairs bathroom and in the men's restroom at work. Things were getting bad.

When I first had Crohn's in my small intestine, stomachaches would last five minutes at most. They had a signature dull wave-like feeling unlike anything else. Now with Crohn's and scar tissue enveloping my rectum, I struggled through every bowel movement.

Writhing in pain on the toilet, my mind grasped for metaphors for what I was feeling. The first was that it felt like I was sitting on an iron railroad spike. Sharp, searing pain split through me as I passed stool out of my body.

The second metaphor was a scene from a music video. These were still the MTV years, back when that channel would actually play music videos. In the R.E.M. video for "Losing My Religion," there are these recreated biblical scenes. In one of them, two men stand next to each other. One man's stomach was sliced open and you can see his insides. The other man stood next to him, fingering the man's open wound. This scene played over and over in my head. The pain that man endured in the video was surely less than what I felt in those moments on the toilet. This vision made me fantasize about being able to physically rip open my stomach and cut out my insides. I would do anything to exorcise the evil inside me by extracting it.

More and more, when I felt finished using the bathroom, I often wasn't finished. I would wipe, stand up on weak, shaking legs that had atrophied in the time on the commode, wash my hands, and exit the bathroom only to feel the urge to go again. Seconds later I was back in the same position on the still-warm toilet seat. I felt bad when this happened at work, where there was just one single bathroom for men and another for women, but I was just in so much pain that it didn't matter.

Then, one Saturday afternoon as I sat slumped over the toilet in my aunt's house, I saw something that replaced the pain with panic. I peered behind me into the bowl and was shocked to see the water was full of blood.

That was it. I cried "uncle" to my Crohn's bully. A phone call to Dr. Flores got him to increase my dose of prednisone to get things under control. But the larger question loomed. Was it time for me to have the surgery? Even if the steroids could steer me back, was this the quality of life I wanted to continue to endure? I practically lived in the bathroom and it would surely impact my life at school more than ever.

It was late July. I had been at the internship long enough so that I could legitimately put it on my resumé. Drew, who had enjoyed having a partner in the art room, had already hired a junior designer who would fill my spot when the summer ended.

I got on the phone with my mom. I told her that I'd contacted Dr. Flores and that he increased the prednisone.

"I'm not doing so good, Ma," I said, fighting back a lump in my throat. I told her about the pain, and the marathon sessions in the bathroom, and the toilet full of blood.

"I'm at my wit's end," I confessed. "I can't go back to school like this. I can't continue to live like this. This isn't living." It felt refreshing to be able to talk openly about this, something I rarely did. I was in a nosedive, and while the steroids would slow my descent, I couldn't keep this up for much longer. Remembering Dr. Boyle's advice, I'd be better off making the decision before I weighed ninety pounds and was knocking on death's door.

My mother let out a sigh on the other end of the phone. "Okay, so what are you suggesting?"

"I think it's time for the surgery," I said, "because even if I get a little better from the prednisone increase, how long is that going to last? I've been pushing it for the past few months. I don't want to be in and out of the hospital for the next year only to arrive at the same conclusion, that I'll need one of those"—I paused because the words in my mouth were hard to say—"colostomy bags."

I was the opposite of The Boy Who Cried Wolf, and my mother knew it. A more accurate fable would be called The Boy Who Didn't Cry, as the wolves crept in and circled the village. I held things inside to the point of exhaustion, usually to a fault. If I was saying uncle, then I meant it.

"Okay," my mother reasoned, "I can call the surgeon's office on Monday morning and we'll find out what to do next."

"Dr. Boyle, right?"

"Is he the one you want to go with?"

"Yes, but we'll have him take out only the diseased portion, not all of my large intestine. Like we talked about."

She agreed that this was a good plan. After hanging up the phone, a huge weight lifted.

Fortunately, Dr. Boyle could fit me into his schedule fairly quickly. Surgery was scheduled for early August, which left me with about a week at home to prepare myself for what was coming.

Because I chronically kept things to myself, when I finally asked for help, things always seemed to get better. I got a small improvement in my health just by letting it out. It felt like off-loading a heavy backpack after a long, long hike. The increased prednisone was also having an effect, so I felt better all around. Yet this didn't present much of a challenge to my decision to have the surgery. I knew in my heart it was time. It was nice to feel better, even if it was only temporary.

I still didn't understand much about the details of living with a colostomy bag. I knew it would be permanent, and that people wouldn't see it because it would be hidden underneath clothing. It would be strange not to use my rear end anymore, but I figured the number of bowel movements I'd had in the past twelve years equaled a lifetime of bowel movements for anyone else. My ass was totaled.

I thought about the boy who'd been my roommate at Children's and the roadmap of scars across his belly. The nurse coming in and showing him what the bag would look like. He couldn't have been older than eight or nine years old. We had a family friend who also had an ostomy from having ulcerative colitis about fifteen years earlier. With that disease, however, a bag comes with a cure. Removal of his colon meant permanent remission. You would never know he had one, evidence that I could continue to keep my poor health a secret, under the cover of clothing. He'd offered to come and talk to me about it, but of course I never took him up on it.

A packet of information arrived and I went through the materials. The glossy marketing brochures from the medical supply companies showed images of elderly people smiling, laughing, and living a care-free life. I had just turned twenty-two, and obviously wasn't the target demographic. There were colostomies, which I was slated to have, which meant there was large bowel remaining. Ileostomies, which was what our family friend had, removed the entire large bowel, leaving only the small intestine. And there were urostomies where the bladder had been removed. One article pointed to an online survey of people who had ostomy surgery. I booted up the beige fixture in our living room that was my mom's Gateway desktop computer and waited to get online as the modem coughed and screeched. I pulled up the website with the survey and spent time analyzing people's comments about having an ostomy. There are basically three ways you would end up with one. The first was inflammatory bowel disease: me, my room-mate from Children's, and our family friend. Another way was colon cancer: seemingly the old people that appeared in the photos in the brochures. The third was major trauma like a car accident or gunshot wound: not anyone I knew.

The online survey data was valuable information in 1998. We were still years away from social websites that let people freely give their views about niche topics. In one way or another, most partici-pants said that they were better off having had the surgery. People talked about how sick they were beforehand, and how they finally felt normal again. I could relate to that feeling based on how I felt after I had recovered from my first surgery. Remission is bliss. The cancer survivors were grateful and said they would gladly have an ostomy as opposed to the other grim outcome. There were only a couple of people that said it was horrible, and now they were sentenced to having to deal with this disgusting contraption for the rest of their life.

As I read through all of the comments, a pattern emerged. The people that needed an ostomy because they were terribly sick were the ones that said they were okay with it. They were severely sick and suffering before the surgery, or were presented with an ostomy as a cure for their cancer. Some of them said it was the best decision they had ever made. The people who hated their ostomies were unanimously the people who had experienced trauma. They were completely healthy and had probably taken their health for granted when they abruptly had some kind of an accident. This seemed understandable to me and gave me a stronger resolve in my decision to go through with the surgery. My health had reached the point where the idea of shitting into a bag for the rest of my life sounded better than continuing to limp along with my failing body.

Monday, T-minus forty-eight hours to surgery. I had an appointment with Dr. Boyle and one of the nurses that specialized in ostomies. After a review of what the surgery would entail and a brief exam, he sized up my abdomen.

"So, as we talked about, the end of your bowel will come out somewhere in this area." He placed his hand on the lower left quadrant of my belly. "We want to position it in a spot that will stay mostly flat."

He studied my abdomen as he had me lie down first, then had me sit up. He felt the contour of my protruding hip, which tickled. He seemed to use that as a guide. I watched him draw an X on my stomach, about two inches southeast of my belly button.

Then the nurse took out one of the pouches from a white box. "Okay, let's see what that looks like," she said. The pouch was round at the top, roughly the size of a paperback book, and funneled together at the bottom where the opening to empty it was.

She centered the pouch over the X, and I stood up and pulled my pants back up. Everything I had read had said that these things were undetectable underneath clothes, but with my pants hanging in the normal position on my waistline, the half-moon shape of the top peeked out above them.

"Can it go lower?"

"No, this is where it should go," answered Dr. Boyle.

He showed me that if it went lower it would come up on the fold of my pelvis when I sat down. "That's going to make it hard to put the appliance on. You want a nice and flat area so you can get a good seal."

I left feeling disheartened and talked out my grievances to myself in the car ride home. What would be different? Most of the time, you still wouldn't be able to notice because my shirt would cover the part sticking out from my pants. I guess when I would go to the beach, I would have to hike my bathing suit up like Steve Urkel. Not that big of a deal because I mostly only ever went to the beach with my family.

I rationalized that I didn't have much of a choice. With my current state of health, I couldn't even go to the beach. I just hoped that when this was all over, I would be part of the group who said it was the best decision they'd ever made.

11

A BRAND-NEW BAG

ON THE MORNING OF SURGERY, I WAS LEGITIMATELY anxious. Was this the right thing to do? My stomach had a steady buzz of soreness from the clean-out, which for the first time wasn't GoLYTELY; it was magnesium citrate followed by several glasses of water. This was a million times easier to ingest. I entered our downstairs bathroom and, for the last time in my life, sat on the toilet and evacuated the remainder of my bowels like a normal human being. I stared down at the tile floor, the familiar lemon-yellow and black pinwheel pattern. Folded in half on the toilet, I had a moment where I reminisced about how much time I had spent in that small room. I skimmed my hand across the cold tile and grout like a prisoner bidding farewell to his prison cell. The next time I would see it, things would be different.

Driving into Boston to the hospital felt like déjà vu. Both my parents in the front seat and me in the back. It felt like the first time we drove into Children's Hospital when I was ten, which would have been twelve years earlier, almost to the day. The tree-lined VFW Parkway hadn't changed, but I felt entirely different from the kid that used to sit in the backseat. I was fully grown and had found art and music and my direction in life. I was in stark contrast to my parents in the front seat. They were exactly the same, traveling as they typically did, without music playing on the radio. My father had been tense from the instant I had returned home from the Cape, stressfully waiting in the yard as I pulled into the driveway. My mother was quiet and composed.

The usual check-in. The nurse behind the desk had me on the list for surgery and asked me the usual questions as she put the wristband on my arm.

"Name?"

"Brad Harris. Bradley Harris."

"Date of birth?"

I looked down at the wristband she was fastening to my arm. "Uh-oh. This is wrong."

Immediately alarmed, the nurse began searching other folders on her desk, which I allowed for a second. "Just kidding, that's right."

Relief laughter erupted between the nurse and my mother. It was a stupid joke, but it was enough to break the tension and get my mother to laugh.

The rest of the morning went as planned. I met Dr. Boyle in pre-op and signed off on the consent form. An IV was started, and the usual drugs were administered to put me off to sleep. By that point, I had learned to enjoy the wooziness that came with them. Fentanyl and Versed swept me away from the hurricane of what I had endured in the past couple of months, with a new struggle on the horizon ahead: recovery from major abdominal surgery.

I smiled as tried to lift my head, which seemed to weigh a thousand pounds. I was in the operating room now. I was transferred from the bed to the cold operating table. A warm blanket covered my body. EKG monitors were attached. A blood pressure cuff squeezed my ankle. I fought to stay awake as long as I could, knowing I would lose the battle in the end.

"Brad." A louder than normal voice in my ear. "I want you to count to ten."

Easy. I'm not even running for the bathroom this time, said the comedian in my head. One. Two. Three. Four...

The surgery had been a complete success according to Dr. Boyle. No complications. I was hooked up to the usual morphine machine with my Jeopardy buzzer for pain control and sent up to a room for the night.

The next morning I was happy to just lie in bed with the covers over what lay beneath them: my new anatomical structure. Soon enough, Dr. Boyle came by to check the dressings on my wounds.

He peeled back the covers and we lifted my gown. A clear plastic bag had been adhered to my stomach, I wasn't expecting it to be transparent. I could see the end of my intestines, which looked like a big red button.

"It'll take a few days for this to start working," said Dr. Boyle. "Your belly has gone through trauma, which happens in any bowel resection, so it'll take a bit for it to wake up again." As he spoke, he gently undid the dressing that was over the midline incision which went from above my belly button to the top of my pelvic bone.

It was a lot to take in. On top of the new colostomy and the vertical incision, I had three bulb drains sprouting out of me. Two in the front and one behind. I turned away as he asked me to roll over on my side so he could check out my rear end, which was now totally sealed off.

"Everything looks good," he said. "Make sure you get up and walk today. That will help to get your bowels moving again. Tomorrow one of the stoma nurses will come by. We like to have you do a couple of appliance changes while you're in the hospital with us. Don't worry, you'll get the hang of it." With a cool smile he said, "You'll do great."

Soon after, my mom arrived. And before I knew it, I was up walking with her.

The word "appliance" seemed to be the term used most frequently for the actual physical pouch, and my first appliance change was a huge failure. The stoma nurse, a middle-aged woman in a white coat, arrived the next day carrying a bulky briefcase of appliance supplies. I hit my morphine buzzer before I pulled myself up in bed and worked my legs over the edge. I had so many things attached to me I felt like an octopus. But I didn't have the feeling that I had from my first surgery where I didn't have use of my stomach muscles, probably because the incision this time was vertical instead of horizontal. I laughed at the irony because the whole point of making that horizontal incision the first time around was so it wouldn't be very noticeable. Now, I would forever be abnormal when it came to waistlines. I stood up and walked with the help of the stoma nurse to the bathroom in my room.

I stood at the sink, catching my bearings. We untied my gown to reveal the cornucopia of bandages, bags, and tubes reflected back at me in the mirror. I tried my best to pay attention to what she was saying, but my stamina was low, and my mind was overwhelmed with my new appearance.

She removed the bag to reveal a round red dumpling poking out of my abdomen, which was the end of my intestines. It was one of the oddest things I'd ever seen. I was inside out.

"It's huge," I said with a tone of both disappointment and disgust. Dr. Boyle had said that the size would vary, but this was the size of a small apple.

"Oh, the stoma will shrink. I promise," she said reassuringly. "You're only two days out of surgery. Everything in your stomach is swollen like this, but it will return to its natural size as you heal."

Still, I was grossed out at the sight of my moist red intestines. I thought I was prepared for this, but in my post-op condition, this was just too much. I started to get nauseous.

"I'm not feeling well," I said. She could tell that I was fading fast and called for my nurse to help me back to my bed. She was able to size and place a new pouch on me before the nurse appeared with a pink pan for me to throw up into. Though my face was probably colorless by that point, I was able to hold it together and I didn't vomit.

They helped me back to bed where I hit my morphine buzzer again and faded off to sleep.

By the time I was ready to leave the hospital, a week after surgery, I had become a bit more comfortable with changing the appliance. Once I got past the abstraction of having part of my insides on the outside, I could focus my attention on the craft of the colostomy bag.

The red knob of intestine that stuck out was called the stoma. It was as if they took the end of my intestine and flipped it out, like how you pair socks together when folding laundry. Then the outside edge gets tucked back down into my abdominal cavity and sewn on so that only the seamless button sits above the surface.

Each appliance has a flat surface called a flange. You cut a hole through the middle of the flange that's the size of the stoma, and then peel off the tape backing to reveal the adhesive barrier that will stick to my skin and completely surround the stoma. The pouch either attaches to the flange in a one-piece appliance, or it's a separate piece that connects like a piece of Tupperware, which is a strange but highly effective use of the snap-on container technology. Then when the bag fills with stool, it's emptied out through the bottom of the pouch which was held together by a scissor-like clip.

The goal is to get a completely tight seal, so no odor or stool comes out. After a few days, the adhesive seal starts to wear off, and the flat flange starts to warp like a potato chip. At that point, the appliance needs to get changed and everything starts over. The mechanics were easy enough to pick up, which was good because there was a lot more to it than just that. Filled with nerve endings, the rectum tells you when you need to move your bowels. Without one, I had no warning. I would just notice that all of a sudden the bag had filled with contents. This was fine, but during appliance changes, I found that I could quite literally have a mess on my hands at any time. So, each change was a beat-the-clock session.

With my parents back at work, I recovered at home taking care of my body as though it were a science experiment. One drain was removed before I had left the hospital, and I measured the diminishing contents of the others. My midline incision was healing well, and my rear end was becoming more tolerable to sit on.

One difference was that the smell of my stool was remarkably worse. Initially, I had hoped that this was going to be like the stoma, which had shrunk down significantly to be a bit larger than a cherry tomato. But even after returning home the rank smell of going to the bathroom persisted. It was equivalent to the smell of really bad diarrhea, the kind that a healthy person might experience once or twice a year. And this was every single time I used the bathroom to empty my appliance, which was three or four times a day.

I brought it up with the stoma nurse during the first post-op appointment I had.

"So, is it normal that my stool smells absolutely terrible? I mean, it doesn't make sense that technically the only different thing is I don't have a rectum. It's not like I lost a large portion of my bowel with this surgery."

"This comes up a lot," she said. "It just seems to smell more because now the stool is being emptied in the front of your body as opposed to behind you. You're more aware of it because it's right under your nose."

"No," I said hesitantly, "it smells not just a little worse but a ton worse."

She didn't agree, which annoyed me. Why didn't anyone tell me about this? No matter, I already knew what my next move was. I left the exam room and scheduled the next appointment for the following week before I went back to school.

By the time I arrived at my next stoma clinic appointment, I was ready. My appliance was full, and when the stoma nurse escorted me to the exam room, I excused myself to the connected bathroom. I emptied the contents into the toilet and the awful smell into the air. I washed my hands and opened the door.

"You seriously can't tell me that this smell is normal," I said to her as the putrid wave of stink crept toward her in the room.

Again she denied it. I was frustrated at yet another dead end. We went through the appliance change, which by this time I insisted on doing myself. I was relieved that I wouldn't have to come to these appointments anymore. I could take this on myself from here on out.

"I can tell you're going to be a pro at this in no time," she said. "I have another patient who had an ostomy at about the same age as you. You're what..."

"Twenty-two," I said.

"Yes, he's twenty-six now and actually he just got married. He met his wife after he'd had the surgery."

I liked this encouraging story. I hadn't let Crohn's interfere with my life up until this point, and I wasn't going to start now. Still, the idea of dating and sex with this pouch on my stomach was going to present some challenges.

As she walked me out to the reception area, I thanked her for her time, and for showing me the ropes. I'd had some good conversations with this stoma nurse because she'd revealed to me that she had Crohn's disease as well. Having Crohn's and being an ostomy nurse made me think that she must have an ostomy, even though only a small percentage of Crohn's patients have one.

"How long have you had an ostomy for," I said.

"Oh," she said, surprised by my question. "I don't have one."

"Well, not yet anyway," I said.

I saw the weather of her face change immediately and her eyes narrowed. I hadn't meant to offend her, but I recognized that unintentionally it had come off as a mean comment. Still, I was a bit stunned by her honest reaction that she became upset at the idea of having one. Of course, needing to get an ostomy was a last resort, but this was her job.

I didn't apologize, just bid her farewell. Walking out I felt for the first time that I had become a failed Crohn's patient. That even with all I had suffered through in the past twelve years, I had given up and surrendered. I wouldn't see another stoma nurse for six years.

After being home for about a week I decided it was time to venture out into the world. Up until that point I had stayed inside. My only excursions were shuttling back and forth to my post-op appointments. The drains had been removed and the midline incision was almost healed.

It was Saturday night, and my parents were going out to eat at Ma Glockner's, a family favorite of ours. They asked if I wanted to go with them, assuming that I would still opt to stay home, but I said yes.

It was time to get out of the loose-fitting gym shorts I had worn around the house and put on some real clothes. The ostomy felt strange with jeans on over it. The top crescent of the pouch stood out above the waist of my pants, but with a shirt on you could barely notice that anything was different. I had always worn my shirts untucked, and that helped too. Still, the appliance was something I would have to get used to. Just walking around or moving from a standing position to sitting made me feel the bag resting against my skin. This must be what it's like for girls when they first start wearing a training bra. It feels strange up against your body at first, then gradually begins to feel normal and invisible.

I grew up going to Ma Glockner's, which was truly a unique restaurant. Located about a mile off of the main road on a side street, it was an old New England restaurant on the outside. The letters "MG" in an Olde English typeface adorned the side of the white clapboard building, which was a series of rooms added on since the original restaurant opened sometime around World War II.

Since it was equidistant from my cousins' house in Rhode Island, we would often meet there on a Saturday night for dinner. Waiting in line often took forty-five minutes to an hour, but once you were there you were committed because there weren't any other restaurants in the area. Going somewhere else wasn't an option. Andy, Julie, Steve, and I were able to sit in a booth by ourselves, our parents in an adjacent booth. Ma Glockner's was famous for its chicken dinner, which was the only meal they served. There was no food menu, just one for drinks. The waiter would arrive at the table and take our drink order, which was always three Roy Rogers for the boys and a Shirley Temple for Julie, and ask how many dinners we would like. Andy and Julie usually split a dinner while Steve and I devoured our own. Our drinks would arrive with four identical garden salads in wooden bowls, already dressed in a fluorescent orange Catalina dressing. Want a different salad dressing? Not an option. The fact that they let Andy and Julie split a dinner was about as far as they would deviate from the menu.

The main course arrived, their trademark chicken, which was

crisp and moist, unlike any other chicken I've ever had. I later learned that this was berched chicken, though I've never seen it on the menu at any other restaurant. On the plate next to the chicken were savory french fries, a cube of cranberry topping, and a warm, to-die-for cinnamon bun.

My father backed the car out of the garage, and my mother and I got in, she in the passenger seat, me in the back. On the drive over to the restaurant, I sat on a square black pillow we had purchased for my post-op period. This was a requirement that would allow my backside to continue to heal. When the hostess showed us to our table, I gently sat down on the pillow which made me appear abnormally tall across from my parents. The waitress arrived and introduced herself, handing us menus.

"Menus? What's this?" I said to my mother.

"Oh, they've changed things since you've been away at school," my mother explained. "It's under new management. They have a full menu now like a regular restaurant."

She could read the apprehension on my face. "Don't worry, you can still get the chicken."

Relieved, I reconstructed the regular Ma Glockner's dinner by ordering a garden salad with Catalina dressing and the chicken dinner. My mother ordered fish and chips, which was her go-to entrée at restaurants, and my father ordered chicken parmesan.

"Boring," I sang when the waitress was out of earshot. "You can get that stuff anywhere. This is Ma Glockner's. The chicken restaurant?"

We talked about school, which I would be able to return to right on time, as planned. Unfortunately, I would have to bring a pillow with me to class for the first couple of weeks. My friends knew I'd had surgery, but they didn't know the details. I would just tell them that it's to help ease my abdomen in recovery. A good dodge.

As I reveled in the nostalgia of eating my Ma Glockner's chicken dinner, I reviewed the past month in my head. I had pulled it off. The worst was behind me, and I could certainly appreciate the fact that the pain was gone. My body was forever altered, and there was a lot to get used to. But for the first time in a long time, I had my health back. Remission had returned.

PART II

12

DISTURBING THE PEACE OF THE AIR

I STARTED MY SENIOR YEAR OF COLLEGE STILL HAVING TO sit on a pillow. I lied to everyone then, too. I told them that I'd had some abdominal surgery and that the pillow helped with the healing. This didn't even make sense, but it was an answer given with confidence followed by a quick subject change. Because after all, the ability to keep the ostomy hidden from everyone was one of the appeals.

Some things are harder to hide than others, though. If someone were to ask me what were the top-three worst parts of having a colostomy bag I would have answered, number one: the smell. Number two: the smell. Number three: the smell. Everything else was manageable.

Since the ostomy nurses didn't think there was anything different about the foul smell of my stool, or more likely, there wasn't anything they could do about it, I went back to school hoping everything would be normal for once. But soon enough, I started getting comments from my suitemates.

"Whoever just took a shit up here needs to get checked out!" one of them yelled from the upstairs bathroom I had just used.

I lived with six other guys in a townhouse-style suite in Cedar

Dell, the on-campus upperclassmen housing. Each of us had our own room, and there were two bathrooms. A full bathroom upstairs, and a tiny half-bathroom downstairs. I needed to strategize how I would empty my appliance without disturbing the peace of the air.

Both bathrooms had fans, but the downstairs bathroom was ideal because it was so small that there was less foul air for the fan to eliminate.

While most people avoid using public restrooms, I began to seek them out. I would freely use the campus bathrooms, only having to put up with strangers making comments about how horrible the bathroom smelled as I washed my hands in an adjacent sink. If I even said anything at all, I would just shrug and say that it smelled like this when I got here, too. Meanwhile, I was shriveling up and dying inside with embarrassment. Fortunately, conversations in men's restrooms are infrequent.

I soon discovered that the student center, which was located near our townhouse, had a single bathroom that no one used. A huge score. It was always unoccupied and clean, and I would use it often when I was home. I could make it there and back to my room in about ten minutes, much preferring the physical hassle than the emotional hassle of smelling up one of our suite bathrooms.

So even though I no longer toiled on the toilet writhing in pain, I still had a good amount of stress around going to the bathroom.

And I was still getting a better handle on the appliance, specifically when to change it. That took about a year to really master, and even after that, there would always be little accidents where the appliance would fail. When the adhesive wore off, the seal would be broken and the odor would get out.

One time we were all at a bar on a Thursday night. By then we were all officially twenty-one, but this was the kind of shady New Bedford establishment where underage kids could use their fake IDs to gain entry. A bunch of us were on the dance floor. All of a sudden it smelled like someone let off a stink bomb, and I knew it was me. As everyone else fanned the air in front of their faces, I briefly pulled my T-shirt up over my nose, Lone Ranger style, and took a whiff to confirm that the offensive odor was coming from my abdomen. Yes, it was me. This was a little trick I had picked up from the ostomy nurses. I spent the rest of the night with my left hand in my pocket, pressing the appliance to my skin to keep the odor from getting out.

Another surprising side effect of the surgery was that gas can escape my body at any time. Without my rectum and those important nerve endings, there was no telling what my body would do next. Because I had most of my large intestine left, I could sometimes feel things moving through and anticipate output. But often there was no warning.

One time I was visiting a friend in a textile design class, which was in a Group Six room that we called The Fishbowl because a bank of windows lined one whole side of the room. Students sat at industrial tables on stools working on their projects. I was standing talking to my friend when all of a sudden a loud farting sound erupted from my direction. Electrocuted by embarrassment, my hand jerked to my stomach to try and mute the sound as my reddening face squeezed out the word "sorry." Everyone's eyes shot to my stomach with questioning looks on their faces. Sometimes in situations like this, I could pass it off like nothing happened because there was never a smell to match the sound. The gas was trapped safely in my appliance. This time was so blatant though.

"Jesus B," my friend said, "You okay?"

"Yeah, yep. I'm okay. Sorry about that."

I hung around for a while longer to not leave the class on such a down note. But walking out of there, finally alone in the hallway, I said quietly to my abdomen, my new sidekick in life, "What the fuck, man?"

. . .

Even with all of these new social trials, I was healthy again, and I was healthy in ways like never before. I began to enjoy the outdoors, especially places that didn't have immediate bathroom access. I had netted out on the positive side of it all, and was happy with my decision to have the ostomy. It gave me a freedom that I hadn't known since childhood, and my laser-accurate instincts about knowing where the closest bathroom was began to dull due to lack of use. Gradually I realized there was no longer a reason to be on high alert all the time. I could be totally comfortable outside, or in the city, or anywhere really. To me, this was such a gift, and for everyone else, it was just normal. Sure, the smell was an issue, but I could be in and out of a bathroom in two minutes flat. That was something that I marveled over for months. I had a noticeable amount of time back in my day. And of course, the pain was gone too.

13

THE CYST

THE FOLLOWING SPRING, I FOUND MYSELF SITTING uncomfortably on a chair in Dr. Boyle's waiting room. Uncomfortable physically because there was a painful mass growing on my rear end that caused me to sit tenderly to one side. Uncomfortable emotionally because I didn't know what it was. My nerves were running rampant at the thought of my body malfunctioning yet again.

In the months since I'd last seen him for post-op appointments, Dr. Boyle had left Deaconess Medical Center and joined the surgical staff at Brigham and Women's Hospital. The Brigham was another hospital located in the renowned Longwood area of Boston. A neighborhood only about a half-mile in diameter holds several of the world's best facilities for medical care. Boston Children's Hospital. Dana-Farber Cancer Institute. Beth Israel. And the Brigham. Many of them are connected by tunnels and bridges, and like the rest of Boston, form a maze you can quite literally get lost in.

I soon found myself in an exam room with Dr. Boyle, explaining to him what I'd experienced. At school, we had a spring formal called the Spring Ball. This was less like the prom with dates and corsages, and more like a regular party except everyone had dressed up. We hosted a pre-game party in our suite that featured a floor-to-ceiling marker-drawn version of a prom backdrop made by a couple of friends that worked at Campus Design. Everyone loved it and rolls of photos were taken of posed couples and groups of friends. Then, it was time to board the Greyhound buses that took us to a mansion in Newport, Rhode Island that hosted the event. In true college fashion, it was a night of drinking and antics. At one point on my way to the bathroom, I passed a room where people were jumping up and down on one of the antique beds.

"When I sat down on the toilet, it felt like something tore on my backside," I told Dr. Boyle. "I patted some toilet paper on it, and there was blood. You can imagine this was terrifying for me."

The tear was like a record scratch in my night. I had gone from about eight-to-ten drinks drunk to completely sober in that moment. The truth was, I had neglected to wash that area when I showered because I hadn't come to terms with the new landscape of my body. Instead of an anus, I had more of an armpit, and when I showered I would just let the soapy water run over it. It was tender new territory that I wasn't ready to explore, so I stayed away from it. Ironically, before the ostomy surgery I spent half of my life wiping myself.

This incident could have happened at any time, in any given bathroom. But of course, this had to happen on a night when I was stranded in Newport, Rhode Island, about an hour's bus ride away from school and the comfort of my single room. Once the return buses started running, I took the first one back, simply telling my friends that I was going to call it an early night because I wasn't feeling well. I sat nervously in my seat with toilet paper wedged in my behind to hopefully stop the bleeding, surrounded by strangers of a nerdier crowd: people who voluntarily took the first bus back.

By the time I was safely in my room with the door shut, the wound had stopped bleeding. I had made an imitation maxi pad with some toilet paper that I wedged in the crease of my backside. With my panic level downgraded, I decided I would go to bed to let everything seal up well, and in the morning I would clean it. Over the next week, a lump started to form.

I was lying facedown on the exam table as Dr. Boyle felt around the area.

"It looks like there's a bit of an infection," he said. "The best thing to do is have me open it up and clean it out as best I can. I can do that right now, here in the office."

Relief washed over me. This wasn't anything major. I was just an idiot who wasn't taking care of himself.

He gave me a consent form to sign because this was technically a procedure being performed. After the hot pinch and sting of several shots of lidocaine to numb the area, he went to work.

"This kind of thing can happen to anyone, especially people in their twenties. The hair you have in this area is really coarse when you're young, and as people age, it becomes finer."

He went on to talk about his move to the Brigham, and how he really liked the idea of it being a teaching hospital.

"Okay, keep this bandaged with gauze until it heals. Make an appointment for two weeks and we'll have another look. Hopefully, we've extracted the offending hair and this will heal up. Though sometimes these things take a while."

I was sore for a few days afterward and had no problem lying to my friends, telling them that it was an issue with my leg, not my backside.

Two weeks later, I returned to Dr. Boyle's office because the lump had returned.

"So Brad," he began, "what you have is called a pilonidal cyst. It's an infection that was probably caused by an ingrown hair. I'm going to clean and cauterize the wound here and we'll see how it does. The problem is, there's a tiny piece of hair that's stuck under your skin and it's trying to get out. If it can't get out one way, it will try to tunnel out another way."

He went on to clean and cauterize this new wound I had, that never totally sealed up, and didn't heal. This went on for a few months. I would return to Dr. Boyle's office every couple of weeks for him to clean and cauterize the area.

I graduated with a degree in illustration that spring of 1999, the height of the dot-com boom. While I had been safely nestled in the college cocoon, the world outside had turned completely digital. My friends that had majored in electronic imaging and graphic design fared much better in the job market, and lots of them were securing positions as early as March in the frenzied era of the late-'90s web market. While my dream was to keep drawing for a living, I realized that I didn't have the talent to become a commercial illustrator. Illustration was a massively competitive field made up of mostly free-lancers, and the more the internet grew, the harder it was to land illustration jobs. There was no way I would be able to go head to head with masters who had been in the field for thirty or forty years. I just wasn't good enough.

Plus, I needed to have health insurance. This was a point that my mother drilled into my head every opportunity she got. And not only did I need steady health insurance, but I also could never have a lapse in coverage, or I would never be able to get back on it with my preexisting condition. I would always have to work.

Fortunately, though, I was able to land a job as a production artist at a golf hat company in New Bedford called Ahead Headgear. This was in downtown New Bedford, an area populated with old brick factories and foundries. Ahead's small, overcrowded office was attached to the warehouse, which held several embroidery machines and ran shifts around the clock. I was one of eight production artists in the art department, which was a glorified name for the 10' x 10' space we were crammed into. We worked elbow to elbow at our computers, which sat not on desks but folding tables. I barely knew any of the computer design programs when I started, but I learned them on the job as fast as I could. I was only making $11 an hour plus overtime, but to me, I had made it. I was putting my degree to work, and making my living creating art. Even if that art was just prepping country club logos for embroidery, the job was fun. I made fast friends with the other production artists, and the job soon felt like an extension of college. Not only did I learn those design programs, I got fast at them. I began to appreciate logo design, typography, and the wider field of graphic design.

I couldn't afford to live on my own right after college, so I moved home to Medfield for one last stint of living with my parents to save money. The drive to New Bedford was an hour of traffic-free highway driving. I drove my Jeep, which had a cassette player, so I unboxed my old cassette tapes from my childhood and listened to Def Leppard, Poison, and The Cars on my drive to and from work.

Eventually, we decided that we needed to take a stronger approach with the pilonidal cyst. It would be a fairly simple day-surgery procedure where he would carve out a deeper section in an attempt to get underneath that lingering hair particle, lodged in the wound somewhere.

The surgery happened on a Friday at Faulkner Hospital, a facility affiliated with the Brigham. The Faulkner was located just outside the city, so it was easier to get in and out. My mom drove me in, and I went through the usual pre-op routine from admission to anesthesia.

After waking up in post-op and getting acclimated with the world again, I was soon ready to go home. The nurse went over my discharge information: a prescription for pain meds, what to expect, and how to care for the wound.

"You're going to leave the packing we have in there for three days," she told me. "Then, you need to pack it with a wet-to-dry dressing. This will help the tissue heal from the inside out."

She went on to show me how to pack the wound, basically making a wick to stuff into this grape-sized hole. She gave me a large care package of medical supplies to get me going and sent me on my way. I left feeling confident with the healing mission I had ahead of me. Theoretically, I would be able to return to work on Monday, with almost no disruption to my life.

There was no way of knowing it then, but the nurse gave me the wrong discharge instructions. I should have changed the dressing the next day, not three days later.

The weekend was a breeze. All I had to do was keep on my schedule of pain meds, and move gingerly around the house, taking special care to sit to the non-traumatized side of my backside.

Monday morning arrived. Anxiety levels were high because of the much-awaited operation of changing the dressing for the first time. I planned to remove the packing in the shower, dry off, pack the wound with wet gauze, put a fresh dressing on it, and get ready for work as usual.

I removed the dry outer dressing before getting into the shower, most of the hair on my upper thigh going with the tape. The running water of the shower should have made the packing come out easily, and it would have if the discharge nurse had given me the correct time frame for removing it. If I had done it the day after the surgery, it probably would have simply fallen out. But I was at the 72-hour mark and despite the water running over it, it was fused to the wound.

Little by little, I pulled at the dressing. With each small tear, pain lit through my body. Blood streamed down my hairy leg and swirled down the drain. Taking pain was one thing. Inflicting pain on myself was entirely different. The ordeal lasted about fifteen minutes, and by the end I was sweating, exhausted, and on the brink of passing out. My vision was waning and I was seeing stars.

I spun the metal faucet to cut off the water. I stepped out onto the bath mat, bold droplets of blood splashing onto it. I ripped open one of the enormous gauze pads and covered the bleeding wound. I wrapped my towel around me, left the bathroom, and collapsed on the couch in the family room, breathing slowly and intentionally, trying to recover by oxygenating myself and staying calm.

After a few minutes, I was able to regain my strength and my bearings and return to the bathroom to properly pack and dress the wound. My mom helped me convert the bathroom floor from a murder scene back to clean tile. After finally taking my pain meds, I finished getting ready, got into my Jeep, and set off for work, wondering the whole time if what I just went through was normal.

At my post-op appointment with Dr. Boyle, I explained the incident, and he confirmed what I'd suspected. That I should have been instructed to begin showering and changing the dressing the next day.

"At the three-day mark," he explained, "the wound would have started healing to the bandages."

"Well, that's what the nurse who discharged me told me to do," I said defeatedly. By then, I just shrugged off the experience and focused my hope toward the idea that everything would heal.

14

BEHIND

BETWEEN GOING OUT WITH NEW WORK FRIENDS OR OLD
college friends that were still at school nearby, my social life was going
strong. After about eight months of commuting to New Bedford
from Medfield, I had enough money saved to move out from under
my parents' roof for good. I found an apartment on Route 6 in North
Dartmouth, right on the New Bedford line. Five hundred and fifty
dollars a month was pricey for that area at that time, but it was worth
it for a huge sunny second-floor space with gleaming hardwood floors.
I loved living alone. I could freely smell up the bathroom without
embarrassment, and because this apartment was surrounded by
commercial buildings, I didn't have any neighbors after 5:00 p.m. I'd
learned to play guitar in college, and now I could play as loud as I
wanted without anyone hearing. Not surprisingly, I had turned out to
be a shy musician, preferring to play alone rather than being vulnerable in front of others.

One night I was at a house party and ran into my friend Gregg.
While we had drifted from the everyday friendship of freshman and
sophomore year, we had remained friends and still hung out occasionally. Drinking keg beer out of red Solo Cups in the basement of this

house, we reunited the way we always did, picking right up where we left off. By this point, we were a year past graduation, and he'd had no trouble finding work with an electronic imaging degree. But the corporate life wasn't for him, and he was trying to figure out a different path. I told him about my job at the hat company, and about my blind spot choosing illustration for my major.

"The job is good, but I don't know. It's not a future. I was so certain that illustration would get me what I wanted. But the web is where the excitement is."

"Totally man," he said. "Web design is where it's at right now."

"I know, and I find myself being more drawn to design. All I want is to make some kind of art for a living. I'm just so far behind."

We went back and forth for a while talking about classmates that were thriving. Some were talented throughout school, and some weren't but seemed to do just as well.

"Dude, you know what you should do? You're living down here now. You should use all of the prerequisites from illustration to take graphic design and EI classes."

I didn't miss a beat. "Yeah," I reasoned, "I don't even need a degree, I just need to know how to do the work and have a portfolio to back it up. So, it's not like I'd need to take any electives or anything."

"Exactly!" he said animatedly. "You should just go in and talk to Howard. He would totally take you into the program."

Throughout the night, as I talked to others, I couldn't stop thinking about this idea. It was right in front of me the whole time but I couldn't see it.

When it was time to go, I found Gregg before I left to say goodbye.

"Hey man," I said, "thank you. I'm going to do this."

He gave me a knowing look and nodded. "I know you are, B."

. . .

What started as two drunk friends scheming a plan together turned into a massive career change for me. I went for it. The very next week I met with Howard Sherman, the head of the electronic imaging department, who gave me the go-ahead to enter the program.

For the next two years, starting in September, I would be back in Group Six.

After I had worked at Ahead for about a year, they moved from the old office in downtown New Bedford to a brand-new building in an industrial park off of Route 140. Gone were the folding tables and cramped quarters; we all had real office desks and a nice cafeteria with vending machines. The work was still flexible because everyone worked hourly. We all punched a clock. So with the blessing of my boss, Vince, I was able to make my own hours. That meant I could go to classes in the daytime, work late every night, and put in time Saturdays. I took two or three classes a semester.

For the next two years, except for going out on weekends, all I did was work. I would go to class, work at Ahead, do homework, and go out on the weekend nights with my friends. It was exhausting and hard, but Crohn's had given me a foundation in overcoming hard things and meeting challenges. The work itself was fun, and it didn't take long to feel that I was improving.

Through all of this, I still dealt with the pilonidal cyst on my backside. It didn't heal after the surgery as we had hoped, which led to more cleaning and cauterizing appointments with Dr. Boyle. He would occasionally have a resident with him and would explain the history of the issue. Most times it was just the two of us chatting, and I was always fascinated with the stories he would tell about working in the hospital and felt a growing bond with him.

Between appointments, I would keep the area covered with a square of gauze and paper tape. Like the ostomy, this was a defect that

I could successfully hide from the outside world because it was hidden under clothing. I also used Nair, the women's hair-removal product, to remove all of the hair in the crease of my backside. The burning cream smelled like celery and seemed to sear off the hair. It did the trick and was a key element in keeping any other hairs from burrowing into the wound.

After another six months of appointments, the second surgery happened and was also unsuccessful in extracting the offending hair. At least I always thought of it as a little piece of broken-off hair that had wreaked all of this havoc. Fortunately, I now knew how to properly care for the wound after the procedure.

The third surgery happened several months later, almost two full years after that fateful night at the Spring Ball in college. This one was the most aggressive. Dr. Boyle carved a two-inch canyon in the area just to the right of my tailbone. The depth of the wound qualified me to have a visiting nurse come out to change the wound dressing once a day.

The first dressing change with the nurse turned out to be much bloodier than she anticipated. Even though I had moved out of my parents' house, I had returned home to Charlesdale Road after the surgery to recover for a few days.

The nurse called my mother into the family room, where I lay on the couch as the nurse tended to packing the wound to stop the blood.

"Do you have any pads?" she asked my mother.

She turned to me, "I know this is going to seem strange, but we need something that's going to be super absorbent to put over this until it starts to heal."

My mother returned with a box of Kotex pads. "Well I never thought I'd be giving these to you," she joked uncomfortably.

The nurse removed one from the box, opened it up, and used it as the meat in a big sandwich of gauze and medical sterile pads and tape. In the end, I basically had a diaper.

But it worked. Both the maxi-pad dressing and the overall surgery were successful. The wound finally closed up and healed. But even with the wet-to-dry wick process that allowed the wound to fill in, I was left with a bit of a divot that made my backside look a little deformed. Along with the stretch marks from high school and the colostomy bag, I was building up a collection of ugliness and scars underneath my clothes.

15

HARD TALKS

THREE YEARS EARLIER, WHEN I WAS HEALING FROM THE ostomy surgery, I noticed that I had trouble getting an erection. Initially, I was able to convince myself that this was normal. After all, my body was recovering from the trauma of major lower abdominal surgery.

But the weeks turned into months, and things never got back to normal. Thoughts and feelings that normally triggered the appropriate physiology in my body weren't doing anything. When Dr. Boyle had talked about the risk factor of becoming impotent, he had referred to nerve endings getting accidentally severed during surgery.

This wasn't it though, I wasn't numb. I could get the mission accomplished with manual stimulation. It was more of a blood-flow issue. It was like something was preventing my penis from filling with blood, like someone was stepping on a hose inside my body, blocking the water from flowing.

I figured that sex with an ostomy would be tricky waters to navigate with girls, but that once I got past it everything would be somewhat normal. Now I had an even bigger problem. I wasn't sure I could even successfully have intercourse.

Sex wasn't something I'd had a lot of. Many people talk about Catholic guilt around sex. While I wasn't raised Catholic, going to health class in the early 1990s had to have been just as bad. The AIDS epidemic had recently shifted from being homosexual-only to an anyone-can-get-it terminal illness. The Medfield Middle School health class translation of this was not that you might get AIDS if you had sex, but that sex would kill you no matter what. AIDS and STDs weren't a calculated risk, they were a guarantee. You weren't having sex with one person, but everyone that person had slept with. While this was technically true, it was a cruel thing to preach to a classroom full of suburban virgins. My wide-eyed and serious former self took it all as gospel and quickly developed an unnecessary fear of STDs.

On top of that, Crohn's didn't help. The natural nerves and exhilaration you get as a guy before you make a move or ask a girl for her number always jarred my bowels and made me retreat to the bathroom. Fortunately, drinking alcohol quelled that problem. Still, I never got the hang of being single and struggled with the games necessary to land a steady girlfriend. I spent most of college being in love with one of my platonic friends, which in turn prevented me from giving any other girls a serious chance. I didn't lose my virginity until I was twenty-one, and the most my sex life amounted to a handful of drunken hookups.

I have always been underweight and tall, which was never exactly what girls wanted. Or maybe it was. I had no way of knowing, because I never had a good read on girls or high self-esteem. When I hit remission after the ostomy surgery, however, I slowly began to get heavier. I put on twenty pounds my senior year of college, and another twenty the year after that. I went from being extremely underweight to skinny to tall and lean.

Having to explain to a girl that I have a colostomy bag certainly put a filter on the kinds of girls I was going to be naked with, although it's not like I was having lots of one-night stands and casual sex before the surgery anyway. Still, there were a few opportunities where girls were interested in me that I didn't pursue because I didn't expect them to have a good reaction to my anatomy.

As far as my erection problem went, I figured I would be able to rise to the occasion when I had the chance. For those first three years, I restricted my experiences to clothes-on, above-the-waist interactions. That way I didn't have to deal with talking about either problem, the colostomy bag, or my bandaged backside with the pilonidal cyst. But by the summer of 2001, the pilonidal cyst had finally healed and I figured I was ready to take things further if the situation presented itself.

Tuesday nights I would usually go to a dark downtown dive in New Bedford called The Bullpen. The main draw was Pearly Baker, a Grateful Dead cover band that performed every Tuesday night. That and they served 85 cent drafts. Most Tuesday nights I was there. People that had seen the Dead before Jerry Garcia died said that Pearly Baker was as close to the real thing as it got. And the band looked the part. The lead singer had powder-white hair and a matching beard. They had two drummers and a guitar virtuoso that could weave through lengthy guitar solos with power and emotion. I wasn't really a fan of The Grateful Dead when I started going there, but became enamored with these guys. I learned to love "Deal" and "Terrapin Station." The bar was on Acushnet Avenue, but it was actually Shakedown Street. They mixed in some classic rock staples like "Miss You" by the Stones and "Tangled Up In Blue" by Dylan, and they often closed with a soaring fifteen-minute version of "Sultans of Swing," a song that practically described The Bullpen on any Tuesday night. The clientele ranged from stoned hippies there for the band, to the regular locals, to the younger crowd just looking for a midweek night out.

I often met Gregg there. He was the one that turned me on to the place, along with other friends that were into the New Bedford music scene. The small dance floor was always full by the end of the night, and I always left sweaty and a little deaf.

Kim was a short, cute brunette who I had seen there a few times before I was lucky enough to be introduced to her by one of my friends. We hit it off right away, and I walked out that June night with her phone number written on a square bar napkin in my pocket.

That Friday night we went out. She waitressed at a sports bar down the street from my apartment. I picked her up after her shift at the restaurant and we went out for a drink. It was a late start, but we were young and it was the summertime so those things didn't matter. After a couple of drinks, we decided that it was a nice night, and we could go to the beach to hang out. She lived in Westport and knew where to go. All I really knew about the town was that it was located at the end this long, dangerous, straight stretch of road, Route 88. Every year several people were killed in a car accidents on that road at night.

I was excited and energized in the moment. Driving down this dark highway with this girl who's a great combination of cool and cute, and we weren't running out of things to talk about. This was the start of something good.

The popular beach to go to was Horseneck, but she had other plans. I pulled my Jeep into a deserted dirt parking lot, draped on three sides by an enormous forest of trees. We got out of the car and could hear the far-off waves crashing. Our shadows were crisp in the brightly moonlit parking lot as we made our way to an opening in the trees.

Kim led me through the woods, on a path that emerged to the moonlit beach. We set up the blanket I had brought from the back of my Jeep and we commenced making out to the sound of the crashing surf. For the first time since the surgery I was with someone I would want to have sex with, but not this quickly. I wanted to have more time with her so I could build up some equity in the relationship before my anatomy was addressed.

While this strategy made sense in my head, it was harder to execute in the moment.

"Let's hold off," I said, moving her hand away from meandering below my waist.

"Oh?" she said playfully. "What's wrong?"

"Um, I like you, so let's wait."

"Oh, o...kay."

I realized then that it was really unusual for the guy to be the one to put on the brakes. And it killed my undersexed self to do it, but I needed to do everything I could to not get rejected.

After a while, we decided we should call it a night, so we headed back down the path toward the parking lot. When we emerged out of the woods to the deserted lot, something was wrong. A dim yellow glow emanated from my car.

"Shit, did we leave the light on?" I asked as we drew closer.

"I don't think so," she said.

"That's really weird," I said.

The light was on because the passenger door was wide open, and when we reached the car we could see that the glass had been broken. The contents of her bag were scattered around the dirt lot. Her wallet was there, minus the cash.

"It's okay," she said. "I didn't make that much in tips tonight anyway."

"What about credit cards, did they take anything else?"

"I left those at home. Most of them. I have to check."

I scanned the area but there wasn't another soul around. My car was mangled. They had pried off one of the crossbars from the roof rack, and judging from the scrapes on the moonroof panel they'd been unsuccessful in breaking through the roof, so they went for the passenger side window.

I swept through my car to see what else was missing.

"Oh man," I said, disheartened, "they stole my tape collection." *Thriller. Hysteria. Heartbeat City. Reckless.* "They're all gone."

We collected everything we could find, brushed away the glass from the front seats, and drove off. We spent the last part of our date at the Westport police station filing a report, which took about an hour. There wasn't much they were going to do anyhow. I'd had the Jeep broken into before, it was just a side effect of living near New Bedford.

I pulled up in front of Kim's house after our visit to the police station.

"Hell of a night," I said to her, and she laughed.

"One for the books," she said back. We kissed goodnight as the sky began to lighten above us.

I turned around and headed back to my apartment. Soon I was back on the familiar two-lane terrain of Route 6 in Dartmouth, and the sun was coming up through my broken passenger side window.

A few weeks later, we found ourselves kissing on my crunchy black pleather couch in the living room of my apartment. It was a Tuesday night, and we had left The Bullpen at intermission to come back to my place to be alone together.

Kim and I had seen each other a few other times since then, and I was able to both get to know her better and strengthen our growing bond. This was at the very least a summer fling, and it had the potential to go beyond that.

I didn't know how to have this serious talk about my body's physiology in the context of our fun and lighthearted times together, but I had been rehearsing different ways of getting the words out. Even if she had the worst reaction ever, she was a perfect stranger. She wasn't connected to my network of friends, so if she ran out of the bedroom screaming my secret would still be intact.

We moved from my living room into the bedroom and slid back into each other's arms.

"Hey, how come you still have all of your clothes on," she teased.

I wrestled out of my shirt, took a deep breath, and started to talk.

"So, I have to tell you something before we go any further." The statement brought everything to a halt. We took the opportunity to dive under the covers to shield ourselves from the cold air that was cranking from my bedroom air-conditioner. I suppose from her perspective, what I was about to say could be very, very bad. But she tucked herself under my arm, looked up at me with her big beautiful brown eyes, and listened intently.

"I have this intestinal disorder called Crohn's disease. I've had it since I was a kid. The best way to describe it is this plumbing analogy. If intestines are a series of pipes, I have a bad pipe. It can be treated with drugs, but when it gets really bad, they take the bad pipe out surgically. It's a chronic disease though, which means it always comes back. When I was a kid, that bad pipe was in my small intestine. They removed that and when it came back, just my luck, because it technically can happen anywhere in the digestive tract, it came back in my rectum. After several years, I got to the point where I was really sick, and they had to take that part out, too.

"So now I don't go to the bathroom the same as everyone else. I have this pouch on my stomach that fills up, and I empty it."

I held my breath and looked to her for a reaction.

"Can I see it?" she asked.

I undid my pants and opened them up to reveal my ostomy, out in plain view sitting above the waistline of my boxers.

"That's so cool," she said examining it. Then, with honesty and curiosity in her voice, "Who knew that they could even do something like that?"

I was pleasantly shocked. Out of the dozens of reactions I had envisioned her having, that was not one of them. Now she was back on top of me as if nothing had happened.

"Does this still work?" she said as her hand slid below my waist.

"Yes," I hoped.

Unfortunately, I was wrong. I was able to get to about half-mast, and I wasn't solid enough for intercourse to happen. I was annoyed and disappointed. I had triumphantly conquered the ostomy communication only to fall short on this unexpected side effect. Erectile dysfunction at the ripe age of twenty-five. Just what I needed.

Kim and I saw each other a few more times, but I was never able to rise to the occasion. If it was a one-time thing I'm sure it would have been written off to nerves or stress, but this had become another chronic problem.

July turned into August, and I could feel her drifting away. Phone calls and plans happened less often, and I slowly started piecing together clues that she was interested in someone else. We were far from exclusive and I took my lumps in stride, vowing to myself that this was not going to happen again.

I had a final follow-up with Dr. Boyle in August, and we officially closed the books on the pilonidal cyst, though I had grown to enjoy our visits. He would always have entertaining stories to tell about working in the hospital environment, and we really began to bond as a doctor and a seasoned patient sometimes do. One time he told me about how disappointed he was in a colleague who left the Brigham for another hospital that paid more.

"I get more out of working here because I get to teach what I know to young doctors," he said. "Sure, I could make more elsewhere, but money isn't everything."

Stories like this made me feel very connected to him like a friend, and I dreaded having to bring up my new problem. Three years had now passed since I'd had the ostomy surgery, and as far as he knew everything had been a total success. This appointment should have been a victory lap for us both, and I was about to ruin it. Hard talks were becoming my forte.

"Well it looks like we finally got it," he said. He was behind me, but I knew he was smiling.

As I put my pants back on, I began, "So, I have to talk to you about something else." I exhaled in a huff. "I can't get an erection. Well, I kind of can, but not all the way."

His eyebrows raised as he answered, "Well your surgery went very well. I know I didn't go near any of those nerves."

"It's not a nerve thing," I explained. "I have all of the right feelings down there. It just doesn't fill with blood like it should. It's like something's blocked. Like someone is stepping on the hose and the water isn't coming out. Maybe something is pressing on the area or something."

"That's impossible. It sounds psychological to me."

I kept rolling with the conversation. "Well at any rate, can you give me a recommendation for a urologist? I think I want to see what my options are. Viagra maybe."

"Sure. All right, Brad," he said.

"Thank you again for everything. Even with this issue, the decision to get the ostomy was the right one. Life is good."

He mustered a quick smile and handed me the name of a urologist. For the first time, there was an issue with my body that even a doctor couldn't explain. We shook hands and parted ways. I wouldn't see him again for almost ten years.

16

LATE BLOOMER

WHEN I GRADUATED FROM COLLEGE, MY MOM GAVE ME A handwritten letter expressing how proud she was of me. When she was my age she received a similar letter from her aunt when she graduated from Connecticut College in the 1960s with a degree in education. Auntie, as we all called her, was also a teacher and someone my mom was very close to. This was my mother seizing an opportunity to keep the tradition of the graduation letter alive. I wish I still had it, but I lost it somewhere along the way. Still, I remembered this one anecdote.

She recognized that I had always been a late bloomer, starting with how I took my first steps as a toddler. I was a very late walker, although I was able to cruise around pretty well despite not being able to stand on my own two feet. The pediatrician had a solution and fitted me with special shoes that would give extra support to my weak ankles. My mom picked out a brown construction boot style. That was all it took. I started walking that very day. By the time my father arrived home from work, I greeted him not with a couple of steps, but by walking across the entire room. Once I got the extra support I needed, my first steps were many.

. . .

That fall when school started up again, I met someone new. I was at the halfway point in my continuing education stint at UMass Dartmouth for web design, and everything was going well despite the heavy workload. Sam was a senior and was a dual graphic design and electronic imaging major. We were in the same electronic imaging class, a six-hour session on Fridays, learning about web design.

I was a couple of years older than everyone, a virtual stranger. She was the alpha of the class and was usually the center of attention. She had a Scarlett Johansson-esque beauty to her and was funny in a playful way. As an outsider, I could tell that the other guys in class were infatuated with her but were also close with her on the friendship level. I knew that approach rarely worked from my undergrad years, but now things were different. I was in the role of being the mysterious older guy that almost no one knew.

The 9/11 attacks happened that September. After that, everything felt different and somehow ominous, like anything could happen. We were at the start of a new and different era.

Things gradually returned to this new normal at work and school. One day in late September while we were on break from class, a bunch of us were hanging out on the carpeted circular benches on the second floor of Group Six, and I somehow mentioned that I was from Medfield.

Sam cut in: "What did you say?"

"...that I'm from Medfield," I said. "It's a small town about an hour away..."

She cut me off. "No you're not."

"I am."

"Nuh-uh."

"I am."

"I would know you if that were the case," she said defiantly, "because I'm from Medfield."

"Oh, seriously? How do we not know each other?" I said, totally stunned.

"I wish you weren't a liar."

"Okay then," I said, pointing my hands back at myself. "Quiz me."

"Okay," she said, squinting. "Who is Bubblegum Bob?"

"He's a guy that used to live up at the State Hospital and ride his bike all around town handing out gum to groups of kids. His go-to joke was to fool you by giving you an empty wrapper instead of actual gum."

That was such an inside-baseball Medfield question that she had to know I was legit, but she continued.

"Oh yeah, well what street did you live on?"

"Charlesdale Road, near the cemetery."

"Oh, so you'd know Aaron Jackson then?"

"Yeah totally. I grew up with the Jacksons. I was closer with his older brothers. They were pretty much my best friends growing up."

"Last question. Who was the art teacher at Medfield High?"

"Mrs. Bernier. Mrs. B. for short."

Her squint turned into a smirk, and she said, "Okay, how do I not know you?"

"Well, probably because I was a huge dork in high school."

"You're suspect. That's what you are," she said as everyone started getting up and returning to class around us.

I now had an in with this girl, common ground. Based on our age difference, she would have been a freshman when I was a senior in a high school of fewer than 500 students in total. We later figured out that we had a mutual friend, Liam, who was also a graphic design major. He was a year behind me and a year ahead of her. He followed me to art school at UMass Dartmouth after hearing me rave about how great the art program was way back when I was a freshman, returning to Mrs. Bernier's art class on a break. Sam followed Liam to art school at UMass Dartmouth in a similar fashion. Between the three of us, we had now come full circle.

Over the next few weeks, we talked more and ate lunch together at the Commuter Caff on Fridays. We talked about everything from design to mutual acquaintances to music, and we just seemed to sync. She invited me to a Halloween party that she was having with her suitemates at their apartment in Cedar Dell.

In college, Halloween was always a renowned hookup holiday. Costumes allowed us to be someone else, which usually led to going home with someone else. I showed up at the upperclassman townhouses to find that her place was just across the parking lot from my old suite where I spent my junior and senior years. I was wearing head-to-toe 1970s garb, rented from the vintage shop where I bought the vintage button-down shirts I wore every day. A full afro wig and brown pleather jacket punctuated by a wide-collared disco shirt tucked into bell-bottom jeans. Sam answered the door looking incredibly sexy in her field hockey uniform.

I was introduced to her roommates and some of the other kids from class were there. It felt great to be back in the dorms with their indestructible fireproof furniture and fluorescent lighting.

After a few Bud Lights and a couple of rounds of Jello shots, Sam turned to me and asked flirtatiously, "So, '70s guy, I have some cool posters in my room. Do you want to see them?"

"Yes," I deadpanned, and she led me by the hand down the hallway to her room.

Less than a minute later, we were making out like our plane was going down. I caught myself. I shouldn't use that Seinfeld quip anymore after 9/11. She had the smallest room in the suite, the A room, which was on the main floor, where outside her door the party was still going strong. Inside her door, she flipped the deadbolt with one hand and pressed play on her stereo with the other.

As the CD spun to life in the tray, she turned to me and put her arms back around my neck. "This is the guy I was telling you about, Pete Yorn."

"Hmph," I said, listening to the lo-fi beginning of *musicforthemorningafter*, "I think he's suspect," using one of her trademark lines on her.

She leaned in and we began to kiss again just as the full band kicked in on "Life on a Chain," finally drowning out the voices in the hallway outside.

It's hard to know if we would have ended up having sex that night if my abdominal anatomy wasn't holding me back. But maybe that was good, because Sam and I seemed to be building something.

When Viagra hit the market in the late '90s I would never have thought I would need it. But sure enough, after a fairly routine appointment with a urologist in the city, I found myself sitting in my car, staring at the doctor's scribbled handwriting on the square of prescription paper, barely making out the "V" and the "a." Soon I stood in line at CVS, the prescription for the tiny blue pills in my hand, nervously awaiting my turn with the young woman behind the counter. Surely when she saw what was written on the small white square of paper she would giggle to herself, or maybe even laugh and point at me.

Finally, it was my turn.

"Hi," I said as I slid the paper across the counter.

She scanned the prescription and just said, "It'll be a short wait, you can take a seat."

Less than an hour later, I was back in my apartment staring at the orange pill container. The label told me that there were only five pills inside and that it was for thirty days. If these worked, I would have to ration them.

I took my first pill that night. My head felt hazy and flushed, and my eyes became a little bloodshot. Nothing happened below the equator until I pulled up some online porn for stimulation. Hard was an understatement for the erection that I had. If I flicked it, it would have made a *ping!* sound.

Relieved that I probably didn't need a full pill, I took out the remaining four pills and cut them in half.

The following week, Sam and I got together for an official date. Two buildings down from my apartment was a popular restaurant called Not Your Average Joe's. A funky atmosphere and delicious food made it a magnet for the college kids and the surrounding area. I'd only eaten there once or twice before when my parents had come to visit.

The waitress came to our table with a basket of focaccia bread and a bowl of their signature dipping oil.

"Seriously what do they put in this, crack?" she said.

"I know, it's amazing."

"You're so lucky to live right next to this place, I would be here all the time if I were you."

"Yeah, I don't know. I guess it would be kind of sad for me to come here and eat alone."

She laughed at that and we kept talking throughout the rest of the meal. Everything felt like it was heading in the right direction.

We got in my Jeep and drove over to Blockbuster to rent a movie for the second half of the night.

The debate of what movie to rent was settled the second she learned that I hadn't seen *Best in Show*, the Christopher Guest movie about overzealous dog show people. The movie was hilarious, yet another example of this girl exposing me to wonderful new things in the world.

Towards the end of the movie, I excused myself to the bathroom where I both emptied my appliance and slipped one of my Viagra half-pills into my mouth, ducking my head underneath the faucet for a sip of tap water to wash it down.

The movie ended, and I had the hazy feeling in my head that told me the drug had started working. This was a detail I would not be revealing to Sam, or any girl for that matter. We started kissing on my crunchy-loud black pleather couch once the movie credits began to roll. My heart was hammering both from having this beautiful girl in my arms and because the time had come to fill her in on my anatomical defect. If I could just get past that, everything would be okay.

We moved into my bedroom and things turned from PG-13 to R. Why did I wait until the last minute to tell her? I guess I hoped that with enough momentum the conversation would be more of a pause rather than a full stop.

"Hold on a sec," I said.

"What's wrong?"

"I have to tell you something."

Again, probably not the best thing to hear when you're about to be naked with someone for the first time. I launched into my speech about how I had been sick when I was younger and the plumbing analogy and how I now had this apparatus on my stomach. Relief washed over me as she told me in so many words that it didn't matter.

After, she got up to use the bathroom, and when she returned, dove under the sheets as if she didn't want me looking at her body.

"Really?" I said flatly.

She turned to me and shrugged.

It blew my mind that she was not only normal and healthy, but beautiful, and even so she wasn't comfortable in her own skin. We talked more, and I told her that if she ever has any questions about my health that I'd be happy to tell her more about it.

I fell asleep that night with her beside me. All had gone well, but still, I couldn't help feel that we should have held out for a bit longer before sleeping together. I guess I was realizing that waiting really did make a difference.

Over the next couple of months, we continued to see each other. It was so nice to be in a relationship over the holidays, something I'd never had up to that point. We carpooled home at Christmas, she met my parents and I met her family. Things were going pretty well.

However, my little blue pill supply was fast becoming depleted. It was 2001, and besides eBay, the internet wasn't yet a place where you bought things confidently online. Despite this, I found a website that would ship me a virtual lifetime supply of Viagra. The website was shady but technically secure, so I put in my credit card info for $200 worth of pills which would arrive via mail at some point in the near future.

Weeks went by without receiving anything. There was no such thing as a confirmation email, and the site I bought them from was so discrete there was no customer service number or even contact information. I began to feel like I had been scammed, and that I wouldn't be receiving a package, ever. I checked my credit card statement when it arrived in the mail later that month and did a search for the company name that had deducted the money from my card. A Las Vegas address came up. "Great," I said to myself, "nothing sketchy about that." I used MapQuest to look up the address, hoping that it would put my apprehension aside by showing me a map view of some Viagra factory in Sin City. The search was a dead end.

Brokenhearted, I called for a refill for my prescription and again went through the humiliating process of getting more pills in person at CVS.

Then, sure enough, after I had given up all hope in the internet and accepted a life of regular trips to the local pharmacy for penis pills, a package arrived littered with foreign stamps. It didn't have a return address, and I tore the box open with Christmas morning tenacity. A brick of bubble wrap emerged, and inside it was a plastic bag filled with 200 diamond-shaped blue pills. I had hit the erectile dysfunction jackpot.

After about three months, things started to fade with Sam. It became clear to her that we were less of a match than we originally had hoped, and she broke it off. We wanted different things. I wanted a girlfriend. She wanted to enjoy her senior year with her friends, and I wasn't mature enough to understand that both could have happened. Even though I was older, she was more experienced in the realm of relationships. At that point, I hadn't ever had a steady girlfriend and my lack of experience showed. We never found the chemistry that would have made us evolve from dating to becoming a couple.

The awkwardness of not being together eventually smoothed out and we stayed friends for the rest of the school year. But by the end of finals, I needed to sever ties with her. I just liked her too much and I wouldn't be able to move on with her in my life. So, while she initiated the breakup of our romantic relationship months earlier, I was the one to end the friendship. I told her over the phone and felt terrible about it, but I knew it was the right thing to do.

The next day, I arrived home from work to find a letter wedged diagonally in my doorjamb. Surprised, I opened the envelope and recognized Sam's handwriting instantly. In the letter, she wrote about what an impact I had had on her over the past year and observed something I would have never thought twice about: that I lived with integrity. I was touched. It was one of the nicest letters I had ever received and it gave me hope. Maybe, as my mother had suggested years before in another letter, I was just a late bloomer after all.

17

THE REDHEAD

BY THE FALL OF 2002, MY STINT IN NEW BEDFORD HAD RUN its course. My continuing education at UMass Dartmouth had ended, and I had the work and experience I needed to get a job in web design. The problem was, there were no jobs in the New Bedford area. Plus, the bulk of my friends had moved away for various reasons. I fell into a hibernation mode, which was probably some sort of mild depression. I slept all the time. Even my easy ten-minute drive home from work was a struggle to keep my eyes open. I had decided to finally move to Boston in hopes of having more fun and adventure than I was currently having. I needed a change and pushed myself to find something new in my life.

A few friends lived in Brighton, which was a neighborhood of Boston and a hub for the twenty-something post-college crowd. It would be a long but easy highway commute to Ahead from there, but it would be a jumpstart for my social life. I found a Craigslist ad for someone looking for a roommate in Brighton for only $600 a month. I was excited and made plans to meet this guy and check out the apartment. I left work early and made the hour-long trek into the city.

I pulled onto Mount Vernon Street and drove past the apartment first, and my heart sank with disappointment. Was this the right address? What a dump. It was a sad-looking white building with a paved yard, with an old white station wagon parked out in front. I kept on driving down the street and pulled over to debate whether or not I should just skip the whole thing and drive home. I sighed and decided that I owed it to myself to at least check it out. The guy on the phone sounded cool enough.

I knocked and instantly got a positive and friendly vibe from the guy that opened the door.

"Hi, I'm Brian," he said enthusiastically.

We shook hands and I followed him up a steep staircase into the apartment where he gave me a quick tour. My tiny bedroom didn't even have a closet. It was literally a bed room. I would have to use the coat closet in the hallway for my clothes. The rest of the apartment had all the makings of a bachelor pad. Mismatched furniture, a bathroom that smelled like mildew, and a small dark kitchen with almost no counter space. But the bathroom did have a fan, which would be a huge plus for me and my bathroom odor issue. Compared to my spacious four-room apartment that I had all to myself, calling this downsizing would be an understatement.

But what the physical space lacked, Brian more than made up for in personality. We clicked instantly. He handed me a can of PBR, my beer of choice in those days, and I said "Great band," nodding to the Lemonheads poster his former roommate had left in the bedroom. Brian himself was Evan Dando's doppelganger, with shoulder-length blond hair on a tall slim frame, wearing thrift-store apparel. He told me that he was a drummer in his own band, S7. After three beers and an hour-long conversation, it was decided. I would be moving in.

Three months later Brian and I stepped out of a cab into the wet slush that covered Washington Street in Brighton. Snowbanks lined sidewalks in front of one of our favorite bars, The Last Drop. The night was still young after a false start in the city at a bar on Boylston Street. Just ordering a drink at this bar lasted a frustrating fifteen minutes because, we noticed, the bartenders were only serving the female patrons. We had no say in the matter and decided to take our dollars elsewhere.

The Last Drop's main feature was that it remained open an hour later than the other Brighton bars. It was a single room with a jukebox, a pool table, and a couple of dartboards. It was 10:00, which meant we had about three hours before crowds would invade from other bars. The place was mostly empty, which was exactly what we were hoping for. I headed for the bar to buy the first round: Captain and Coke for me, and a PBR for Bri, who was at the jukebox to queue up our first round of songs, which always included "Free Bird" by Lynyrd Skynyrd because it was ten minutes long. More bang for our buck, we reasoned.

We reconvened at the dartboards and continued our conversation about Brian's band, S7. They were a 3-piece bar band that played gigs, or concerts, as Bri always called them, at small bars in the surrounding Boston neighborhoods. While they did have a couple of good songs, the dynamic of the band was our most popular topic of conversation.

In the power trio, Brian played drums, Pete was the bass player, and Lee was the singer and guitarist. Lee was very handsome and flamboyant and straight, but everyone assumed he was gay. He had a girlfriend that no one had ever met.

"The thing about his girlfriend," said Bri, "the reason he's with her, is that Lee likes pretty things. His guitar is pretty. His hair is pretty..."

"He even has that song he wrote about his pretty puppy," I said.

"And his girlfriend's a model," said Bri. "I've only met her once. No one else has ever even seen her. She's just another pretty object that makes him look like a heterosexual guy."

"Meanwhile, there's Pete, who's actually gay," I said.

"Right, I mean Pete's in his 40s. He's basically Yoda to younger gay men. But man, I wish he was a better bass player. We had band practice this afternoon and Pete kept flubbing his base lines and missing the choruses. And Lee is great, but we keep telling him to stop talking to the crowd between songs. His stupid banter alone is making us worse."

As we played darts and continued to philosophize about the band, a guy I went to college with, Glenn, entered the bar with one of his friends and a girl. We greeted each other and he introduced me to his friends. I needed a refill, so I walked over to the bar with them. He was very excited about the girl they had with them.

"Hey man, that redhead? I just met that girl! My friend and I were on the 57 and started talking to her. She lives a few streets away from here, and I convinced her to get off the bus and have a drink with us."

Glenn was glowing with pride. I didn't know him too well at school, but a familiar face is a familiar face, and the fact that we knew each other was grounds for a conversation now that we were out on our own.

When we returned with drinks in hand, the redhead was talking to Bri. She was tall, not quite six feet but close. Bri and I were both 6' 2", which put the three of us at a different elevation than Glenn and his buddy. She was fun and laughed easily. As the night went on, it was clear that she was having more fun talking to us, but she would leave us to go and talk to Glenn for a few minutes, feeling bad for not spending time with them. After all, she wouldn't be talking to us if Glenn hadn't recruited her from the bus.

By 12:30, the bar started to fill up as prime time at The Last Drop started to get underway. The regulars were forming a line outside as the bouncer checked their IDs. We had really hit it off with the tall redhead, spending the night laughing and bantering about the band, our jobs, and everything else that went into being single in our twenties.

Glenn, on the other hand, was visibly pissed but still hanging in there. I felt bad, but any other night I would have been the guy that recruited the girl only to lose her to someone else in the bar.

As The Last Drop transformed from quiet and empty to loud and packed, we decided to call it a night. We collected our coats, and once we emerged into the cold night air, it was time to make an awkward decision.

Glenn began, "Hey, it was really nice meeting you — would you want to go for a nightcap at my place?" He nodded his head to the left, down Washington Street, the direction of his apartment.

"Oh, no thanks Glenn, I'm going to head home," she said, pointing to the right, up Washington Street. "It was nice meeting you, too."

"We're headed the same way," I said in the nicest way possible because Glenn was still in earshot.

The three of us staggered up the snowbanked sidewalk, continuing to joke and have fun together. Several blocks later we stopped.

"This is me," she said, tipping her head toward her street. I can't remember who threw the first one, but we spent the next few minutes throwing snowballs at the Dead End sign at the intersection.

"Welp, it was nice to meet you," said Bri, and he started walking away, leaving us together.

I took a breath. "Hey, if you want you could come back to my place and continue the night..."

"I'd love to," she said as she put her gloved hand in mine.

My heartbeat quickened, and anticipation warmed my veins. With each step, I became more elated, and a bit more nervous. My sobering mind began to strategize how I was going to navigate this encounter. I reasoned with myself as we continued to chat. I was feeling lucky and pretty damn drunk, and since I'd only had success with the ostomy and girls, why not just see where the night led?

It was a relief to enter the heated apartment. Year-round Christmas lights were a good theme and atmosphere for our bachelor pad, and they gave off a dim romantic mood. Earlier that day we'd taken down our Christmas tree, which had been decorated with about fifty empty PBR cans. We reached the top of the steep stairs and Bri quickly said goodnight to us, retiring to his room and closing his door.

We stood at the top of the stairs, removing our coats.

"Do you want to see what we have to drink, or..."

She finished my sentence by leaning in and kissing me as her arms wrapped around my shoulders. We made it into my room, also lit by Christmas lights, and I relaxed as our hands explored our clothed bodies. Before long, she was completely naked, and I remained fully dressed.

She sat up and started unbuttoning my shirt to even things up.

"Hold on a sec," I said. Moment of truth. I could easily stop here and we could just pass out. But, I wanted to continue, and to do that I needed to give her my talk.

"So, I have to tell you that I have something that's a little different going on with my stomach." I gave a short, drunk version of my speech.

"Oh," she said, "for a second there I thought you were going to tell me that you had a girlfriend. I would have had a problem with that. But this doesn't sound like a problem at all."

She proceeded to undress me, but unfortunately, we were both just too drunk for much of anything to happen. Still, we were both happy with our night together. We slid between the sheets and finally passed out.

· · ·

Predictably the morning brought a headache, but unpredictably it also brought a challenge. No doubt, a night like that makes for an awkward morning, but those social fumblings paled in comparison to the fact that I did not remember this girl's name. I simply hadn't paid attention when we first met, and much of the rest of the night was blurry at best.

I didn't expect Bri to be up for a couple of hours, so there was no way to ask him. She got up and headed for the bathroom and I quickly realized that this was my only chance.

I snuck out to the living room, where her coat and purse lay on the couch. I opened her purse, hoping to find her wallet, and inside the wallet her driver's license. Nothing in the bag looked like a wallet. "Come on," I whispered as I heard the toilet flush through the wall. She got into the bar, so there had to be a license. Finally, I found a hidden zippered pocket on the inside lining that held her wallet. Yes! This was it. I could hear the sink running in the bathroom. Almost out of time.

I opened the wallet and the familiar Massachusetts state license appeared behind a clear plastic window. My heart sank. Her name was Katherine. Damn. Is it the full Katherine? Or Kate? Katie? Too many options. I put the wallet back in the zippered pocket and lay the purse gently down on her coat. Nothing to see here. I could hear the bathroom door opening down the hall, and I walked out to meet her.

Five minutes later we were dressed and emerged from the warmth of the apartment into the blistering cold New England morning. Our feet crunched on the snowy ground, and we got into my Jeep. We managed small talk as I drove out to Washington Street, retracing our walk home. I turned right at the Dead End sign covered in melting snowballs from our target practice session just hours earlier.

I had made it this far without knowing her name. But my conscience was stabbing at me from the inside. I stopped in front of her apartment and put the car in park.

"Well, that was a great night. I'd love to see you again, but I have to admit something," I said, looking down at my hands. "I'm sorry, but I never got your name."

She stared at me blankly and sighed, "It's Kat."

I never would have guessed that.

As she dove into her purse for a pen, I looked away and smiled. I might have come off as a jerk, but at least I was an honest jerk. She handed me a scrap of paper with her name written in three large letters, her number scrawled next to it. Kat got out of the car and walked up to her front door. I waved, put the Jeep in drive, and drove home.

We talked the next week, and went out one night the following weekend, but didn't hit it off. Regardless, it was another win for me and my new anatomy.

18

SECOND-CLASS PATIENT

B Y T H I S P O I N T, T H E S T O M A C H A C H E S W E R E C O M I N G A N D
going about every ten minutes. I wasn't sure exactly what was wrong,
but I began to piece together a theory. I'd had intermittent pain all
day, and I hadn't gone to the bathroom in over twenty-four hours.
That's normal for the average person, but for me, it's like not going
for a week. Initially, I enjoyed the break, but then I caught myself. My
body doesn't allow for little vacations like this. Something must be
wrong. Then I realized that the mild stomachaches I'd been having all
day were slowly worsening.

It was a quiet Friday night in March, and Bri and I were just home
hanging out watching a Red Sox spring training game on TV. I made
some spaghetti for dinner, something fairly easy on my stomach. But
after eating I became nauseous. It was clear by now that what was
going in wasn't coming out. Throwing up was something that I rarely
did. For as weak as my lower gut was, I had a strong upper stomach
built from a childhood of taking prednisone and an iron supplement
every morning. Both medications are known to cause stomach upset,
and I took them effortlessly, with or without food. With all of the
drinking I had done in college, I only vomited once.

I held it for as long as I could, but eventually lost the battle with myself. Bri had gotten up to go to the kitchen, and before I could get off the couch, I threw up all over our red living room rug. Vomiting made me feel physically better but emotionally worse. I wasn't nauseous anymore, but now I knew something was really wrong.

"Holy shit dude!" Bri said, re-entering the room. "Did you just throw up?"

"Yeah," I said, "I think I need to go to the hospital. Can you drive me?"

With the nausea subsiding, I was able to clean up the mess a bit while Bri got ready to leave. Newton-Wellesley Hospital would be the best place because at least my primary care physician's office was there. I still didn't have a gastroenterologist. I wasn't a kid anymore so I couldn't see Dr. Flores, and I figured I didn't need one because I was in remission and wasn't having symptoms. I guess that was different now. But these stomachaches didn't feel like Crohn's stomachaches. It was more of a pressure pain than the dead-dull pain of a Crohn's ache.

Traveling down Route 9 in Bri's old white station wagon with his drum kit in the back, I told him for the first time that I had Crohn's disease. I used the plumbing analogy and explained that I'd had surgery before. I kept it simple and said that I think what's going on must be connected to Crohn's somehow.

"Jesus dude," he said with his eyes fixed on the road.

"I know, it's just something I live with."

But inside, I didn't know what was wrong and I needed serious help. The stomach pain felt like contractions, each one getting worse. This must be what pregnant women feel like. Painful contraction, relief. Painful contraction, relief. The nausea hadn't come back, at least.

After about twenty minutes we were there. Bri swung the white station wagon around to the front of the hospital in front of the red Emergency Room sign.

"I'll call you when I know more. Thanks for the ride."

"Are you sure you don't want me to stay with you?" he said.

"No, no. I'll be okay."

It was a Friday night, so of course the waiting room was packed. After about an hour and a half, they called me in. I explained my story to the emergency room doctor. He had the nurse draw blood work and start an IV so they could give me some relief for the pain. Plus, he said, I was probably a bit dehydrated from the vomiting. He said that the best thing to do would be to get a CT scan of my abdomen so they could get a look at what was going on.

The nurse returned and put the IV in my arm. She started the IV drip and returned a few minutes later with a thin needle-less syringe with a small amount of fluid in it. Pain meds. She screwed the syringe into a hub in the line, pushed the plunger and the liquid entered the line. Then she removed the syringe and flushed the line with saline. As my heart pumped the medication through my veins, a wave washed over me and I finally felt relief.

Hours later, after the CT scan results were in, the doctor came in and explained that my intestines were severely dilated because they were obstructed. The segment of intestine where I'd had my first surgery, about a dozen years before, had scar tissue around it to the point where a stricture prevented anything from passing through. Because of this backup, all of the food I had eaten in the past day or two was packed in the bowel north of the stricture. Those intestines had increased to three times the normal size. The vomiting occurred because my entire system was blocked, and my stomach was pushing food out the other way. I was literally a clogged sink.

He explained that there were things they could do to help get things moving again, but if they didn't work then they would go in and surgically remove the stricture. This was my first blockage, so he felt that things would most likely get moving on their own. But they would admit me to the hospital until they did.

"The first thing we have to do is have an NG tube placed, which will relieve the pressure from the top of your digestive tract."

"NG tube? Is that the..."

"Nasogastric tube. It's a catheter tube that goes up your nose and pushes down into your stomach. We'll put the tube on suction so it'll both relieve the pressure and remove the contents of your stomach."

The blood drained out of my face. I remembered this from my first surgery at Children's. A vision appeared of the nurses holding me down as they shoved the tube up my nose, and I started to panic inside.

Two nurses returned with the tube and a cup of water with a straw. My heart began to beat faster, pumping dread through my veins. The nurses were talking to me loudly and directly, explaining what was about to happen. One of the nurses stood in front of me holding a clear tube, the end of it doused with lubricant.

"We're going to insert this in your nose. When it reaches the back of your throat, we need you to drink from the straw." The other nurse stood next to me holding the water.

"Wait a second," she said as she reviewed my chart, "they have you as NPO which means you can't have anything by mouth. You'll just have to swallow as hard as you can when I tell you to."

I clenched every muscle in my body and braced for forced entry.

"Here we go."

The tube was cold and wet in my nose, and once it reached the cartilage I felt an overwhelming pressure. The nurse aggressively pushed the line in, and I felt the cold in the back of my throat. I fought the tender urge to gag.

"Swallow! Swallow!"

I did my best to dry-swallow the tube down, and finally, it stopped.

"Okay, good job!"

The assault was over, which brought some relief. One of the

nurses started the suction machine to confirm that it had reached my stomach. When brown stomach bile started to travel out of the tube, the other nurse taped the tube in place on my nose. I tried to keep my head still. My nose was sore, and it was uncomfortable to move my head left or right.

The transport person arrived, and I was wheeled up to my room in the ER bed. It was the middle of the night by now, and my room was dark. The guy I was sharing a room with was asleep. I carefully climbed into my bed. The night nurse came in and asked me a bunch of intake questions. She was an older woman with a heavy Spanish accent.

"You have colostomy?"

"Yeah," I said.

"Mmmph. How long you have?" she asked.

"About five years, since I was twenty-two."

She clicked her tongue three times and shook her head, "Such a shame. So young."

This made me feel worse than anything I had endured that day. Here was someone who dealt with patients all the time, with all kinds of ailments, who viewed an ostomy as some kind of defeat. Something to be pitied for. This is exactly why I don't tell people about it. This is why I keep this entire chronic illness hidden. I refuse to be pitied.

I repositioned myself in the bed as I tamed the anger brewing inside. "Actually, it was one of the best decisions I ever made. I get along pretty well with it."

"Hmph," she said.

She rattled off the rest of the questions, turned the light off so I could sleep, and left the room.

"Fuck you, lady," I said quietly as I tenderly settled myself in a spot that felt comfortable enough for me to fall asleep.

· · ·

The night nurse wasn't the first time a health care professional made me feel bad for having an ostomy. A few years earlier I had set out to find a new gastroenterologist. I had aged out of Dr. Flores' pediatric practice, and even though I was in remission and without symptoms, my primary care physician thought I should have someone officially on the books.

"I like to send people to Dr. Barry," he said. "He's local, and a lot of my patients with inflammatory bowel disease see him."

"Okay," I said. "I guess it couldn't hurt."

"Exactly. We know that Crohn's isn't curable, and it'll come back at some point. This way when you need someone, you have someone. Okay? And hopefully, that won't be for a long time."

A few weeks later, I found myself sitting in the quiet exam room waiting for my new doctor to enter. In my mind, I pieced together my medical history into a quick speech I could give him. Reviewing everything I had been through, I felt grateful for where I was. Sure, I had the ostomy, but I was feeling great and no longer spent extended periods of time in the bathroom. I was pain-free, and things were going well.

A soft knock on the door was followed by a middle-aged man entering the room. He shook my hand and introduced himself as I scanned his slicked-back receding hairline. Before I knew it, I had launched into my story.

I told him how I was diagnosed with Crohn's at age ten, and how I'd had surgery in seventh grade. How Crohn's came back during my sophomore year of high school, this time in my rectum, and how I had held out until the summer before my senior year in college before getting an ostomy. I told him how sick I was that summer, about the toilet full of blood, and how I was able to get the ostomy surgery done in August so I wouldn't miss any school.

"Honestly, I think it was the best decision I ever made. It really gave me my life back," I said proudly.

He had been scribbling notes in the stereotypically illegible hand-writing all doctors have. He paused and sat back in his chair.

"Well Bradley, in my experience, I don't think that level of disease would warrant a permanent colostomy. For me to send a patient to have surgery like that would certainly need to be really ill and presenting more severe symptoms."

With those words, all sense of confidence I had about living a successful life with Crohn's drained out of me, and anger filled the void. Why would a doctor ever question such a major decision like that? Even if he's right, he certainly wasn't concerned about my feel-ings on the subject. Sure, I probably painted my picture a bit rosier than it was, but he wasn't giving me, or my previous doctors, the benefit of the doubt. Plus, it's not like I could snap my fingers and have my anatomy back to normal. While I truly believed the decision to get the ostomy was the right one, not a day went by when I didn't wish I had my normal, flat stomach back. After that surgery, I slowly became envious of the smooth contours of other people's stomachs. In public, I would casually view the profiles of people's abdomens and think, "they don't know how lucky they are." Thin people, fat people, and everyone in between. A slow jealousy grew inside me and has been there ever since.

Back in the exam room, Dr. Barry had flung himself into a speech of his own about my apparent medical misdirection. I had stopped listening. His voice trailed off and I knew three things. One, this guy was not going to be my new doctor. Two, maybe I needed to tone back the whole "best thing ever" angle to my colostomy bag and talk more about how debilitated my life was before the surgery.

The third point cut deeper. For the first time, I felt like a second-class patient. It seemed to me that the goal of a gastroenterologist was to keep people out of the operating room at all costs. As the saying goes, if all you have is a hammer, everything looks like a nail. A doctor practicing Western medicine has one main tool, drugs. A surgeon's tool is surgery. For a doctor to recommend an ostomy, which seemed to be the ultimate gastrointestinal surgery, was thought of as a failure. Like I had become blacklisted.

After allowing Dr. Barry to examine me, the appointment came to a close. I held a poker face with him as we shook hands and parted. I stopped at the reception desk before leaving, as I did with every appointment, to make sure there wasn't anything else they needed.

"No, you're all set. Would you like to make a follow-up?"

"Not right now, I'll call if I need him," I said, knowing that would be never, and exited the office.

After about twelve hours with the NG tube, things began to move in the right direction again. I'd never been so happy to see stool in my bag. The ER doctor's prediction was right, things worked themselves out without the need for surgery.

I never saw the night nurse from the previous shift again. The day nurse came in and announced that the doctors had given the okay to remove the NG tube. Sliding it out was just as unnatural as placing it. It was a hot three seconds of discomfort, followed by a relaxing relief at the tube's absence. I could move my head around again.

They advanced my diet to include solid food on Saturday night, which didn't cause further problems. My gut felt tender, but everything moved through. Sunday I was discharged with a promise made to get set up with a gastroenterologist. Given that all of this happened at Newton-Wellesley, it made sense to see someone affiliated with the hospital. So, I made an appointment with Dr. O'Neil, who coincidentally was in the same practice as Dr. Barry.

I returned to work on Monday like nothing ever happened.

19

THE SWITCH

"Let's head to The Green Briar," I said. "Bri said he'd meet up with us after his show."

It was about ten o'clock and my friend Dave and I walked out of O'Brien's, a one-room rock club in Allston, just as the opening band was taking the stage. We got into Dave's car and headed back to Washington Street in Brighton. Dave was one of my closest college friends who'd relocated to Boston. He had a punk-rock style. His typical uniform was a black Ramones T-shirt and ripped jeans, coupled with tattoos and ear expander plugs which were permanent fixtures of his appearance.

It was a Friday night in late April, the first warm night of the spring, and everyone was out. Both the relief of the end of winter and the promise of summer put us in a great mood. Brian was out playing with his band at a bar in another part of town.

I had been seeing a girl for about a month, but that relationship had just fizzled out. It was a fun fling, most of the time spent drinking at various bars in the area, but there wasn't anything underneath the haze of intoxication. I was in search of something more.

The Green Briar was your typical Boston Irish pub, located a few blocks from my Mount Vernon Street apartment with Bri. It had a traditional Irish interior with a mix of wood paneling and exposed brick, and a range of clientele spanning from regulars to older folks to the younger twenty-something crowd that filled the bar on Friday and Saturday nights. The sound of the cover band playing "The Gambler" filled the night air as we opened the door. We got the first round, a PBR for Dave and a Captain and Coke for me, settled into conversation, and waited for Bri to show up, but he was nowhere to be found at the moment.

The next thing we knew we were talking with two girls. The first was Nicole, a cute brunette with pretty eyes and a short-cropped haircut. The cover band in the next room broke into the opening riff from "Even the Losers." We exchanged comments about our mutual admiration for Tom Petty, and then there was a shift in how we were all standing, and suddenly I was talking to the other girl, Kate. She was taller, with long dark hair, pretty, but with a completely different vibe from the first girl. No matter, I was happy to talk to her. Yet something seemed to draw me back to Nicole. In situations like this Dave always ended up talking to the cooler girl.

Kate threw back her head flirtatiously and laughed at something I said that was only mildly funny. What was wrong with me? She was easily one of the best-looking girls here, and any other guy in this bar would have been psyched to be in my position right now. Yet I'm focused on the fact that she's wearing too much makeup and over-laughing at everything I say.

"You're so funny!" she said, flirtatiously touching my arm, and raising her empty glass and giving me a will-you-buy-me-another-drink expression.

"What are you drinking?" I said reluctantly as I reached for my wallet.

"Sam Light," she said with a smile.

The drinks arrived and after paying I turned around to see Kate had rejoined the larger group with Dave and Nicole, and a few others. Nicole and Kate were roommates and lived in a triple-decker right on Washington Street. There were three others with them. Tali, who was their other roommate, and Kyle and Derek, who lived in another apartment in their building. Tali and Derek were clearly together because they'd been talking quietly and closely the whole time. I read Kyle as just a friend. He was a cool, laid-back guy with a Cheshire grin.

"Hey," Dave cut in. "I have to work tomorrow morning, so I'm going to call it a night," he said as he extended his hand for me to shake. "Nice to meet you all," he said to the group. He turned and headed toward the door and was gone.

Nicole started talking to Kyle, and I returned to my conversation with Kate. As she talked I began to strategize. Could I somehow switch from Kate to Nicole? Dave is out of the picture and he didn't seem to get Nicole's number or anything. I don't think she was Dave's type, so that made sense. What if I could somehow get over and start talking to her instead of Kate? The problem was, from the outside it looked like everything was going great with Kate and me. If I was going to make this switch, I needed to do something bold.

"Hey, if we leave now we can get a jump on the crowd at The Last Drop," Nicole said.

Kate and Kyle agreed, and the rest of the group worked on finishing their beers.

"I'll grab our coats," said Nicole, and she walked off in the direction of the bathrooms.

Thinking fast, I excused myself and said, "I'm going to hit the restroom before we leave," and I followed Nicole. I caught up to her and got her attention.

"Hey." She spun around surprised to see me. I'd caught her off guard.

"Oh, hey," she said.

"I think your roommate is cool, but I'm interested in talking to you more."

Surprised at how bold my words sounded, I realized this could be the end of my night. I didn't know if this girl had a boyfriend or not, or if she even liked me. I thought she did though, but it was really just based on a snap judgment that I'd made when we'd met initially.

"Well, are you going to the next bar with us?"

"Yep," I said, nodding.

"Okay then," she said with a smile. All I could do at that point was hope that this would work out, somehow.

We rejoined the group and began to walk toward the exit.

"We'll be able to get a cab pretty easy now," I said.

"A cab?" They laughed. "On a beautiful night like this? Dude, we are walking there."

Washington Street in Brighton is the main stretch of restaurants, small businesses, and houses, which are mostly classic Boston triple-deckers. On the fifteen-minute walk from bar to bar, the four of us rotated walking partners several times. I walked with Kate, who reached for my hand to hold. I joked that I didn't hold hands with girls I had just met, hoping to get a laugh out of Nicole. I was right about Kyle, who was just a friendly guy who lived downstairs. Tali and Derek were attached at the hip and bid us all goodnight when we passed the triple-decker where they all lived.

By the time we reached The Last Drop, I was glad there wasn't a line outside because by then I really did have to pee. When I walked out of the men's room, I made my way through the crowded room to the bar, where I found Kate leaning over with a $20 bill in her hand. Nicole and Kyle had found a good space at a high-top table nearby and were waiting for us to return with drinks.

"I got it," I said, taking out my wallet.

"No. I have it," she said with a serious tone in her voice. For the first time that night, she wasn't smiling.

"Come on," I said.

"Well, how about this. Who do you think will get the bartender's attention first, you or me?"

I glanced down the bar, which was all guys, shoulder to shoulder, trying to order drinks. Kate was the only girl trying to order and might as well have had a stage spotlight shining down on her. Sure enough, the bartender walked right over to us.

"Ladies first," he said.

"Three Sam Lights," she said, and after paying, brought them over to Nicole and Kyle behind us.

The bartender pointed to me and I ordered my usual Captain and Coke. Just one, thanks.

I walked over to the table where Nicole had saved the barstool next to her for me. "Thank you," she said, raising her beer. "Kate said you bought this for me."

Shocked, I looked to Kate and said thank you. She smiled and just raised her beer at me.

Nicole and I continued talking and soon we were holding hands. Kate began mingling with other people, and some UMass Dartmouth people showed up at the bar. One of them was a pretty blonde with light-blue eyes, who I'd known mostly from parties. She typically hung around with the frat guys, but was one of those people that was friendly with everyone. She came over to me and saw me holding hands with Nicole and smiled at me.

"Well, you're having a good night, huh?"

I laughed and agreed. "You have no idea, my friend," I said.

Nicole and I talked the rest of the time we were there, sometimes together, sometimes with Kyle. She was from Portland, Maine and had gone to Wellesley and was quick to correct me that it was not an all-girls school, but an all-women's college. After last call we walked outside, once again commenting on the unseasonably warm night the way all New Englanders do, with constant repetition.

At this point we were all waiting for Kate, who had found the company of a new guy in the time we were at The Last Drop and was saying her goodbyes.

The four of us made our way back up Washington Street to their place. Kate and Kyle disappeared inside, leaving Nicole and me in the light of the streetlamps and the smell of Chinese food from Hoy Hing, a tiny restaurant right next door to their place. She met me halfway down the steep stairs that led up to the first-floor landing from the street. She stood on a step higher than me to make up for our one-foot difference in height, put her arms around my shoulders, and we started kissing.

"Do you want to come inside?" she asked.

"No, I should probably take off." It was the perfect time to end this night on a good note. "But I'd love to get your number so we can do this again."

I pulled out my cell phone and started a new contact. Nicole. I put in her number.

"What's your last name?"

"Parent," she said, "like mom and dad."

Too risky to make a joke about her unusual last name. I closed my phone, kissed her one more time, and we parted.

Walking alone down this quiet two-in-the-morning version of Washington Street, I basked in the warm night air and my own luck. Three days earlier one fling had ended, and here was a new one starting up.

"I love this town," I said to the empty street as I made my way home.

20

LOVE IN THE ER

I DID EVERYTHING WRONG ON OUR FIRST DATE. Everything prior had gone well. We had a good origin story with our meeting at The Green Briar, and the pair of phone calls through the week had gone smoothly. When I suggested that we go bowling she loved the idea. She'd just been bowling a couple of weeks before with her friends for her birthday. They didn't like the idea of going bowling, but it's what she really wanted to do, so they went along with it.

I parallel parked in front of their triple-decker on Washington Street. After being buzzed up, I climbed the creaky stairs to her second-floor apartment. She and Kate were in the kitchen, which unlike the dark, outdated kitchen that Brian and I had was bright and clean. Cookbooks filled a shelf on one end, with a refrigerator covered in photos of them and their friends at the other. The centerpiece of the room was the life-sized cardboard standee of Aragorn from *The Lord of the Rings*, which they introduced me to as if he was their fourth roommate.

"Kate and I were making speculations on what kind of car you drove," Nicole said.

"A Jeep Cherokee," I said.

"Aw," they said in stereo, laughing.

"We thought you would be one of those tall guys that drove a tiny car," Kate said.

"Sorry to disappoint," I said, smiling.

We talked a bit more, and then Nicole and I headed out.

Kings was a fairly new establishment next to the Prudential Center in Boston. Half bowling alley, half restaurant, it had a cool retro Vegas-y vibe. We sat down to eat and ordered the same thing, a bacon cheeseburger with fries. Everything was going so well that I think the excitement just got to me. I spent the whole meal talking about myself. I talked at length about the running joke that Brian and I had about his band and the strange homosexual dynamics with Lee and Pete. By the end of the meal, Nicole was questioning whether or not I was gay or straight.

After dinner, we went to the other half of the place to bowl. We got our bowling shoes on and sat down to figure out the scoring, which no one really understands anyway. Kings knew this and had an automated system that scored for you. The first string was slow and serious and kind of boring. All around us, the other groups of people seemed to be having way more fun. Through some combination of having a couple of drinks in me and realizing I needed to shake things up, I decided to change the rules.

"Okay," I announced, "this time we have to bowl with our eyes closed."

"Okay," she said, and bowled straight into the gutter.

She turned around laughing. This was good, she was game for some fun. We did this for a few turns and then I added a twist. We would spin each other around pin-the-tail-on-the-donkey style before she would bowl. I spun her around, making sure her eyes were still closed, and pointed her in the direction of the lane. She was lined up perfectly. She wound up and released the ball and it flew out of her hand diagonally and into the neighboring lane, right into their gutter.

No one was hurt, but the couple bowling in that lane was not happy because Kings' automated system had scored a gutter ball on their scoreboard. We apologized but they were clearly annoyed at us. We awkwardly finished our string. We changed back into our regular shoes and walked across the soft patterned carpet toward the exit.

"Welp, that's a story we can tell our grandkids about," I joked ironically, because this night had not gone well.

But, she laughed and the mood lightened up a bit. I drove her home, kissed her goodnight, and hoped things would keep going.

For our second date, we went to Carlo's, a tiny hidden gem of an Italian restaurant in Allston, a neighborhood of Boston that's known more for its rock clubs and college scene. While the conversation was much more balanced this time around, we just didn't have the spark that we had that first night when we met. That felt like magic, this just felt like talking.

She was telling me about the camp her parents owned in Maine when she was young.

"What do you mean a camp?" I said. "Like a summer camp?"

"No," she said, "more like a cottage. In Maine we call them camps."

"Oh good," I said, "because I'm retired from camping. I had enough of that when I was in Boy Scouts. I'm an Eagle Scout by the way."

"Really?" she said curiously, leaning forward in her chair.

"Yeah, I guess you wouldn't know it just looking at me because I'm not an L.L. Bean-style Eagle Scout. But yeah, I stuck with scouting and made it all the way through.

"That's so awesome," she said, and I could hear a hint of awe in her voice. Somehow, she was interested in this Eagle Scout business. We talked a bit more about it and I slowly realized that it had rekindled the fire of the first night. I thought being an Eagle Scout would strengthen my resumé. I never expected that it would impress a girl.

This was a turning point in the relationship. We had taken the T to Carlo's, and after finishing a bottle of wine at dinner we stumbled through the streets of Allston holding hands. We kissed on the train tracks and once again it felt like this could go somewhere.

"Okay, where to," I said when we got into my Jeep, ready to set out on our fourth date. We had been out for sushi the week before, and we had made a deal that this time, she would pick the restaurant.

"Okay," she said as she fastened her seatbelt, "have you ever had Ethiopian food?"

"Ethiopian food?" I started to make a skinny joke and she cut me off.

"Seriously I know a great place in the South End. It's an experience if you've never had it before."

"Let's do it," I said, and shifted into drive.

The restaurant was downstairs in a building in the South End. It was fun, we sat on pillows, and food came in a giant shallow basket. The bread was our utensils, and the food was flavorful and mushy. We emerged from the restaurant feeling light and good. On the walk to the Jeep, we held hands. The rich warmth of her hand filled my body and settled somewhere in my chest. This was going really well.

Part two of the date was going to see Bri's band play in Jamaica Plain at a dive bar called The Midway. We detached hands and got into the car. It was about a twenty-minute drive to JP, and as we made our way down Route 9 I began to feel off. I was starting to get queasy. Every minute of the drive my stomach felt worse than the last. I kept our conversation going, but in my head, I was in full-on medical analysis mode. Please, I pleaded to myself, don't let this be my Crohn's acting up. The bowel obstruction incident was about two months behind me, and once I'd started eating a regular diet everything had gone back to normal. Maybe it was just that Ethiopian food? I didn't have stomach pain, which was good. I had eaten the same thing as Nicole, and she seemed okay.

By the time I parked in the wooded area behind The Midway my face must have been a pale shade of green that would have blended in with the surrounding trees. Nicole didn't seem to notice, so I kept the nausea to myself and toughed it out. Hopefully, it would pass.

We entered the dark bar and I introduced her to Bri and the band, who she had heard so much about. Pete gave me a firm handshake, and of course Lee greeted me with a hug and a kiss on both cheeks. I ordered us drinks at the bar, a Newcastle for Nicole, and a PBR for me. Sipping the cold beer only made my nausea worse. After about ten minutes, I couldn't take it anymore. It felt like my teeth were sweating.

"Hey, I'll be right back," I said to Nicole. "I have a weird feeling that I forgot to lock the car."

"Okay," she said.

I flashed her a smile, placed my full beer on the high-top table next to us, and exited the bar. Successfully leaving the group to be alone was exhilarating. I started counting to twenty out of habit. That's all I would need to get back to that wooded area behind the bar where I parked. The perfect spot to throw up.

In front of my car twenty seconds later I bent over, my hands on my knees, and my stomach still refused to give up its contents. "Come on," I said out loud, knowing that my stomach had been conditioned to not throw up. I needed to feel better. I reached my finger into my mouth and pulled the trigger in the back of my throat. That did it. The entire country of Ethiopia seemed to erupt from my stomach onto the grass below. I stood up and assessed my body. I was sweating and empty, and I didn't have any stomach pain. Compared to how I felt a minute earlier, I was a new man.

I walked back to the entrance of the bar and squatted down with my back to the brick exterior, catching my breath. I felt so much better. By then it was dusk and I watched the cars on Centre Street go by as I collected myself. I had pulled it off. I was wiping my brow when the door swung open and Bri appeared.

"Dude! Where have you been? I have to tell you, that girl is really into you!"

"I know," I said, "that's the girl I've been telling you about. Listen man," I said in a quiet voice, "don't tell her, but I just went out back and puked."

"You just threw up?" he said. "Oh God, are you going to have to go back to the hospital?"

"No, I don't think that's it. We went out for Ethiopian food tonight. Her idea. I don't know, it just didn't agree with me. So, I went out back and pulled the trigger."

"Holy shit dude," he said.

"I feel a million times better now though," I said, standing up. "Seriously, I'm okay. Don't say anything."

"Okay," he said, looking serious.

We went back inside and rejoined the group.

"Announcement!" Bri said loudly. "Brad was just out back puking!" Bri said, laughing.

I flung my hands up in the air, giving him a blank stare. He'd blown my cover and was loving every minute of it.

I huddled with Nicole for a minute to see if she was feeling okay. She was. Puzzled because we ate the same food off of the same plate, I still chalked it up to the Ethiopian food.

The band played. We drove home after and called it an early night.

The next time we saw each other was a Wednesday night. Every date before then was a Friday or a Saturday night, so this felt like an advancement in the relationship to hang out on a Wednesday. Her roommates were out for the night, and she invited me over to watch a movie.

We got takeout from Hoy Hing, the Chinese restaurant next door to her triple-decker on Washington Street. Calling it a restaurant was an overstatement. It was really just a kitchen with a cash register and a small area to order your food off of yellowed menu signs.

We ate in her kitchen, surrounded by the aroma of Chinese food fryolators floating in through their open windows. She had chicken fingers, and I had my go-to General Tso's chicken with crab rangoons. She said that Hoy Hing was her favorite Chinese food and I disagreed, which spawned the beginning of a long debate about where the best Chinese food in Oak Square was.

"I think it's great that you live next to this place, but The New Hong Kong's food is way better. You can't beat their crab rangoons."

"Well, we'll have to go to The New Hong Kong next then."

"It's on," I said as we continued to devour the greasy food.

We watched *Muppets From Space* on DVD, which Nicole insisted was her favorite of all the Muppet movies. I joked about the title, calling it everything but the real name. Muppets go to Mars. Muppets: Out of This World. Planet of the Muppets. Did I really want to sit through a Muppet movie? No. But it would be a great segue to hang out with her in her apartment, sans roommates. Plus, regardless of what we watched, it was pretty great to lie on the couch together holding hands.

I wasn't sure if we would have sex that night. It certainly seemed like a strong possibility, and now that I had my virtual lifetime supply of Viagra I could be prepared like a good Boy Scout. I had my fractured blue half-pill in my pocket and slipped it into my mouth after the movie.

We started kissing and made our way into her bedroom. Here we go. At this point, I had an undefeated record with my colostomy bag speech and presentation. Even though I felt really good about Nicole up until this point, I was still nervous to reveal my vulnerability. Still, I said to myself, I doubt she's going to run out of here screaming. We had a lot of time together in the past month getting to know each other and were getting more and more comfortable together.

After I finished the explanation, I felt relieved. She took it well and was okay with my health issues. She said that it gave me an edge, like I had been through some shit and survived. This was a nice conversation that brought us closer, although for that night the mood had faded. Still, we lay in her bed embracing, talking into the night.

"You're so warm," I said. "You're like a furnace." Her body seemed to be a good ten degrees warmer than mine, which always ran cold.

"I can be your furnace," she said, and pulled closer to me.

In September, Nicole and I made a two-part trip to New Jersey. Our first stop was to Hillsborough for me to meet her sister, brother-in-law, and baby niece, Zoe, who was almost one. Then we would travel an hour to North Haledon to meet up with my friend Ray from high school.

Ray had moved to New Jersey with his mom a few years earlier. His father had died when we were in college, and in the aftermath, he and his mom relied on one another. Ray had always been a family man, and after Ray graduated, they moved to New Jersey to be close to relatives and begin a new chapter of their lives. We remained friends and made time to meet up when we could.

After a nice visit with Nicole's sister's family, we arrived at Ray's house on Saturday. He was so happy we were there, and had a grand plan for us, taking us to his favorite restaurants and bars in his neighborhood.

I can't remember what it was that I ate that began to give me stomachaches. It must have been something I'd eaten at lunch at the restaurant where Nicole and I had stopped. In my head, I launched into analytical mode once again. Dull pain was coming and going every twenty minutes or so. Maybe I had something with onions in it? Ever since I had that bad chow mein at the Chinese restaurant on the Cape when I was a teenager, I was convinced that I had an allergy to onions. The pain constricted in my gut, like a clenching fist. And I realized that I hadn't been to the bathroom in several hours. All I could do was hope it would pass.

While this was going on internally, Ray enthusiastically led us from bar to bar. He'd met Nicole only briefly a few months earlier when he came up to visit me in Brighton for a weekend. Nicole and her roommates had a party on Saturday night, and I was excited for Ray to meet her. But based on a quick phone call I'd had with her before we went over, I could tell that they had started drinking early. Not a good idea for three petite girls who had a long night ahead of them. Nicole spent most of the night passed out in her bed, missing her own party, and never getting to hang out with Ray.

It was early evening and the three of us were at the beginning of what would surely be a night filled with laughing and retelling stories from our past. But inside I felt that I might need to derail the fun.

As my stomach pain contracted at increasingly closer clips, I tried to be a good sport and keep it together. By this point, we were about three stops into Ray's tour. Ray and Nicole had plenty to talk about, comparing their notes about me, so it wasn't too obvious that I was being more quiet than normal. But, small bouts of nausea had started to set in, and I feared what the unfortunate outcome would be: a trip to the emergency room.

When Ray left us to use the restroom, I explained to her that I needed to throw in the towel for the night, a strange comment because it was only about eight o'clock.

"I'm not feeling well. I think I might have another blockage." I had previously told her the story about how I had to be in the hospital for a few days back in March, which was about a month before we had met.

"Oh no," she said. "Okay, well what should we do?"

"Well, let's just head back to Ray's house and hang out there for starters. Maybe it'll work itself out," I said.

Ray returned and he read the concerned expression on our faces right away.

"Uh, what's up?" he said.

"I'm not feeling that great dude. I know you had all this bar-hopping planned for us tonight, but maybe we could just hang at your place instead?"

"That sucks dude. Yeah sure, we could go back by my place."

"Thanks, yeah, it's just my stomach thing. It'll probably be okay."

But by the time we made it back to Ray's house I was really nauseous. My knees hit the cold tiles of his downstairs bathroom floor, and I stared at the rim of the toilet bowl. I sighed, leaned forward, and threw up.

I emerged from the bathroom a few minutes later.

"It's probably not a big deal," I said to them, downplaying this as much as I could, "but I have to get to a hospital."

I filled Ray in on more of the specifics of how I felt with an intestinal blockage underway. Concern and confusion set in, but of course, he would get me to a hospital. There was one in a neighboring town. Even though we had been friends for so long, I kept the specifics of Crohn's quiet as much as I could. He knew that I had Crohn's and intestinal problems and was always so great at waiting for me while I clocked time in his bathroom when we were teenagers. Even with a good friend like him, I kept my health cards tight to my chest.

"Thanks. Yeah, unfortunately it's the only way this is going to undo itself at this point."

In the car, I apologized and explained to them what would most likely happen.

"They probably won't even keep me overnight. They'll just snake a tube up my nose for a while. I'll be good to go in a few hours."

There's a saying that goes, the pessimist complains about the wind, the optimist expects it to change, and the realist adjusts the sails. The wisdom of that statement is simple: it's more practical to be a realist. I'm not a realist though. In that anecdote and in my own life I've always been the optimist. Driving in the passenger seat of Ray's car, through my haze of internal questioning about why I was sick once again, I reassured myself that I would be okay.

"Everything will work out, you guys," I said, trying to defuse their worried looks. "You'll see."

Two hours later I was lying in a large open room in the ER at the hospital, NG tube uncomfortably placed in my nose. My stomach was still clenching in pain, on and off. The time was nearing midnight, and I was wide awake. My nerves were starting to get tense. The most important thing for me was to get out of this hospital so that Nicole and I could drive back to Boston. I needed to be back at work on Monday. I also didn't know this hospital, therefore I didn't trust it.

Nicole came in periodically to check on me as Ray sat patiently out in the waiting room. She was there when the ER doc came in to check on me.

"Hello Mr. Harris." She made her way over to examine the beaker that was slowly filling with the contents of my stomach via the NG tube they had placed.

"So, I'm hoping I won't be here much longer. Like I said earlier, I'm from Boston and I have to get back up there tomorrow."

The ER doctor, a young woman with dark skin, looked at me with the same concerned eyes that Nicole and Ray had been using.

"How about this," I said. "I'll stay here for a couple more hours, and then you can discharge me. If I'm still feeling bad when I get up to Boston, I'll check myself into my hospital up there."

"Mr. Harris, you're not going anywhere tonight," she said. "The CT scan shows that you have an intestinal blockage. That's serious. If it doesn't clear on its own, we may even have to consider surgery. We're not there yet, but I'm going to admit you for the night, and we can see how you're feeling tomorrow."

I stared at her blankly for a few seconds. "No. I need to not be here," I said.

I continued to fight a battle I would lose. Technically and legally, they couldn't keep me there. But I also knew they were right. I wasn't showing signs of improvement yet and leaving would put me at tremendous risk. Many people die of bowel obstructions each year. Even though I was in unfamiliar territory, any hospital was safer than a five-hour drive back to Massachusetts. Plus, if I made it to Boston, they'd have to put another NG tube in, and that was the last thing I wanted.

The doctor left the room, and I consulted with Nicole.

"I just need to be at work on Monday," I said, my head falling back on the pillow.

"Why? What's going on that's so important?" she questioned.

This was a strong point. I didn't have anything major happening at work, but Nicole didn't yet know how stubborn I was about not having Crohn's interfere with my life. I had worked at Ahead for four years, and no one knew I had a chronic illness. I was enjoying a nice period of remission that was coming to a fast close. Plus, if I called in sick, I didn't get paid unless I used one of my vacation days.

"Well yeah," I said, "I don't have anything super important going on, but you have to work Monday too. I feel bad."

"Don't," she said, leaning in to hug me. "I'll call my boss and explain what's going on. It's not a big deal for me to miss Monday. I want to be here, with you."

My defiance came to a halt. The intent of what she was saying meant so much more than her actual words. She was saying that this was okay. She would stay with me through this ordeal, and I wouldn't be alone anymore. Because she was with me. She wasn't bothered by the darkness that I tried so hard to keep hidden. It was then that I realized what she and I had been building together for the past five months. In that exact moment, lying there in that emergency room bed with an NG tube in my nose and her warm hand clasped in mine, I looked into her eyes and summed it up in three words.

"I love you."

They discharged me on Sunday afternoon, and we stayed over at Ray's house on Sunday night. Nicole had stayed there the night before while I was in the hospital. She had already developed a rapport with both Ray and his mom, who was one of the friendliest people in the world. Despite this unexpected twist in our weekend, the expected results came through. These people that I truly cared for had gotten to know one another.

We returned to Massachusetts different from when we left, only days before. In the vast majority of unmarried couples, most won't have to deal with major illness or hardship. Even most married couples won't have those kinds of problems until decades have passed. I've always known that wouldn't be the case for me. I had finally found someone that I could be truly open with. Someone who was willing to shoulder the burden of living with Crohn's and still love me, scars and all.

21

A THANKSGIVING

The day before Thanksgiving I woke up still feeling nauseous from the night before. Constricting stomach pains were coming in waves, and my heart sank as I felt my flat appliance to realize that nothing had moved through during the night. Not again. I made my way through my morning routine, showering and getting ready for work. I didn't eat anything, and hoped my GI tract would start to move again.

Things got progressively worse during my hour-long drive to work in New Bedford. Howard Stern yammered away on the radio as I breathed through the stomachaches and focused my attention on not throwing up. Maybe things would improve, and I could make it through the workday.

That fall had been rough. Ever since we had returned from our trip to New Jersey I'd become hypervigilant about what I ate.

"Think of it this way," said Dr. O'Neil, my new gastroenterologist, after examining me. "Your body is like a sink. You can't put, say, pasta down the sink or it'll get clogged. Everyone is different and you need to figure out what it is that you can and can't eat."

Ironically, my go-to meal had indeed become pasta because it was easy for my body to break down and digest. I avoided roughage like salad, and I kept to fairly bland food. Dr. O'Neil had slowly started me on some oral drugs for Crohn's to keep things quiet. And things were quiet from a Crohn's perspective. I didn't have active disease like before, but the two incidents where I'd had blockages were concerning. If I watched what I ate, then I would be okay, in theory.

I pulled open the heavy outside door at work and was thankful that no one else was in the hallway when I punched in on the time clock. I quickly entered the warehouse bathroom and felt grateful that it was empty. I flew into the stall and knelt facing the toilet. I let loose the spaghetti that had sat in my stomach since the night before when I had practically force-fed myself. Rising from the floor, the nausea subsided. But the pain had increased.

Instead of going to my desk like I normally would have done, I went into the cafeteria and put my head down on the cool surface of one of the white tables. What am I doing here? I breathed through the sharp pains, hoping they would subside.

Just then, my boss, Vince, walked into the caff with a crisp dollar bill in his hand, heading for the vending machines. He took one look at me and stopped in his tracks.

"Woah. Are you okay?" he said, with worried eyebrows.

"Yeah, yeah. I'm okay," I said, picking my head up.

"You don't look okay. You kind of look like shit. I know we have a lot going on, but I don't think you look like you should be here."

"Yeah," I said, "you're probably right. I don't think I can contribute much like this."

"This is the stomach thing you were telling me about, isn't it?"

"Unfortunately," I said.

After the New Jersey incident, I had told Vince about my Crohn's. As usual, I had kept it light, and assured him that it probably wouldn't be a big deal. But here it was, presenting itself to him in full effect.

"Well," he said, "why don't you go home, and we'll catch up next week."

Relief instantly swelled inside me, as the burden of having to struggle through a workday vanished.

"Okay, yeah. Thank you, Vince."

"You're really okay?"

"Yeah, yep. I'll be okay. Happy Thanksgiving."

"You too, happy Thanksgiving," he said, with the same worried expression.

A minute later I was back in my Jeep with my worsening stomach pains. Twisting the key in the ignition, I knew exactly where I was headed. Home to Medfield to someone who would be able to help me. My mom.

"Alright, Charlesdale Road here I come," I said as I shifted into drive and drifted out of the parking lot. It was borderline dangerous for me to be driving in the condition that I was in, but the roads were pretty empty, so like always I just decided to tough it out.

The day before Thanksgiving was one day of the year where I knew exactly where my mom was: baking pies in the warmth of the kitchen and singing out loud and off key to her *Neil Diamond's Greatest Hits* cassette. At this very moment I knew she was rolling out pie crusts to the sound of "I Am, I Said," "Song Sung Blue," and "Cracklin' Rosie."

An hour later I opened the front door to the sound of her favorite song, "Sweet Caroline," and the sweet smell of blueberry and apple pies cooking in the oven.

"Hey Ma," I said as I collapsed on the floral print couch in the living room.

"Hi hon," she said, turning down the music and looking at me questioningly. I wasn't expected until later that evening.

I was moaning quietly by this point as another stomachache enveloped my abdomen. When it passed, I broke the news to her.

"I gotta go to the hospital, Ma."

After securing where she was in her baking process, we were off. I hunched over in the passenger seat, feeling thankful to finally not be driving that morning.

"What's Nicole doing for Thanksgiving?" she asked. My parents had met her earlier that month and liked her instantly.

"She's up in Portland with her parents."

Another stomachache came on, and I faded back to silence. My mom and I were seasoned dance partners at this. She knew not talking to me was okay. She dropped me off at the entrance, parked, and met me in the waiting area. She couldn't stay long because she needed to get back to baking. Here again, to my own mother, I downplayed what I knew would have to happen so she would leave me and not worry too much. I told her I would call her when I found out what the plan was.

With all I had been through with Crohn's up to that point in my life, these blockages were as bad as it got, pain-wise. I knew the routine by now. IV pain meds. CT scan. The dreaded NG tube. Admission to the hospital. And eventually, everything would start working again. I was going to miss Thanksgiving, but even if I could have gone, I couldn't have risked eating all that food. What was I going to do, sit at the table and watch everyone eat? I was better off being here for now.

This time, the doctors were alarmed at the CT scan, which showed that my stomach was majorly distended and enlarged. They strongly felt that I would most likely need emergency surgery and were going to closely monitor me for the remainder of the day and into the night.

I assured them that they were overreacting. I'd done this before, twice that year in fact, and everything will be okay. They'd see. They admitted me, wheeled me up to a room, and I settled in for the night, finally falling asleep with a dose of the IV pain meds.

I woke up on Thanksgiving morning to a middle-aged doctor entering the room.

"Hi Bradley, Fred Millham," he said, extending his hand. He resembled Keith Olbermann from ESPN. He was young to be the chief of surgery at a major hospital.

After examining me and asking a few questions, he pulled up a chair and sat next to the bed.

"I came in this morning fully expecting to be in the operating room with you, but you seem to be beating the odds here." He was shocked that I was improving. My stomachaches were down to about a quarter of the pain I'd had the day before. He settled into a chair, and we talked. I liked him instantly. He told me about being a surgeon, and how he hated the old-boys-club practice of hospital business getting done on the golf course.

"I just focus on doing my best for my patients," he said.

I told him about my life, my job, and Nicole. We talked for at least thirty minutes that Thanksgiving morning. This level of bedside manner wasn't something I had ever experienced before. We had developed a mutual respect for one another in a short amount of time.

Still, he felt that I needed surgery. This was a much more severe blockage than I had back in March, based on the CT scans. The stricture wasn't going to improve and would be a greater risk with further blockages. He felt that there was probably some active Crohn's behind all of this, but surgery would be the only real way to tell. He wanted to wait a few days to let my gut settle down.

I had talked to my mom the previous night after I made it up to my room, and I called my aunt's house in Rhode Island in the middle of the day to wish everyone a happy Thanksgiving. I spent the day lying in bed, salivating at food commercials, and watching the typical Thanksgiving programming.

I was slated for surgery on the Monday after Thanksgiving, which gave me four days in the hospital for some R&R. But at the crack of dawn every day, just before 6 a.m., a team of residents came charging in, asking questions and poking around at my belly. So much for the R&R. Apparently, they'd all had Thanksgiving off, because they weren't around the day before.

The band of doctors was a mix of young men and women of all different ethnicities. Some quiet, some outspoken. All of them tired. The team was headed by a haughty overweight doctor who was the alpha resident. He was probably the chief resident, the queen bee. He led the daily interview in a loud and obnoxious way that seemed unnecessary. I pocketed my judgment because by then I had a great respect for residents. They have it worse than anyone on the hospital staff. They're doctors, but they're still learning their craft and proving themselves. They basically live at the hospital, hardly make any money, and are essentially at the bottom of the career food chain.

Nicole came home from Maine early so she could visit me. She took the T out to the hospital on Saturday, and we had a nice visit. Here again, I was lucky to have her in my life. My parents came to visit too, and I called Vince to tell him about the aftermath of me leaving work that day. He was understanding of course, and I let him know that I'd be out for probably a couple of weeks because I needed to have surgery.

I was feeling better by Sunday, which was a good sign. I wanted this surgery to be as successful as possible, and Dr. Millham said that the more my intestines could recover from the trauma of the blockage the better.

Monday morning finally came. I was taken down first thing, and after signing the consent form with Dr. Millham, I was off to the operating room. They started the anesthesia, and soon I was off to sleep. Anesthesia turns off your sense of time passing. Once you nod off it feels like the next minute, you're in the recovery room.

"Brad, the surgery went well," a loud voice announced in my ear.

And that was when the trouble began.

In the post-op recovery room, I kept coming in and out of consciousness. I'd wake up in pain, groaning. My stomach seared until they administered more pain meds, and then I'd fall back to sleep. This cycle happened every hour, based on the round clock next to me on the wall.

There was concern in the voices around me. I was able to mumble out some words to ask what was wrong. They said my blood pressure was low and that they had to watch me closely. At one point, they said that they couldn't give me any more pain relief because my blood pressure was too low. More pain meds could stop my heart.

My stomach felt like a forest fire being put out by a pelting rain of razor blades. I moaned in agony as a new feeling emerged. I felt a release in my belly like a dam had given way, and my stomach stretched out, pressing against the sheets. I called the nurses over and explained this to them. I turned my head and saw that the clock read 4:20. I nodded off again.

Eventually, they announced that I'd be going back into surgery, which was a huge relief because that would mean they would give me anesthesia which would make the pain stop. I had a hazy conversation with Dr. Millham before I was wheeled back through a dim hallway into the operating room. I focused on the table filled with an array of sterile metal surgical tools, lying on a blue paper tablecloth. The anesthesia finally took over. I closed my eyes one last time, and I was out.

. . .

It was bright and it was morning. I lay in a large sun-filled room in the ICU. Two nurses were moving around, tending to me.

I was back on a morphine drip for pain management, my old friend the Jeopardy buzzer back in my hand. I hit it when the nurses announced that they needed to change my sheets. Why they needed to do this, I had no idea. They were efficient regardless of the pain this caused me, performing a synchronized routine of rolling me to one side and back, and they removed and replaced the sheets underneath me.

They talked as they worked, and I tried to follow their conversation because they were talking about what had happened to me the day before.

"Dr. Love. That man saved your life," one of them said.

"Yep," the other nurse said, "that Dr. Love, he knows what he's doing."

"Dr. Love?" I asked. Then they told me what happened.

The symptoms I experienced in post-op meant that I was bleeding internally. My blood pressure had dropped because my heart wasn't just pumping blood through my veins, it was filling my abdominal cavity. This explained the dam-breaking sensation. One of the residents was assigned to me, and even though I was clearly showing signs of hemorrhaging, didn't do anything about it.

Fortunately, the shift changed late in the afternoon, and a different resident took over. Once he was briefed on my situation, he called Dr. Millham to let him know what was happening. They immediately decided to bring me back into the operating room to find the source of the bleeding and patch it up.

"If he hadn't made the call, you probably wouldn't be here," the nurse continued. "He saved your life."

"He saved my life?"

"Yes."

"And his name is Dr. Love? Is that really his name?"

"Yes."

"Okay."

I laid my head back down on the soft, clean pillow. The nurses exited the room, and I was alone with my thoughts. Though I was tired and weary, I was filled with gratitude.

The timing couldn't have been better because not five minutes later the door swung open and the team of residents began to file into my room. There had to be about a dozen of them today, and I couldn't believe that somehow they'd followed me to the ICU. I scanned the small crowd, thinking that one of them was the one that had saved me.

If my mother had been there, she would have been on the hunt to persecute the mistake maker. Always the disciplinarian, she would have demanded to know who had almost killed me and would have scolded them. However, I hadn't grown up to become my mother. Knowing what I knew of residents, I saw a different opportunity.

The big alpha resident was at the helm as usual.

"Well, Mr. Harris," he said, reviewing the paperwork he held in his hand, "you clearly had a bit of a rough day yesterday..."

"Hold on," I said, raising my palm to him. I had cut his morning monologue short and now I had everyone's attention. I winced as I repositioned myself in my bed.

"I have to know, which one of you is Dr. Love?"

They all stirred, and their gazes turned to a young man in the back. The residents in the front parted, and he walked forward into view. Everyone fell silent as I spoke to him.

"The nurses here tell me that you saved my life yesterday, and I believe them. Yesterday was hell for me. You saw it, and you made the right call by having the surgical team come back in."

Dr. Love nodded.

"Thank you," I said directly to him. I extended my hand and he made his way over to me and shook it.

The alpha resident resumed the daily exam using as few words as possible. When he finished, the other residents began to file out of the room to see their next patient. Dr. Love hung back and stood at the foot of the bed, beaming with pride.

"Thank you, Mr. Harris." With a great smile on his face, he turned and caught up with the others.

Praising one of them in front of their peers was the best lesson, knowing that another one of the residents in the pack would have been the one that failed me. Later I learned that it was the big alpha resident.

Just before six o'clock the next morning, back in a regular room, the residents arrived. They did their typical questioning and exams, and as they turned to leave Dr. Love once again stayed behind.

"Hey," he began, "I just wanted to thank you again for saying that to me yesterday."

"Well thank you for doing what you did," I said back.

"I was so happy that I told my parents last night when I got home. They were so proud of me. And it meant so much for the other residents to hear it as well. Thank you."

I never saw the big alpha resident again. For the rest of my stay at the hospital, Dr. Love was mainly in charge of tending to me. The other residents treated me with caution and distance, rushing through their questions and exams as quickly as possible. They seemed to be a little afraid of me.

There was a huge snowstorm in early December when I was recovering. Roads were closed, but Nicole took the T out to visit me. She came in a few times and we had nice visits. My parents didn't come in as much as they usually did. I guess I was an adult now, and things were beginning to change.

On my last day, Dr. Love came in to remove the staples from the vertical incision that divided my stomach. We talked and had a great respect for one another. Maybe I had more power as a patient than I initially thought.

22

GOOD THINGS

AFTER I RECOVERED FROM SURGERY DR. O'NEIL STARTED me on Remicade, an immunosuppressant drug administered by infusion, to once again attempt to keep me in remission for as long as possible. Whereas prednisone simply controlled the inflammation caused by Crohn's, Remicade would block the attack by my immune system. A fair analogy would be to compare Crohn's to a sunburn. All they used to be able to do was apply aloe to the burn so the skin could recover. Prednisone was the aloe. But Remicade was like a high SPF sunscreen, blocking the sun from the skin before any damage could be done.

The big difference was the administration of the drug. For the first time, I wasn't just taking a pill in the morning. I would go into a medical facility and a nurse would start an IV for an infusion which lasted three hours. After the initial ramp-up period, I only needed an infusion once every six weeks to keep a therapeutic level of Remicade in my system. Though my fear of needles wasn't as severe as when I was a kid, I wasn't thrilled to have to get stuck that often. It allowed me to work on squashing any more lingering anxiety. Instead of spending my morning worrying about that needle going into my arm,

I challenged myself to not think about it until the moment the needle was unsheathed by the nurse putting in my IV. I found that the little pinch wasn't that bad after all, a ridiculous thing to waste my time thinking about.

Remicade worked well for me, and I liked that it forced me to take a half-day off from work every six weeks for the infusion. Once I was hooked up, I could just relax into the oversized vinyl recliner and read for three hours straight. I wasn't ever interested in reading when I was younger, books were just pretty shells. I loved the cover designs but never found anything exciting in the pages within. It wasn't until after college that I began to get enjoyment out of it.

My gateway drug came to me in the form of Henry Rollins' *Black Coffee Blues*. The rawness of his writing was a million miles away from the boredom I had found in everything else I had read. My college years were filled with art critiques. We'd work on a project for a few weeks, then everyone would put their work up on the wall in class and we would dissect them one by one. Those critiques taught me how to interpret and understand art in a way that English classes never had, and once I applied that knowledge to reading everything began to make sense. A new world opened for me and I began to devour books.

The infusion unit at the health care facility I went to for Remicade was six reclining vinyl hospital chairs and a desk where the nurse who ran the unit sat. People went there for all kinds of infusions, not just Remicade, so it was a busy department. At first, an efficient young woman ran the department. She was a disciplined multi-tasker and moved quickly from one patient to the next. She was too good though. Soon she was promoted out of the department and on to more important jobs than starting, monitoring, and finishing people's infusions. One day there was a new nurse at the desk.

"Have a seat, and I'll be with you in a minute," he said.

About twenty minutes later he was ready for me.

"Hi, I'm Paul," he said, and shook my hand. He was an older man who reminded me of Quint from *Jaws*. He took my name and information, got my vital signs, and then finally called down to the pharmacy to tell them to mix the medication. I couldn't believe how slow he was. The previous nurse would have had the infusion going by now, and he hadn't even called the pharmacy to have them mix the medication yet.

Over time I heard him tell his story to others. He was a retired ambulance driver. "I was in the streets for about thirty years," he would tell people. I couldn't believe it. This guy? I imagined traffic pulling over as his ambulance crept past at ten miles an hour. But as my visits to the infusion unit turned from months to years with Paul, I started to understand and appreciate him. He was calm and he took everything one step at a time, two traits that must be essential for being an EMT. From that perspective, Paul made sense.

"You're on," he said after I had been there nearly an hour.

"Thanks," I said back to him, not looking up from my book.

By then I had finally left my job at Ahead for a web design position at Jack Morton, a marketing agency in Boston. My friend Pam from college was an art director there, and she offered me a perma-lance position because she had extra work. I would go in every day, she would pass off work to me, and I would get paid for what I worked on at a freelance rate. I jumped at the opportunity, figuring that at least it would get me out of Ahead, and out of New Bedford for good. Plus, I would learn tons about design from her and build up my portfolio. The agency was located on Berkeley Street in Boston, which happened to be only two buildings down from where Nicole worked at Houghton Mifflin.

The only downside was that I wouldn't have insurance through them because I was essentially freelancing. So, I would need to switch to COBRA insurance for the time being. Knowing better, I didn't tell my mother about this detail until I was past the point of no return. She had drilled it into my head for years that because I had a preexisting condition, I would always need a full-time job for health insurance. When I finally told her, everything was lined up. I had agreed to the new job at Jack Morton and given my notice at Ahead. All she could do at that point was worry, which was a major hobby of hers. She would never risk a stunt like this, and always followed the rules. The older I got, the more I realized that rules could often be overlooked. Plus, COBRA worked perfectly for this kind of situation.

As I had predicted, everything worked out. My initial read on the job was that I would be there for three months. I would get industry experience, and with more web design work in my portfolio I'd be able to find something full time. But the work at Jack Morton was exciting, I was making good money, and I had found another great group of people to work with. Soon I was brought on full time. What I had predicted to be a three-month gig turned into seven solid years doing fun and exciting design with fun and talented people.

Besides the Remicade infusions, Dr. O'Neil also suggested that I see a stoma nurse for my ostomy. Not because anything was wrong, but I needed to be seeing someone at least once a year for a checkup. Specialized nursing like this can be hard to find, so I ended up scheduling an appointment with a nurse that worked with Dr. Boyle at Brigham and Women's.

I had managed my ostomy care by myself for about six years at that point and hadn't talked to anyone about the specifics since I'd recovered from that surgery. I had essentially put myself on a deserted island, and it was an enormous relief to finally have a boat appear on the horizon.

Diane was an expert at ostomy and wound care, and became someone I could be totally open with. So, appointments with her had a dual purpose. The first was for my body, a functional medical session where we did an appliance change, and she could examine my stoma and the surrounding skin and give me tips on how to take care of the whole area. The second purpose was for my mind. It was a reassuring therapy session where I could tell all of my war stories for the first time. Appliance fails, accidental public flatulence, and of course the smell.

"Tell me more about the smell. Have you ever put anything in the pouch for it?" she asked.

"Well, I remember hearing people used mouthwash in their pouch. I tried that a few times, but it didn't work."

She was rummaging through the small suitcase of ostomy supplies she brought with her as I spoke, and finally found what she was looking for. She handed me a small white bottle.

"This is called M9. Most of my patients love this. If it doesn't take care of the whole smell, it'll take care of most of it. You can order it with your other supplies so your insurance will cover the cost."

"Okay cool, I'll give it a shot."

She put a few drops in the new appliance that she had fixed to my stomach. It was Windex-blue and odorless.

I continued to tell her stories about living through my twenties with an ostomy. Nicole and I had been dating for about a year at that point, but I'm not even sure I brought her up because I had so much else to talk about. It was the first time I was alone with someone where I could verbally and physically bare all.

"I just live my life as though I don't have an ostomy. I just don't tell anyone I have it, and no one knows." I had never actually said this strategy out loud, but it was a natural summary of all of the stories I had told.

"That's really impressive," she said. "I have so many patients that aren't as active as you. Where you say that you always go out, they always stay home."

Forty-five minutes had passed. I thanked her and scheduled a one-year follow-up appointment. I left feeling hopeful with the tiny bottle of M9 in my pocket.

The drops worked. The few she put in my pouch at the end of the appointment curbed the smell enough to notice. While the recommended amount was 4-6 drops, I ended up putting in 4-6 full squirts of the bottle, probably 10 times that amount. But it worked. I could now use the bathroom in public and have the smell range from nothing to a normal bowel movement smell. The only downside was that I had to use it every time, so wherever I was I'd sneak the small 1-ounce bottle in my pocket before heading to the bathroom. Managing that was easier than the dread and embarrassment I felt for years of scurrying away from bathrooms I had just air-polluted. I felt so much more confident and at ease with my day-to-day life with that tiny white bottle of blue drops nearby.

In the months that followed the surgery, I slowly began to realize that I didn't need Viagra anymore. I had fully expected to be reliant on the little blue pills forever, so the realization happened over a few months where I gradually noticed that things were back to normal. This felt like a miracle, I couldn't believe it. It was a completely unexpected side effect that coincided with that surgery. I can't explain why it happened, I just theorized that all of my organs just settled differently after the surgery with Dr. Millham, because the feeling that something was damming the blood flow was gone. For me, it proved that this was indeed a physiological issue, as I had guessed all along. It was another instance of having a clearer understanding of my body than the doctors.

In April of that year, Nicole and I planned a weekend out in Boston to celebrate our two-year anniversary. We got a room at the Park Plaza, a historic hotel in Back Bay, and designed an itinerary of favorite places and things to do.

"I know what we can do, Meesh," I said to her one morning, lying in bed. Meesh was an affectionate nickname we had for each other, a completely made-up word that we just started using early in our relationship. She called me Meesh, and I called her Meesh. Sometimes we would speculate about its origins, but neither of us could remember. Whereas other couples might use babe or sweetheart or honey, we had our own word that no one else had. We had playful variations like meeshie and an abbreviated "M" for signing notes. We never used it in front of others because that would just be obnoxious. Our first names were reserved for when we were mad at each other.

"We could get FuGaKyu sushi on our way into the city, and eat it for lunch in the hotel room. That could be the start of the whole weekend."

"Well, I'm not going to say no to that," she said. Eating sushi became a pastime of ours, as much as we could afford it anyway. FuGaKyu was our favorite Japanese restaurant, saved for special occasions. We weren't picky though. We frequented sushi buffets, take-out-only sushi joints, and of course our tiny neighborhood gem Asahi, where we had gone on an early date. At Asahi, the chef always gave out an extra two pieces after you finished. And that was going to be how I proposed to her.

That morning, I checked in to the hotel early to get the room ready. I had a bouquet of flowers, and some other things to drop off in the room. I got us upgraded to a suite when I checked in by telling the hotel clerk that I was about to propose to my girlfriend in the room.

I drove back to Brighton to pick up Nicole, we called in our order at FuGaKyu, and soon we were in the hotel room finishing the sushi. As we went through the ritual of dividing up the last pieces, the sushi in my stomach turned to butterflies. All of a sudden, I was nervous.

"Okay," I said after we finished, "now it's time for dessert."

"Dessert? What kind of dessert are we having with sushi?"

I walked over to my black duffel bag that I had brought up with us, and with sweaty hands unzipped it to reveal a small black sushi takeout tray with a clear plastic lid, sitting on ice. Earlier that morning, on my way to pick her up, I had gone to a different sushi restaurant and picked up two pieces of salmon nigiri sushi. Wedged between the twin pieces of fish was the ring.

She was still sitting, and I stood above her with the tray. My hand was shaking, and I fumbled through an unrehearsed line about how the last two years had been the best of my life, then I kneeled down to reveal the ring between the sushi.

"Will you marry me, Nicole?"

She said yes.

23

THREE

"Shit, I missed my turn," I said, my hand shielding the blinding early morning sun that hung low in the February sky.

"Are you fucking serious right now, Brad?" Nicole said.

"Just hold on, I'm all turned around."

I tried my best to navigate through the concrete maze of streets that was Boston's Longwood area. Leave it to me to get lost rushing my pregnant wife to the hospital. Fortunately, it was a Saturday morning and the salt-stained winter streets were mostly deserted.

"If I can just get back out to Route 9, I'll know where we are."

"Can we just get there?" She quietly turned away and sighed in pain.

I wasn't used to this role of being the support person, and clearly, I wasn't very good at it. Finally, I found Francis Street and realized where I was. I pulled in and had them valet my car while I ushered Nicole inside.

The day before, Friday the 13th, turned out to be a real-life horror show. We were up all night, and Nicole had suffered through about fifteen hours of back labor. This meant the back of the baby's head was positioned so that it ground down on her tailbone. The only thing we learned about back labor from the all-day birthing class we took a few months earlier was the nurse saying, "Back labor... well, let's just say you don't want to have back labor." And then she went on to the next birthing topic.

We had called the hospital a few times through the night, hoping the doctor would let her come in and get the pain medication started, but no luck. Her actual contractions, which were hard for her to decipher from the blinding pain in her lower back, were still too far apart. At dawn, I had an idea.

"Meesh, I bet this doctor is just on the night shift. They usually change first thing in the morning. Maybe your doctor will be the one on, and she'll have you come in."

"Okay," she said from the tub, where she was trying to get some relief. Back labor didn't have breaks like contractions did. It was a steady sharp pain that completely wore her out.

"We'll call at 7:00. That's when the shift change usually happens," I said.

I coached her on how to act on the phone. Each time she had called during the night, she'd pull herself together and had what sounded like a regular conversation with the on-call doctor. I knew this all too well because I used to do the same thing, trying to muster up my best self while in agony.

"When you talk to her, really let her hear your anguish. They need to hear that you're in pain and that you're exhausted. They're listening for it. You've been up all night, let them hear it in your voice."

"Okay," she sighed. "Good idea."

Sure enough, when she called she was connected to a different on-call doctor. Not her obstetrician but another doctor in her practice. Someone with a different opinion on the situation who decided they could make her more comfortable in the hospital.

. . .

It took a couple of hours, but finally we were in a room on the labor floor, her epidural had been placed, and she was pain-free. Friday the 13th was behind us, and today was Valentine's Day.

We slept. We played Scrabble. We spent the day talking and speculating what it would be like to have a little boy or girl with a Valentine's Day birthday. When I would venture outside to the kitchenette, I could hear the sounds of birth happening in other rooms. The patterns were the same every time I heard it. *Push! Push!* Followed by the first cries of a baby entering the world. This was no ordinary hospital floor. This place was magical.

They started Nicole on Pitocin, an IV drug used to move the labor along more quickly. Real contractions began, but Nicole was numb from the epidural. All she had felt was the back labor.

By about nine o'clock that night it was time for Nicole to start pushing, and that's when the complications began.

"You grab a leg," the delivery nurse said to me, "and I'll grab a leg."

"Got it," I said.

Now, I was in my element. I had the paper johnnie and hat on and was ready to help as much as I could. The nurse and I were on opposite sides of Nicole, and we both grabbed one of her legs and pushed them back toward her head while she pushed. This wasn't the movies. Nicole was totally naked in the dimly lit delivery room, the nurse and I were using all of our strength to lift her legs back toward her, and her vagina was the centerpiece of this hot sweaty scene. The doctor was down the hall delivering another baby because Nicole wasn't ready yet. It wasn't Nicole's doctor that she had spent the last nine months seeing in appointments, but someone else in the practice. That was okay though, we rolled with it. We liked her.

All of the monitors said that the baby's heartbeat was dropping when she pushed. We stopped, and the doctor came in and explained the situation in a loud, clear voice.

"Nicole, we need to get the baby out. The best way to do it is what's called a vacuum delivery. I'm going to put a small suction cup on the top of the baby's head, and that's going get the baby out in a couple of pushes. Without this, you're probably an hour away from being able to do this on your own, and that's too much of a risk to the baby."

"Okay," Nicole said, nodding her head.

The next thing we knew the room was filling with people. Nurses. Pediatricians. Other doctors.

"I guess modesty goes out the window with this kind of thing," she said to me, totally naked in a room full of about ten people.

The first big push with the vacuum advanced things significantly.

"Dad, do you want to call the sex? I think the next push is going to do it."

"Yep, I know the difference so I can do that," I said, trying to make a joke that totally bombed in a room full of serious people.

I took a deep breath. We had waited to find out the sex, and here we were in this moment of excitement. A boy or a girl. This would drastically alter the direction of our lives in one way or another.

Nicole pushed again, and that was it. A tiny purple baby emerged.

"It's a boy! His name is Cooper. And he looks just like his mom," I announced. It was 10:00 at night, and we had our Valentine's Day baby. In that instant, his face really did look like Nicole's to me. But unlike all of the other births I had heard out in the hall earlier that day, our room was silent. The baby wasn't crying.

They whisked him off to the baby warmer in the corner of the room, where they examined him. This wasn't the plan. Everything we had learned said that after the baby comes out it goes right up to the mother's chest for some essential one-on-one time. They made it sound like if you didn't have this experience the instant the baby was born, they would surely grow up to be a serial killer.

"What's going on? Is he okay?" Nicole said to the nurse who seemed to be assigned to staying back with us at the bed.

"Yes, dear, they just have to get the Apgar score," she said. "If the baby is born crying, that checks most of the boxes."

Nicole and I huddled together on the bed while a small crowd of doctors hovered over the warmer in the corner, examining the baby. Through their shifting bodies I could see the baby's skin slowly turning from purple to pink, a good sign because that meant that he was breathing.

After what felt like ten minutes, but was probably only two, Nicole called out to them.

"Is he okay?"

One of the doctors stepped back from the warmer and took in a wider view of the baby.

"Yes, he is. I think he's just a laid-back kid."

A nurse scooped him up from the warmer and brought him over to Nicole.

"He looks like an alien," Nicole said.

"Oh, that's just from the vacuum," the doctor said. "His head will be back to normal in a day or two."

It was true that he looked more like Marge Simpson than a newborn, but we didn't care. Here was this tiny life who was taking his first glances around at the world. We talked to him and introduced ourselves as his parents.

After our new family of three had a little time together, the doctor announced that he would have to go to the NICU to get an IV for antibiotics. There was a risk of infection either because of the vacuum delivery or the fact that his heart rate dropped when Nicole started to push.

"He has to go now?" I asked.

"Yes," she said, "but we'll bring him up to your room in an hour or so once it's placed."

They took him away, and we spent another hour there while Nicole birthed the placenta. We called our parents to let them know they had a new grandson. Eventually, Nicole was ready to get transferred to a wheelchair to get transported upstairs to the maternity floor. Turning back for a last look at the room, there was so much blood on the floor it looked like a massacre had just occurred.

Finally we were alone in our own clean room after the transport person dropped us off.

"You did it, Meesh," I said, and I leaned over and kissed her forehead. "I'm proud of you."

"It sounds weird," she said, "but it feels like something is missing."

"I feel it too. He'll be back with us soon," I said.

Just then, a nurse entered, wheeling Cooper back to us in the clear plastic bassinet. Without him, there was a distinct emptiness that was instantly filled by the return of this new life that was now sleeping safely in Nicole's arms.

Now, we were three.

24

HOPE IS A DRUG

"I just want to point out that you are talking about diabetes like it's one condition and it's not. Type 1 diabetes is an autoimmune disease that has nothing to do with overeating."

A year and a half later I drove in my Jeep listening to an NPR call-in show on Halloween about the evils of sugar, obesity in children, and the rise of type 2 diabetes. After they addressed the caller's issue and confirmed what she was saying was true, I turned off the car stereo, and drove in silence.

My mind raced with this new knowledge, as a new theory began to take shape. My grandfather was a type 1 diabetic, but I never knew that it was an autoimmune disease. In almost every way, my grandfather's genes had skipped a generation and landed inside me. We were the tallest in the family, though he was an inch taller than me at 6′ 3″. We had the same lanky frame and knobby knees. And we were both the artists in the family. In retirement, he focused on carving birds. These were delicate life-like renderings he would create in his basement shop, where he had industrial drills and band saws and a lathe. He would use photographs from *Field and Stream* magazine for reference to create beautiful life-sized renderings. After mastering cardinals, mallards, and chickadees, he moved on to other interesting birds. These treasures were not for sale. They were gifts that he would give out to the family at Christmas. Three cardinals, one for each of his daughters. The grandkids got things like planes and wooden Rolls Royce cars. Years after his death, these carvings live on as family heirlooms on everyone's mantels.

And now this, an heirloom just for me. We both had autoimmune diseases. As a kid, his diabetic routines seemed incredibly difficult to me. He gave himself an insulin shot every morning when he woke up, a practice that shocked me. How could he stick himself with a needle every single day? This alone made him seem like some kind of superhero. He was vigilant about avoiding sugar, something else I couldn't imagine. No dessert? No candy? Of course, that didn't stop him from small infractions like eating leftover pieces of pie crust at Thanksgiving or sneaking a lick of someone's ice cream in the summer.

I became inspired by this new connection to him. Maybe our conditions were somehow linked. Maybe a solution for me was hiding in plain sight. What if I cut sugar out of my diet? Maybe that alone could keep my Crohn's symptoms under control.

After a few years of remission, my Crohn's began to creep back. Remicade still worked in a decent capacity on a six-week cycle. I would get my infusion and feel good for about two weeks. The middle two weeks would be just okay, and then symptoms like sluggishness and more frequent bowel movements would start to creep back in the last two weeks. Then I would get my infusion and bounce right back. Nicole called Remicade my Magic Juice because it would bring me back to life.

The Remicade infusions weren't the only thing that Dr. O'Neil had me on. I also took another Crohn's maintenance drug called Asacol, and 6-Mercaptopurine, 6MP for short, which was a chemo drug that also helped Crohn's patients.

I had often lamented the fact that the internet wasn't available when I had been diagnosed back in the 1980s. Now, people had easy access to alternative solutions to typical Western medicine. One thing I'd been doing for the past few years was chi gung, which are sets of slow movements similar to tai chi, to optimize health and longevity.

The idea of cutting sugar out of my diet was the start of a new direction for me. I researched and found a book on digestive health which was the story of a man who had cured his Crohn's through diet alone. Eliminating sugar was part of the diet's regime. After tinkering with that diet for a month or so I learned that his plan was based on a more widely known diet called the Specific Carbohydrate Diet, commonly referred to as SCD. It didn't just stop at sugar, it went way further, outlawing most of what I ate, including processed carbohydrates. With the new year on the horizon, I made SCD my new year's resolution.

Before starting the diet, I called up Dr. O'Neil to get his take on it. I expected him to have a negative opinion and dismiss it. Most Crohn's-related diets dealt with reducing the amount of roughage that moved through the digestive tract. Keeping a patient's weight up was still of paramount importance, so therefore carbohydrates were key.

After giving him a quick overview of the diet, I waited for his opinion on the other end of the line.

"Well, I've never heard of it, but you can try it. It doesn't sound like a good idea for you to cut out carbs. We both know they're an easy source of calories."

"Okay," I said. "I'm going to do it then."

After hanging up the phone I knew I was going to be on my own, but I was getting more comfortable with that idea. The defiant side of me fantasized about becoming so healthy that Dr. O'Neil wouldn't be able to ignore this new diet I had found. This excitement about the possibility of putting Crohn's to rest through diet inflated me with hope, as if hope itself were a drug. I challenged myself to find success and never have the need for surgery again.

SCD was a hard diet to implement, but I did it. Similar to other ketogenic diets like Atkins and paleo, I had to get my calories from protein and fat, not carbohydrates. There were four main rules: No sugar. No grains. No starches. No dairy. I couldn't handle a lot of roughage like salad and nuts, so this left me with little variety. All I ate was meat and cooked vegetables. Besides bananas, there wasn't anything quick and easy that I could eat, so I spent hours in the kitchen boiling, broiling, baking, sautéing, and of course washing mountains of dishes. In a way, the goal of the diet was to shift the time spent in the bathroom to the kitchen.

By the end of the first month, I had lost about fifteen pounds even though my massive daily intake of food was somewhere in the area of 5,000 to 6,000 calories, no easy feat considering that I wasn't eating any refined sugar or processed food. A typical meal would be about a pound of meat like chicken, pork chops, or hamburger patties with green beans or cooked carrots. I made my own homemade SCD yogurt, which was also part of the diet because it provided good bacteria in massive amounts. Fortunately, we could afford the food bills each week, which had doubled from the pre-SCD days. Carbs and processed food are cheap. SCD foods are not. At checkout, the belt would be filled with two-pound bags of carrots and frozen green beans, several bunches of bananas, and a hill of brown butcher paper packages from the meat and fish counter. Nicole and Cooper, who'd just had his second birthday, usually ate separately because our different meals were just too difficult to coordinate. Plus, I needed to eat as much as I possibly could to try to keep my weight up.

SCD started as a book called *Breaking the Vicious Cycle*, a terrible read because it's written by a biochemist and cell biologist, not a dietician. Online resources made it better because people posted SCD-legal recipes on blogs, and there was a podcast that was put out by two young guys that had success with the diet. They developed resources for the diet and highlighted success stories in people with a range of intestinal disorders. Listening to them each week was also a big influx of hope. I wasn't experiencing the success that they advertised yet, but it would happen for me eventually.

I hit cruise mode with the diet by the third month, leveling out at around 4,000 calories per day. I was feeling good and was ready for my appointment with Dr. O'Neil to report on my new diet and other supplements I had been taking.

"So," he began with hesitation, scanning the report from recent blood work that had been taken. "Your labs are a bit off. Quite a bit, actually. Your liver is being taxed from whatever you're doing."

"Well, that doesn't make sense because I'm eating only real food, nothing processed," I protested.

He shrugged and raised his eyebrows in a look of compassion. "Sometimes this happens with lots of supplements though. What are you taking?"

I listed off about a dozen supplements I had started taking, ranging from Betaine HCl, which helps to break down food in the stomach, to cod liver oil for its omega-3 properties, to SCD-legal probiotics.

"Well, that's certainly a lot. You need to stop taking them. After your liver gets back to normal, you can start adding them back one by one. That way we'll find the culprit."

"What do you mean 'stop taking them?' All of them?"

Inside I was panicking. I had thoughtfully curated these supplements that were helping me to feel better based on internet research I had done. It was a carefully constructed house of cards, and there was no way I was going to stop all of them.

"Well let's put it this way. If I didn't know you and I just saw these lab numbers, I would guess that these were the labs from an alcoholic."

I sighed, knowing that he was pointing out something serious. We wrapped up the appointment with me saying to him that I would stop the supplements, and to myself that I would go online and figure out what would cause my liver numbers to spike like this. Surely it must be tied to one of them that I can simply stop.

I can't remember what it was, but I was able to figure out the offending supplement and eliminate it. I stayed on the diet month after month, and while I was feeling good, it never put me back into a state of full remission.

25

BAD DOCTOR, GOOD DOCTOR

EVEN THOUGH THINGS WERE GOING WELL WITH THE Specific Carbohydrate diet, Crohn's always seemed to blindside me. This time it came in the form of another intestinal blockage.

It was a difficult year to be on a hard diet. We moved out of our small condo to a house in Canton, a suburb about thirty minutes southwest of Boston. We loved our new house, but the kitchen was falling apart so we decided to remodel after only living there for two months. Without a kitchen, takeout is key, but there was so little I could eat at restaurants. I managed SCD with a microwave for the two weeks it took the contractor to get our kitchen up and running again. At the same time, I started a new job at Cramer, a marketing agency in Norwood. And through all of this, Cooper was going through the terrible twos.

Somewhere inside me, Crohn's decided to join the chaos.

It was a Saturday night in April, and we had just finished eating dinner. I grabbed the leash and took our dog out for a walk around the block. Suddenly I started feeling the first pains of a blockage. The labor-like contractions started slowly, with dread and disappointment following close behind. Not again. It had been eight years since I had felt this, but the feeling in my stomach was unmistakable.

By about ten o'clock that night, I knew I was going to need help. The pain was getting gradually worse, and nausea was setting in. I still had a window of time where I could tolerate the pain, and I hadn't yet vomited, so I drove myself to the emergency room at Newton-Wellesley Hospital. It was only about a twenty-minute drive, and Nicole could stay home with Cooper.

I parked in the garage and checked myself in. Like every emergency room on a Saturday night, the waiting room was packed. I slumped down in an open chair and doubled over in pain. When they finally took me in, they put me through the usual regime. IV fluids to hydrate me. Narcotics for the pain. A CT scan to confirm the blockage. And an NG tube placed up my nose to begin to relieve the pressure and remove the contents of my stomach.

Given my history of Crohn's, the resident doctors were worried about me. I had a different angle on my history, pointing out that I had experience with blockages.

"This has happened to me before. You'll probably just have to admit me for a day or two, and things will start moving again," I assured them.

If I felt that I needed surgery, I would have gone to the Brigham. Two years earlier I'd had surgery with Dr. Boyle once again, this time for was a stoma revision. Crohn's had developed near my stoma, which distorted it and made it difficult to pouch.

They were skeptical and kept me in the ER for the night to monitor me. Plus, they had to constantly flush my NG tube because it kept getting clogged from the spinach just sitting in my stomach from dinner.

As it goes in hospitals, the early morning shift change produced new doctors who took an interest in me, specifically a young woman with short dark hair who immediately started bossing around the residents. The NG tube they had placed was a narrower gauge than she would have selected. It turned out that the reason they had given me a thinner tube was that they didn't have anything larger on hand, so at least I wouldn't have to go through an NG tube removal and reinsertion. The smaller tube, however, was the reason for the repeated clogs.

After a conversation with me at 5:00 in the morning, she came to a fast conclusion.

"Well Mr. Harris, it looks like we're going to be operating on you today to alleviate your blockage," she said in an all-knowing tone.

"No, I don't think so," I said. "I'm not going to need surgery. I've had blockages before, and they almost always work themselves out on their own. You'll see."

Her eyes narrowed, surprised at my opposition to her recommendation. "Well, your scan shows that your stomach is completely distended. Cases like this almost always require surgery."

"Well, even if you're right I wouldn't have the surgery here because my surgeon is at the Brigham."

"Who's your surgeon?"

"Dr. Boyle."

Now she was pissed. In all of my experiences with doctors, I've never seen a doctor so mad at me.

"He did my ostomy surgery," I said, "and he's one of the..."

She cut back in. "I know who Don Boyle is. He worked with my father for years."

Not knowing what she was talking about or how to respond, I just watched her vent.

"So, if Don Boyle is your surgeon then why did you come here? Why didn't you go to the ER at Brigham and Women's?"

"Well, two reasons. One, I'm not going to need surgery. And two, Newton-Wellesley is closer to my house. I drove here myself, it's not like I came here in an ambulance."

At that point, one of the residents had returned to tend to the suction on my NG tube.

"Tell me something," she continued. "If you know you're not supposed to eat spinach, why did you eat spinach? I've never understood that, and I see that all the time. People with food allergies eat what they shouldn't eat. And then they always end up in here."

"Well that's the thing," I said calmly. "Up until this point spinach hasn't been a problem for me. I guess that's Crohn's for you."

The surgeon turned on her heel and exited the room in a huff.

"Thanks," I said to the resident who was flushing the spinach out of my NG tube. "Is she always like that?"

He smirked and shrugged, which told me all I needed to know.

An hour later I learned that an ambulance ride to Brigham and Women's had been arranged for me. Whether this was because the surgeon really thought I would need surgery, or because she was just completely disgusted with my decisions, I will never know. But I was about to learn that fate works in mysterious ways, and soon I was riding in an ambulance from one ER to the next.

By then it was officially Sunday morning, and after getting established in my curtained off area in Brigham and Women's ER, a new doctor entered.

"Hi Brad," he said extending his hand to me. "Matt Hamilton."

I shook his hand and registered a positive feeling from him. I liked him instantly. He was the attending gastroenterologist on the floor, another young doctor who couldn't have been much older than I was. He was wearing casual clothing, as was the norm for doctors on call during the weekends. I gave him the rundown of the previous night's events. While I was proud of myself for how I handled the surgeon at Newton-Wellesley, I was still awestruck at her obnoxious behavior. I had never seen anything like it before.

We talked for about fifteen minutes. As I went through my story he nodded thoughtfully and asked questions. He examined my belly in the typical way that all gastroenterologists did.

"You're still pretty distended," he said, "so we're in a wait-and-see pattern. Given your history I think you have a good sense of your own body at this point, so let us know if you start feeling worse. We'll keep the tube in and keep you NPO until things start to move. The surgical staff will be around in the morning, and I'll let Dr. Boyle know that we talked, even though his services most likely won't be needed. And I'll contact Dr. O'Neil as well and let him know what's going on."

After he left, I replayed the interaction. The caring, thoughtful nods he gave me and the extra time he spent talking to me. He was really listening, not waiting to prescribe his opinion. I could see the gears moving in his head as I spoke, and there was nothing about him that showed an ego. He honestly wanted to connect with me. That was something I hadn't experienced in a long time.

After I was admitted, I called my creative partner at work and gave him my Crohn's rap. We decided it would be best to keep the fact that I was unexpectedly hospital-bound quiet, and just say that I would be out sick for a couple of days. I told him that I would be back in the office by Wednesday, and he said that he'd be able to cover things while I was out.

I climbed out of bed and closed the door, positioning my IV pole in a way that I would be able to do chi gung. The last time I had a blockage was before I learned it, and I was interested in the prospect of having a new tool to help to unblock my intestines. My arms arched in gentle circles and my entire torso began to relax and let go. Halfway through, my nurse entered.

"Oh." She paused in the doorway trying to assess what I was doing. "Oh, you're doing exercises. I'll come back later."

I continued and finished the set. I felt much looser and relaxed, and lay down in bed and closed my eyes for a well-deserved nap.

I ended up spending three days at the Brigham before being discharged. The last time I saw Dr. Hamilton I asked him some questions.

"So, are you only stationed in the hospital here, or do you see patients?"

"Oh, yes I see patients in the clinic here at the Brigham. We all switch off on having shifts in the hospital, and you came in on my week."

"Okay, awesome. I would like to see you again somehow."

"Sure, that would be great," he said, and he handed me his card. "At this point, I only take IBD patients, that's my specialty. Of course, you would qualify."

A few months later, I became symptomatic again. Stomach pain made me feel another blockage coming on, and fortunately, I was able to fast on my own and it worked itself out before I needed to go to the hospital. I called Dr. O'Neil and left him a message, feeling that at the very least we needed to talk about this over the phone. I had been on Remicade for nine years, which was longer than most people, and I felt like it had run its course. I pride myself on not being a complainer. This way, I figured, when I ask for help I'd get it. Or, I should get it.

Dr. O'Neil wasn't giving me the attention I deserved when I called his office. He didn't call me back the day that I called in distress, and I could practically hear him shrugging his shoulders through the phone line when he did call the next day. It was time for a change.

I called Dr. Hamilton's office, and even though I wasn't even a patient of his, got an appointment the very next day.

"There he is," he said when he entered the exam room, remembering me instantly. He met with me for forty-five minutes, a new record for any doctor visit I'd had to date. It was such a fruitful conversation filled with his thoughtful nods to what I was saying.

Whether he knew it or not, this appointment was half a second-opinion meeting and half an interview for being my new gastroenterologist. What would he think about the Specific Carbohydrate Diet?

"SCD, sure," he said without missing a beat. He knew about it. And with that, I talked about all of the other alternative treatments I had tried over the past few years.

He set me up for blood work where he would test to see if my body had built up antibodies to the Remicade. I didn't even know a test like that was possible. But I did know one thing. Dr. Hamilton was going to be my new doctor.

I met with Dr. O'Neil one more time to let him know that I would no longer need his services. It was a hard appointment that felt like a breakup. In the end, he knew I was going to do well with Dr. Hamilton and he gave me his best.

I now had my three most important practitioners at the Brigham. Dr. Boyle for surgery. Diane for my ostomy care. And now Dr. Hamilton as my gastroenterologist. Besides being at the top of their fields of expertise, they all knew each other and worked together at one of the best hospitals in the world. I finally had a care team that I felt really good about. And I was going to need it.

26

DEATH AND LIFE

THE HOUSE FELL SILENT AS MY FATHER SAID GRACE.

"Dear Lord, bless this food to the nourishment of our bodies, and may we remember those who are not with us today." His bowed head glanced sideways at the empty chair next to him. "Especially Sally."

A dam broke inside him. His face crumpled and his large teeth clenched as he broke down crying. This was the second time in my life I had seen my father cry. The first was decades earlier at his mother's funeral. I was a little boy sitting in the church pew looking over at his silhouette choking back tears. Today was different though, this was a full-on sobbing.

Our whole family was seated around the dining room table of my parents' house in Medfield on Easter Sunday. My uncle put his hand on my dad's bobbing shoulder to console him, as eyes around the table welled with tears. Nicole, who was eight months pregnant, turned to me and gave me a what-is-happening-right-now stare as she tended to Cooper, who was three years old and ready to eat. As everyone began to pass food around, filling their plates and changing the subject, I sat squinting at my upset father, trying to process what was really going on here. Later I would realize that was the exact moment when I knew my mother was going to die.

She had left the house an hour earlier because there was an opening at the hospital for an MRI, a test she needed to have done. She had been experiencing cancer symptoms for the past month, though she'd been reluctant to admit it. She was sixty-five and had retired just a month ago from her job as an administrative assistant to the CEO of a bank.

Two years earlier she had been diagnosed with multiple myeloma, bone marrow cancer. By all of the reports from her appointments and treatments, everything was optimistic.

"There are several new treatments in the pipeline, and for many patients, this is more of a chronic disease than a death sentence," she told me one night on the phone.

She had chemo, lost her hair, and after about two months she returned to work like nothing had happened.

This time around, her symptoms were worse. The doctor discovered a lump on her head the size of an egg, and she didn't have an explanation as to what caused it. Then a week later she started to have pain in her jaw, which prompted her to finally get to the oncologist.

She returned later in the afternoon on Easter after having the MRI, and I could tell she was less anxious.

"At least it's done, and I've done everything I can do at this point," she said. She was just happy to be back at home with everyone, especially Cooper.

After she ate a plate of reheated food, a few of us grabbed the bag of plastic colored eggs she had filled with candy and coins and hid them in the backyard. Once the eggs were in place, my mom led everyone out back to get ready to watch Cooper find them. He was the only one in the family under the age of thirty, and the light of my mother's life. This was the one part of the holiday she wanted to experience firsthand. For those ten minutes, she forgot about her looming illness as she followed Cooper around the yard, finding eggs.

As April turned to May, the trees had filled with leaves and my mom was doing better. One Sunday she and my father came over to our house after church for a visit. They found us in the backyard, pushing Cooper on the swing set underneath our big cherry tree. That tree was in bloom for only one week a year, and we were right in the middle of it. We were surrounded by bright pink blossoms and covered in shade.

As usual, my mom rushed through hellos and immediately became absorbed with Cooper. This had become a joke with Nicole and me because she would sometimes go an entire visit being so completely enamored with Cooper that when it was time for them to leave, she realized that she hadn't talked to us at all, saying, "oh and how are you guys doing?" She just loved being a grandmother. This was okay with us, and we were happy to take a much-needed break from the terrible threes, a continual stream of, "I can do it by myself," even though he couldn't, followed by frustrated tears. The simple task of putting on his shoes in the morning became a twenty-minute test of my sanity as I became later and later for work.

I took a snapshot in my mind of that day. The weather finally warm. My mom smiling, pushing Cooper on the swing. His shaggy blond hair waving in the breeze as he swung back and forth with a huge grin on his face. Mom was happy and seemed to be feeling okay despite having strong sessions of chemo for the past couple of weeks. She had her wig on and had made it to church, probably telling her friends all about Cooper in the coffee hour following the service. My father stood sipping a Heineken, talking to Nicole about how much he paid for gas on the way over, and the Vernon Cancer Center at Newton-Wellesley Hospital where they were going for her appointments. He always referred to the facility by its full name, the Vernon Cancer Center, like it was as well-known and prestigious as Harvard or NASA. The reality was she was getting best-in-the-world care because her oncologist was a conduit for another doctor, at Dana-Farber in Boston, who was trying to get her into a trial and advised her oncologist based on their cutting-edge research.

After taking in this scene in my backyard, I walked over and joined the conversation with my father and Nicole. I didn't know it then, but it would be the last good memory we all had together.

With baby number two on the way and no idea how Cooper would welcome a new baby brother or sister, Nicole and I signed up for a siblings class at Newton-Wellesley, which was where the birth would be taking place.

When people hear the word hospital, they usually picture a neatly organized tower of rooms, departments, and elevators. Newton-Wellesley Hospital constructed the opposite of that vision, a funhouse maze of confusion. Even though I had spent so much time there going to appointments since the Dr. Flores years, I usually stopped to study the map, as I did that Saturday morning to find the siblings class.

After walking around for ten minutes, we found the correct location, an open carpeted room where all of the kids had gathered in a circle on the floor. They were surrounded by tired fathers holding Dunkin' Donuts cups and full-bellied moms resting their swollen feet in chairs. A happy and enthusiastic nurse facilitated questions to the kids about their future brothers or sisters, and they spent the rest of the time putting diapers on baby dolls.

After hugging and kissing the faux future siblings, the nurse collected the dolls and led the class to the elevators. We were going up to the maternity floor to visit real live babies in the nursery.

When we arrived at the wide window that peered into the nursery, the kids climbed up on a wooden bench in front and pressed their faces to the glass. Instead of a room full of babies, there was a single hospital bassinet that held one tiny, sleeping, swaddled newborn. The parents smiled, the kids asked more questions. What was this baby's name? Where were the parents? Did the baby like chicken nuggets too? Finally, the teacher announced that the class was over, and everyone started to shuffle away from the nursery. Everyone except Cooper.

"I love the baby!" he said pointing at the glass. "We can't leave without the baby."

"Oh, no Coop, that's someone else's baby," I said with a laugh. "Our baby is still in Mommy's tummy." I pointed to Nicole's nine-month-full belly.

Cooper nodded, slowly processing the news that we wouldn't be bringing a baby home with us yet. Nicole and I had a whispered conversation about how this had to be a good sign. He might be okay with a sibling after all.

"Hey Coop," I said, kneeling back down, "Gram's in the hospital upstairs. Do you want to go see her?"

"Yes!" he said excitedly.

"Okay, well I have to tell you that she's not going to look like you're used to seeing her. She's going to be in a big bed, and..." I paused. "Well because of how she's sick, she doesn't have any hair."

"Okay!" he said, clearly either not understanding or not caring what her state was. He just wanted to see Gram.

Five minutes later we entered my mom's room and she lit up when she saw him. Her pale white scalp reflected the overhead light, and she leaned over to the side of the bed to hug Cooper.

She had been in the hospital for two days at that point, having been admitted after a Thursday morning checkup appointment with her oncologist where she had been weak and short of breath. She felt better knowing she would be in the care of the hospital staff.

"The doctor actually wheeled your mother over to the hospital himself," my father said, eyebrows raised. Another check in the plus column for the Vernon Cancer Center.

After Cooper explained what happened in the siblings class to his grandma, we said goodbyes, and I assured my parents that I would be by tomorrow for Mother's Day.

The original plan for Mother's Day was to go to Legal C Bar, a branch of the famous Legal Sea Foods chain in the northeast. This way, Mom wouldn't have to cook, and we could all see each other. However, the reservation was canceled when we realized she wouldn't be out of the hospital by then.

The next day Nicole and Cooper stayed home, and I went into Newton-Wellesley to visit her myself. With flowers in hand, I entered her room, and at a glance I realized quickly that things had changed. My parents had seemed chipper the day before, but today they were drained and tired. My mom's ashen face hovered over a tray in front of her holding, of all things, a can of chocolate Boost with the straw pointing in her direction.

They explained that they'd just talked to the doctor and had gotten the results from a series of scans they had done.

"The good news is that there's a possibility that a lot of this is viral," said my father.

"The doctor will be in shortly, so you can hear for yourself," said my mom.

This was good because I really didn't have a clear picture of what was actually going on. All of the information went through the filter of my parents' brains before reaching me, and I was suspicious of what kind of spin they were adding.

The doctor entered and took a seat, settling in for a long conversation. He explained that based on the images, the cancer in my mom's skull had most likely metastasized in a couple of other areas, her liver and her lungs.

"There's an outside chance that this could be some kind of virus, but the fact that she has stage 4 multiple myeloma would suggest otherwise," he said.

This was the first time I had heard that she had stage 4 cancer. It was at that moment that I realized just how much my parents, especially my mom, had been sugarcoating her disease from the start. When she was diagnosed two years earlier, she had advertised the fact that there were new treatments and that many patients were able to manage their symptoms for decades. There was nothing contradictory to this angle, like saying, "but on the other hand, I do have stage 4 multiple myeloma, so perhaps mileage may vary."

Even now, my father interjected, "so, what you're saying is that there is a possibility that this might be just a virus?"

"Dad. That's not what he's saying at all," I said.

My mother pulled herself up in bed, remaining quiet.

"Well, we are still assessing everything and are putting together a plan," the doctor continued. "The good news is that right now, Sally, you're awake and alert and have a clear sense of everything that's going on. I think we should talk about what your wishes are in case things take a turn for the worse."

My mother, knowing exactly where this conversation was going, said, "I'd like to be DNR. I don't want to be put on life support. If my time comes, then it comes," she said, giving a faraway glance to no one in particular.

That was a bit dramatic for my taste, but such was my mother's way. I couldn't help but cheer myself up in my head by sarcastically thinking that this was the best Mother's Day ever. I'm in this hospital room with my bald mother and scared father talking about her death sometime in the near future.

"Okay Ma, I think that's a good decision," I said.

The doctor gave her the forms for her to sign, and my father and I cosigned as witnesses. He collected the paperwork and exited the room.

I stood up, realizing in that moment that I needed to be the support system for my parents, the same way my mother had been for me for years.

"Hey Ma, how does that Boost taste?" I said sarcastically to lighten the mood.

She answered with a wince, turning her nose up.

"Come on, you have to drink it," I said, seriously now as I moved the can closer. "Take a drink."

I saw the straw darken with the chocolate color moving through it briefly. I don't think she would have done it if I hadn't been the one making the demand. She knew how much I had endured with having to drink Boost and Ensure when I was a kid.

"Have you been up to walk yet?"

"Not today," she said. "Yesterday I made it to the door."

"Come on, Ma. I don't have to tell you how important it is to walk. Let's go. I'm getting you up."

I went out to the nurse's station and got her nurse, who helped her get her IV tubes organized. She stood with her weight balancing on her own two feet and hooked her arm under mine.

"Brad, I don't know how far I can make it."

"That's okay, one step at a time," I said. "Let's just make it to the door first. That's it, one thing at a time."

She shuffled forward, and I could not believe that this was the same person who had been pushing Cooper on the swing in my backyard just two weeks ago.

We reached the door and went down the hallway for a short distance before she wanted to turn back.

"Okay Ma, but you know if I was the patient here that this would be an unacceptably short distance for a walk."

"I know, hon, but I'm just so tired," she said. "Thank you, Brad."

After she got back in bed, she had more visitors. One of her best friends and her husband came in on their way to their daughter's for a regular Mother's Day celebration. I couldn't help but be a little bit jealous of them and their normal plans. That's how it goes sometimes though, I told myself. Still, my mother and I had just made a very special transaction, a Mother's Day gift. For all of the times my mother had aided my weak post-surgical self around hospital floors, this was one time I was able to do the same for her. After all, I acquired my drive to heal from her all those years ago at Children's, even if she didn't have it for herself in the end.

I had barely gotten to my desk at work on Monday morning when my phone started vibrating. I saw my mom's cell phone number light up on the screen.

"Hey Ma, how's it going today," I said.

"The doctor wants to have a family meeting at 1:00 today. I want you and Steve to both be here."

"Okay, I'll be there," I said without hesitation.

"I don't want to say more about it over the phone, it will be better to talk in person."

"Of course, Ma. Let's hear what he has to say, and not get too worried about this."

We hung up, and I remembered this was similar to how she had told me that she had cancer in the first place, two years earlier. She called and left a message saying to call her because she had something important to tell me and it wasn't something she could leave as a voicemail, which of course left me anxious until I was able to talk to her.

I went through the rest of my Monday morning on an emotional edge that I was not used to. During a meeting, my phone rang again. This time it was the Medfield number. It must be my dad calling from home. I stepped out of my meeting and picked up once I was in the hallway.

Out of everyone I've ever met in my life, there isn't a single person that's worse at keeping a secret than my father. Secret keeping plots on a spectrum for most people. Some secrets stay locked away in a high-security vault, others are free to roam in conversations when applicable. My father's secrets are running for public office. His mouth acts as the loudspeaker attached to the roof of a political caravan driving the streets, announcing them to anyone within earshot.

He gave a big sigh and began.

"Brad, your mother doesn't want me calling you, so you can't tell her that we're talking. I have to tell you what the doctor said." I could hear him choking up on the other end of the line. "They have a treatment for her, but he thinks she only has a few months to live."

"Okay Dad, well, let's just wait until we hear what the doctor has to say this afternoon before we get upset. Let's hear the plan he has for Mom."

"I know, okay," he said. I could hear a palpable sense of relief just to be able to tell me about this. It was too much for him to take.

He said he would see me at 1:00 in her room. He'd just gone home to get a few things for her, though I suspected that he'd just needed an excuse for some time alone.

A few short hours later at Newton-Wellesley, the four members of my immediate family were in my mother's hospital room when an older man with a kind face in a white coat appeared in the doorway. My dad stood up and introduced Steve and me to the doctor the way he does with anyone.

"I never call him Steve, always Steven. He's in finance. This is Brad, he's the artist..."

"Jim," Mom said from her bed, and gave him a look that said, *stop talking, this is serious.*

Steve and I shook the doctor's hand and found chairs to sit in. Once we were settled he began.

"Based on the scans we have, we have two treatment options with two different corresponding timelines. The first is that we can start her immediately on a new cocktail of chemo that should really do a number on the cancer that's currently attacking her body. The second would be to do nothing and keep you comfortable. Unfortunately, we don't see this going back into remission, we're just trying to buy you as much time as we can. Like the exercise you went through yesterday with the attending doctor, it's good to make these decisions when everyone is present and we're all awake and alert.

"If we decided to go the chemo route, I would estimate that you would have three to four months to live. If we do nothing, probably one to two months."

It was a unanimous decision to agree to start the chemotherapy. In my mind, I mapped out the upcoming months in my head. The baby would be born in June and she would be gone by the end of the summer. It was going to be a long few months.

After the doctor left, Mom pulled us in for a hug. As firmly as ever, she told us that she didn't want us to change our lives around because of this.

"I don't want any sudden engagements or weddings," she said to my brother, who'd been with his girlfriend for about four years. She turned to me. "And I don't want a baby named after me. I want every-thing to just proceed as it normally would."

Steve and I said goodbye and returned to our busy lives at work. I didn't know it then, but I'd just had the last real conversation with my mother. They started the chemo the next morning, Tuesday, and it hit her like a truck. I visited her only a couple of nights that week because I was bracing for a marathon of hospital visits over the next few months. She was sleeping every time I was there, her body doing everything it could to survive.

By Saturday morning, just five days after the meeting with her doctor, we were all being called back into the hospital because it was time to make another decision. The chemo wasn't working. She had been declining rapidly all week. It was time to stop her treatment, keep her comfortable, and let her pass away. The whole family who lived in the area was notified, and because it was a Saturday everyone was able to come in.

I stepped outside through the lobby of the hospital and made phone calls to two of my mom's best friends. I let them know that we were taking her off the oxygen tank and that the end would be soon. I invited them to come to see her, but they declined, saying that they felt that family should be with her. Still, I was glad that I had called for them because she treated her friends like sisters.

I put my phone in my pocket and sat on the high curb of the sidewalk, gazing into the curtain of tall trees that surrounded the entrance. I inhaled the warm May air and felt my emotions finally taking over. I was alone, and for the first time since I was a kid, I didn't fight the tears that were coming. As I looked up through the trees at the blue sky above, I began to cry.

It was as if a switch deep inside my chest had flipped back to the factory setting. I felt like a child again, and that was okay. All of the dread and anxiety that had been building over the past month washed out through my eyes, and onto my cheeks. And I felt better.

As I rose to go back into the hospital, I knew this was the last gift my mother would give me. The ability to soften in hard times and cry.

By late morning everyone was in her room. If she could have planned it herself, she would have wanted to leave this world exactly like this, surrounded by her family. Her husband. Her sons. Her two sisters and brother-in-law. Her niece and her niece's wife. And her college roommate who had been her lifelong friend. My father had the minster of the church come in to pray with us.

The nurses had removed most of the machinery that was in the room and now asked us to go to the family waiting area so they could take out the rest of the lines and tubes in her, leaving her with just a morphine drip. We all wanted a few minutes alone with her, and I took the first shift, staying with the nurses as they disconnected her.

At one point they pulled a thick tube from her neck and she started bleeding.

"Can I help?" I asked, sensing they could use an extra set of hands.

"Oh yes, sure, if you don't mind, just keep this gauze pressed up to her neck."

I took hold effortlessly, and the nurses looked at me with a tentative gaze. Apparently, they weren't used to having a patient's family member with such a hands-on approach.

"Are you a physician?" one of them asked.

"Ha, no. Just a lifelong patient. I have Crohn's, so I've had my fair share of this kind of stuff."

I was happy to help, and it really meant something to me to be able to care for my mom in such an intimate way.

After the nurses left, I spoke quietly to my mother for the last time. I couldn't help but notice the irony, because it was the first time that she couldn't hold up her end of the conversation. She couldn't voice her opinion. We couldn't argue. She couldn't tell me that I looked thin, or that she loved me. Or that I needed to be careful. All she could do was listen to me tell her what a wonderful job she had done in raising me, and how proud I was to be her son.

The others had their time with her, and soon we were all back in the room together. As we passed the time quietly, my father approached her side and said something to her that I couldn't quite make out between his whispered tone and his heavy Boston accent. He sat there holding her hand for a long time, and I tried to figure out the puzzle of what he'd said. He was a man who showed little affection or emotion, and here he was losing the person he loved most in the world. Then what he said hit me. He had said, "I got a broken heart."

Shortly after one o'clock, surrounded by her family, my mom took her last breath. The doctor came in and confirmed it, and now everyone was crying. And I was crying along with everyone.

Twenty years earlier when I was in high school, the whole family was at my grandparents' house for Thanksgiving. Everyone had finished eating the big meal and a small stack of old photos was being passed around the table.

I was descending the stairs from the second-floor bathroom, having had the third or fourth bowel movement of the day, when I heard some excitement in the dining room.

"Oh my God, look at this one. It's Brad!" I heard my mother say.

I walked over to her and she handed me a sepia-toned photo framed in heavy brown ornate paper. The man in the photograph sat leisurely on a park bench with a suit on. It was my great-grandfather, my grandfather's father, circa 1905. And he looked just like me.

Though my grandmother was a kind, gentle, and easygoing woman, nostalgic items weren't of much interest to her. My mother knew this well. There was a risk that she would either lose it or throw it out accidentally.

"Please," my mom said to my grandmother, "keep this. I want Brad to have it someday."

The someday she meant seemed far off back then. She hinted about a time when my grandparents wouldn't be there anymore, which didn't seem possible. They hosted every holiday and led active lives.

Those days did arrive though, about ten years later.

In the months that followed my grandmother's death, my grandfather began to decline and moved out to an assisted-living facility. My mother and aunt spent half of their weekends for an entire year cleaning out their house. They knew this was coming; it was an enormous excavation project that had loomed like a dark cloud for years. The basement alone was packed to the rafters with relics of bygone eras, from my grandfather's hunting rifles to a cabinet full of ancient liquor bottles they had received as gifts even though they didn't drink, to the industrial shop equipment that he used to carve his birds.

There was a running list of what items people wanted, and one by one, items were checked off the list as my mother and aunt undertook this as a gigantic archeological dig. My cousin Julie got the crafty pineapple lamp that my grandmother had made in the 1970s. I acquired the mid-century chrome-and-Formica kitchen table they'd had since the 1950s. My grandfather's carvings and my grandmother's jewelry were divvied up. But one thing was never found: that sepia-toned photo of my great-grandfather as a young man.

"I told her," my mother said to me toward the end. "I told her specifically that I wanted her to save that photo for you."

Items were collected. We filled a large dumpster with trash. We had a yard sale for things we could sell. The house was sold and their estate was settled. They decided the best way to divide up the remaining old photos was to give some to each of the three sisters. So, my mom got a box, and my two aunts each got a box. And that was the end of it.

Until my mom died ten years later.

My parents' house in Medfield became home base for family and friends as we prepared for the wake and funeral. The day after she died, we started to plan everything together. My aunt had brought her box of photos from my grandparents' house, and we passed them around looking for good ones for a slideshow that would play at the wake. There were photos of my mom as a kid playing dress-up. Posed photos with her sisters and brother. Prom photos of her in my grand-parents' living room wearing a poofy dress.

Food arrived and everyone got up, following the smell of hot pizza in the kitchen. I sat down next to the box and continued to sift through the few remaining photos. And there at the bottom of the box, the very last photo, was the sepia-tone shot of my great-grandfa-ther that we thought was lost so many years before.

"Oh my God," I whispered to myself.

My vague memory of seeing the photo decades earlier immedi-ately filled in with dramatic detail. His eyes, ears, and the bone struc-ture of his face were mine. His bony hands and knuckles were mine. The sharp-cornered frame of his body that protruded underneath his suit was mine. And the telltale knobby knees and broad but thin shoulders were mine too.

This photo that I didn't think existed anymore was now in my hands. I couldn't believe it. I felt like Charlie Bucket holding that last golden ticket, or an orphan finally coming face to face with a blood relative.

This was the one thing my mother wanted me to have, and somehow I was now holding it. The gravity of the situation made me dizzy as I stood up and walked to the kitchen to show everyone else what I had found.

"Honey, wake up!"

A month later, I awoke at 2 a.m. to Nicole crouching on the floor next to her side of our low platform bed.

"My water definitely just broke," Nicole said. She had sensed it and rolled out of bed, soaking the hardwood floor instead.

"Okay, I'll call Steve," I said as I picked up my phone.

With Cooper asleep in the next room, we prepared everything for the hospital. My brother was on the way to babysit and get Cooper off to preschool in the morning. Nicole, who was starting to have contractions, sat at the dining room table sending off work emails and buttoning up her projects.

My brother, who was notoriously late for everything, arrived over an hour after I called him, even though he only lived thirty minutes away. Nicole was in pain by then, and we flew down the highway to Newton-Wellesley Hospital, a route I knew all too well at this point.

Things moved quickly this time. Soon we were in a labor room with a nurse assigned to us. Without back labor, Nicole was toughing it out and experiencing normal contractions as she tried different positions and environments. She tried the bathtub while the nurse and I took turns spraying her back with warm water. We took a few walks in the hallway. All the while her contractions were growing closer together.

"What else can I try?" she said to the nurse.

As the nurse showed her a way of positioning herself at the end of the bed and holding on to the frame, the sun was coming up outside.

"Hey Meesh, this is all great, and you've done an awesome job so far with the labor."

She shook her sweaty head, and nodded.

"But, the window is closing for getting drugs. They're not going to be able to place the epidural if you go much longer."

"I got it," she said.

"What do you mean, you've got it?" I said.

"I'm going to do it," she said, breathing heavily, "without the drugs."

While we couldn't predict what kind of labor and delivery we were going to have, this certainly was not the plan. If she was going the no-drugs route, she would have prepared for it by learning and practicing ways of dealing with the pain. But, the pain ended up being much more tolerable for her than she thought. That was up until the last twenty minutes, when the pain became almost more than she could take. But she stuck it out, and six hours after her water broke in our bedroom, she gave birth to another baby boy, Redding.

And just like his brother, he entered the world without a peep. The doctor again took him over to the warmer that was across the room while Nicole and I became anxious.

"Is he okay?" Nicole said to the nurse.

"I think so," she said back. "You did great."

"You did it all without pain meds," I said. "I can't believe it, Meesh."

Nicole was beaming. The tremendous pain she endured at the end had turned into an enormous sense of pride for having done it herself. Before we knew it, the doctor brought Redding over to us. He had a full head of dark brown hair and was looking up at us as we introduced ourselves as his parents.

In the middle of the day, I drove back to Canton to pick Cooper up from preschool so he could meet his baby brother. Cooper was both proud and curious when I brought him in to meet Redd.

"Hi baby!" he said.

"Do you remember what his name is?"

"Redd," he said quickly. "He has long legs. And ears," he said as he examined the baby.

"I bet he has all the same things that Cooper has," I said.

"I love the baby. Hi baby!"

Cooper squeezed him in a strong brotherly hug and announced that Redd was his best buddy, a name he would call him for about a year. He was never jealous of the newborn attention, he honestly loved having a little brother, even though he didn't do much for the first few months.

My dad came in later that day. It was unusual to see him alone, without my mother. He sat down and we placed the swaddled baby in his arms as he smiled down at him. Redd was a welcome distraction from all the grief we were still feeling.

It was tragic that my mom was missing this, and everything that would follow. She had left us just twenty-six days earlier in the same hospital. And here we all were again, surrounding a precious life with love as he entered the world in the arms of our family.

27

FAST METABOLISM FOR BAD NEWS

Six months later, winter was slowly creeping in. I moved through my morning routine, getting ready for work, which involved an appliance change. I'd had the ostomy for about fifteen years by then, and the routine cycle of changing it every few days was completely normal. Remove the old appliance. Shower. Dry off. Adhere the new bag. That morning though, something was off.

It probably wasn't anything, but I felt a dull pain in my midsection. Most likely it was due to some hair on my lower abdomen being pulled as the adhesive of the appliance gradually loosened over the past day. That's what it felt like anyway. But when I explored the area in the shower, the pain wasn't just on the surface of my skin, but deeper in the tissue. As I poked and prodded the area, the dreaded something's-wrong-with-my-body-again feeling took hold. I took a deep breath and self-diagnosed it as Probably Nothing and wrote myself a mental prescription for Wait and See.

I finished getting ready for work trying to convince myself that everything was okay, but I had a nagging emotional feeling in my gut telling me that something was amiss.

Distraction was easy in my life at that point. Both of our kids were hard babies because they had infant reflux, which meant that stomach acid backs up into their esophagus. It's a condition they just have to grow out of as their stomach develops. The result was that they both cried inconsolably for several months straight. With Cooper, it lasted three months, but Redd was still screaming strong at six months. He would arch his back and howl for most of the time he was awake.

The dull ache in my stomach continued for the rest of that Monday in December, and by the next day, I knew that something bad was brewing. It had grown into a small lump, and it felt like some kind of infection or abscess. Memories of my battle with the pilonidal cyst shocked my system like an electrical current. It was the same kind of pain. I fought the mixture of sadness and frustration with my body and decided to call Dr. Hamilton's office. Good, bad, or otherwise, he would know what to do.

With chronic illness comes chronic disappointment. This boomerang effect of the disease throughout my life has given me a fast metabolism for bad news, and sadness doesn't linger long. If I could get out of the Unknown Paranoia stage and into the We Have A Plan stage, I knew I would feel better.

Dr. Hamilton was able to fit me in that very afternoon. As usual, he took his time, and thoughtfully assessed my abdomen.

"There's something building there, and it's hard to know what," he said. "I think we should have Dr. Boyle look at it."

"Seeing as I'm in here now, can you find out if he can see me today?" This was a perfect opportunity to test the unity in having all my care in one facility.

Dr. Hamilton left the exam room to call for Dr. Boyle, and when he returned he told me that he was in surgery all day, but that in this case, he'd be able to see me. He arranged for me to head over to the surgical area, and he would find me between cases.

. . .

Similar to Newton-Wellesley, Brigham and Women's Hospital presented a complex structure to navigate. Like the city of Boston, it's been cobbled together over decades with each area segmented out in an illogical map. The surgery and testing departments were underground, connected by long whitewashed hallways.

I met Dr. Boyle in the surgery department, and he led me through a few behind-the-scenes hallways. We passed nurses and other unidentifiable people in scrubs. As we walked, I explained the abscess to him as he searched for a private area for us. I felt grateful for this VIP treatment, and the fact that he was taking this so seriously.

We found an empty gurney for me to lean against as I pulled up my shirt so he could have a look himself.

"Well, it's definitely an abscess," he said as he prodded my stomach gently with his fingers. "Sometimes things like this will open up on their own. But, if you feel that it's getting too uncomfortable, then you can come and see me in the clinic, and I can lance it."

"Ugh," I said. "Okay, well thank you so much for seeing me like this. Honestly, I feel better just knowing that you've laid eyes on it."

He told me that he would be in the clinic on Thursday and Friday if I needed him. We shook hands and he directed me how to find my way back to the elevator.

That was Tuesday.

By Thursday I was on Tylenol around the clock for the pain. The lump had grown into a mass the size of a ping-pong ball, and it was right below the surface of my skin. If I missed the window of seeing Dr. Boyle I would have to spend the weekend like this, so I called in. I took an open slot that he had in the early afternoon.

I left work at 10:00 because Cooper had a Christmas pageant at his preschool, which was only about five minutes away. This was one of the perks of working so close to home: I could leave for an hour and get to have these kinds of experiences.

Cooper's preschool was located on the campus of Massachusetts Hospital School, a state-run facility designed to educate physically disabled children and young adults. These were mostly wheelchair-bound kids with cerebral palsy and muscular dystrophy. The preschool was in a building right next to the parking lot, so we usually didn't have much of a view into the full campus. But the kids were just part of the school pageant that took place in the auditorium.

Unlike the rest of the world, the buildings were designed primarily for wheelchair access. The auditorium was no exception, with wide aisles and docks that faced the stage so the students could watch. After waving to a couple of parents, I took a seat in the bleachers that were above all of the kids in wheelchairs. I noticed Cooper's teachers leading his class into the auditorium. The preschool was two classes of twenty kids, and I sat there marveling at the fact that all of the kids were attentive and following the rules, something that I rarely could achieve with just one of them. I spotted Cooper, with his long blond hair, following right along.

"Hi Daddy!" he said as his face lit up when he spotted me waving from up above.

The pageant was cute. All the kids lined up in one long row on stage, with teachers at both ends giving them visual cues to help them along. They sang "Jingle Jingle Little Bell" to the tune of "Twinkle Twinkle Little Star," as they rang little bells in their hands. They yelled the words to a couple of other festive songs that I couldn't quite make out over their clapping hands and pantomimed gestures. A couple of them were doing their own performances for the crowd.

It was enough to take my mind off of my stomach abscess, and the dreaded appointment I had lined up in the afternoon. But after they finished and I stood up, I was quickly reminded of the awkward ache in my midsection.

I headed into the city, figuring that I could have the doctor's appointment and be back at work in time for our holiday-themed year-end company meeting at 4:30. I could zip into the city, get the abscess taken care of, and be back in time for the meeting.

Sitting in the exam room waiting for what would almost definitely be an unpleasant experience, I tried to convince myself that this would be a short-term-pain, long-term-gain scenario. Dr. Boyle entered and went to work examining the abscess after we said quick hellos to one another. It was located below my belly button and the skin over it was tight. A portion of it extended underneath my appliance. It was a tricky situation and I felt confident that I had made the right decision to be there.

"Have you ever had a fistula before?" he asked.

"Nope," I answered confidently.

I knew that fistulas were nasty business, both one of the most profound things a human body can do, and one of the most disgusting. By general definition, a fistula is an abnormal canal between two hollow spaces. Blood vessels, intestines, or hollow organs. In Crohn's patients, they occur in the intestines and the anus. An amazing thing can happen with an infection; the body will do anything to push it out. It can perforate intestinal walls, tunnel through connective tissue, muscle, and even bone in an effort to export the bacteria. The tunnels become sinus tracts that can link to adjacent organs like the bladder, uterus, kidneys, other parts of the intestines, or in my current case, to the skin.

"Okay good," Dr. Boyle continued. "There's a chance that this could still be a fistula, but the fact that you've never had one is a good sign. Still, we won't know what it is until I open it up, drain it, and see how it heals."

"Sounds like a plan," I said. I signed the consent form and an assistant came in to help with the procedure.

After cleaning the area, I felt the pinch and burn of the lidocaine shot. The first one always feels the worst, the needle shooting hot pain into an already tender spot. He followed that up with several more, making sure the area was good and numb. After a few minutes, he tapped the surface and I could feel nothing.

"Well, the good thing about having me do this is that I can make the incision here." He pointed to the part of the bulge that wasn't covered by the ostomy. "So that way the wound will drain and your appliance shouldn't interfere."

He made the incision and something unexpected happened. The room filled with the smell of stool. I don't remember what the drainage looked like, but I knew something was wrong with that potent smell in the air.

Fearing the worst, I risked a question. "So, if it's a fistula, how long does it take to heal?"

"Fistulas don't heal on their own. You'll need to have surgery," he said flatly.

That was information I could have used two minutes ago, before he cut into me. But, I reasoned with myself, this wasn't just going to resolve on its own, especially if it was truly a fistula.

"Well that odor can't be a good sign," I said.

"Yes, but we won't know if it's an active fistula until we see how it heals."

While this conversation was going on, he expressed the area, trying to get the maximum drainage out. In a final push, pain erupted and I let out a loud moan as he hit an area that was too deep for the numbing medication to hit. He was done. He bandaged me up.

"I'm going to call in some oxycodone for you because you'll be pretty sore after the lidocaine wears off. I'm going to also put you on a short course of antibiotics."

"Okay, great." I checked my phone and figured I would have enough time to get the prescriptions and still be back at work for the start of the company meeting. He gave me directions on how to tend to the wound and gave me a small bag of supplies to get me started.

"Okay, fingers crossed that it heals up," I said.

He agreed, we shook hands, and I headed out.

Forty-five minutes later, I was sitting in my Jeep in the Walgreens parking lot with my prescriptions. I tore into the white paper bag and two orange prescription bottles fell onto my lap. As I read the labels on each bottle, I built up the saliva in my mouth by making sucking and spitting gestures with my mouth closed, a technique I had taught myself in Boy Scouts to secretly take pills on camping trips without water. I figured I could start the antibiotics when I got home, but I wanted to get the pain meds going ASAP. I put the white, bitter-tasting pill in my mouth, swallowed, and pulled out of the parking lot. Work was only ten minutes away, so I figured that I would feel the effects by then.

I pulled into the Cramer parking lot in the fading December afternoon light. Walking in, I ran my hand over my bandaged abdomen and it finally felt okay. No pain. The mass was gone and so was the pressure. I could sense that the pain meds were kicking in.

I walked inside and entered the large, high-ceilinged cafeteria where everyone was gathering for the holiday-themed meeting. Members of the executive committee were wearing Santa hats, and serving snacks and hors d'oeuvres to the employees. I sat down at a table with the rest of the graphic designers and breathed a sigh of relief for the week that I'd survived. A slow feeling of euphoria was rising inside me, which was either the opioids in my bloodstream or the Christmas spirit kicking in. My pain was gone, and all was right with the world.

"Mr. Harris?"

"Ah, thank you, Mr. Wood," I said to my boss, who was carrying around a tray of cider. He had no idea about what I'd been through, or even that I had Crohn's disease. I raised my plastic glass to him.

"Merry Christmas," he said.

"Here's to feeling good all the time," I said before sipping the hot cider.

I settled into my chair with the warmth of the cider in my hand and the warmth of the oxycodone running through my veins as the CEO stood at the podium, cheerily calling for everyone's attention. Everything was going to be alright.

Three months later, I lay on an exam room table in Dr. Hamilton's office as he gave me a puzzling gaze.

The wound hadn't healed, and it was a full-blown fistula. This meant that stool exited my body through a tiny hole underneath my belly button, where Dr. Boyle had made the incision months earlier. To tend to it, I covered it up with gauze and tape, and would change the smeared gauze when I went to the bathroom. It was a huge annoyance, but other than that I felt okay.

"This is troubling to me," Dr. Hamilton said, "because at this point we've narrowed Crohn's patients into a few different categories. One of them is for fistulizing Crohn's, and up to this point, you weren't in that category. We've found that it's unusual, really rare in fact, to have people change from one to the next. But you clearly have."

"Well, according to Dr. Boyle," I said, "the only solution is surgery. But I've found a regime online that says that you can cure fistulas with a mixture of elements that you flush through the canal with a dropper. I figure it's worth a try."

"Hey, if you think that will help, go for it," Dr. Hamilton said.

I went on to explain that I made a mixture using oil of oregano, dimethyl sulfoxide, and colloidal silver. Oil of oregano contains natural antibiotic, antifungal, anti-inflammatory, antiviral, anti-everything properties. Dimethyl sulfoxide helps to speed up the healing process. Colloidal silver is somewhat of an outlaw. In the early part of the twentieth century, it was commonly used to fight infections before penicillin was discovered. If you look it up online you'll find pictures of people whose skin has turned a Smurf blue color from using too much of it, an incurable condition called argyria. I figured I was using a small amount, and it wouldn't be an issue. I would fill a dropper with the mixture and flush it into the canal of the fistula, hoping that it would narrow the passageway and eventually close it.

Dr. Hamilton didn't approve or disapprove of what I was doing, so I continued the treatment. I just really didn't want to have surgery again, and anything I could do to keep myself out of the OR, I was going to try. I treated myself for months without success and finally gave up. As with the Specific Carbohydrate Diet, the internet seemed to flaunt success stories of people curing their fistulas through this naturopathic method. But for me, it didn't work.

I explored other alternative treatments through the spring and summer of that year. One was a very expensive elemental drink that was put out by the same person online that had the fistula fix. It was straight nutrients that were easy to absorb by my weak digestive system. I bought a juicer for the same reason: rapid absorption of nutrients. Meditation was something I'd always wanted to try for stress, so I found someone to teach me transcendental meditation.

Everything offered hope, but nothing worked. The fistula continued to act as an additional exit point that I did not need. I felt okay Crohn's-wise, but not great. I was still having symptoms in the last two weeks of my six-week Remicade cycle, and Dr. Hamilton and I were talking about switching to Humira. I saw Dr. Boyle every few weeks to check on the fistula, and we debated the pros and cons of my situation.

I could have carried on the way I was going with the traditional steady decline of symptoms, or I could have Dr. Boyle operate to repair the fistula. His preference was to operate on me in the light of day, when I was still feeling healthy. Plus, the fistula could decide to fork off in a new different direction at any time. Having it exit through the wall of my abdomen was actually the least complicated form. I would be in worse shape if it decided to join my bladder or link to other parts of my intestines.

"If we're just repairing the fistula then we most likely won't have to take out additional intestine," he said. "Being healthy is the best option. That said, I never know what I'll find until we get you in the operating room."

So, I planned to have the surgery in September. This would hopefully make my day-to-day easier after I recovered. The plan was to repair the fistula, and he would also examine my bowel to locate other areas of active Crohn's.

No one at work knew that I had Crohn's at this point. With the surgery date on the horizon, I sat down with my boss and explained the basics, using my tried and true plumbing analogy. He didn't need to know the details, and I didn't want him to be concerned for me. I didn't need to gross him out by telling him that my body had decided to tear itself another asshole and that I've had stool leaking out of my abdomen since the company meeting back in December. "Well, actually I have two holes in my stomach if you count the colostomy bag that I've had for the past fifteen years..." No, just the plumbing analogy will do.

"They open me up, take out the bad pipe, and reconnect the two good halves."

He reacted sympathetically, but also didn't pry for more information. The subject changed quickly to coverage for me while I would be out.

In early September, I lay in a pre-op bed with Nicole seated next to me. Nurses and doctors came in and out of my curtained-off area. I was anxious but not nervous. I knew I was in the best possible hands with Dr. Boyle, and that I was diving into another surgical cycle where it would be painful and hard initially, but that every day I would get a little better until I hit full remission.

A young woman with short brown hair entered and introduced herself.

"Hi Mr. Harris, I'm Dr. Erin Teeple, the fellow in colorectal surgery. I work with Dr. Boyle."

"Hi Dr. Erin Teeple, you can call me Brad. What exactly is a fellow?"

"Oh, that means I've finished my residency and am getting further specialized by working in the area where I want my focus to be."

"Ah, gotcha."

She went on, clearly in awe of Dr. Boyle. "He's truly just one of the best in the world at his craft, and I'm incredibly lucky to be working under him."

"I agree," I said. "He and I go way back. Unfortunately."

She laughed.

"He actually did my colostomy surgery when I was younger."

"Yes, you've clearly been through a lot. Well, you know you're in good hands. I'll be in the operating room as well, and I'll be following you in post-op."

"Okay then, I'll see you on the other side."

She left and the anesthesia doctor came in wearing scrubs. He went through the usual questions. He had my anesthesia notes from prior surgeries, so he knew what to give me and what to expect. Dr. Boyle stopped in and I signed the consent form for surgery. Before long I was kissing Nicole goodbye as the relaxation drugs were administered. The nurse wheeled me out of my curtained-off area, and I felt the coolness of the air-conditioning rippling past me.

In the operating room, they moved me from the gurney to the operating table. The usual monitors were attached as the anesthesiologist administered the full dose. Their voices seemed amplified when they spoke to me.

"How are you doing, Brad?"

"Mmmm. Fantastic," I said, enjoying my drift off to sleep.

Remission was on the horizon. When all of this was over, I would be better.

PART III

28

THE WORST PAIN

I was so much worse. September's surgery had fixed the fistula, but my health Crohn's-wise had steadily declined in the past five and a half months. There was a good amount of Crohn's in other parts of my intestines that needed to be removed during the surgery, and despite that, I never achieved a remission period.

By February 2014, I was in full-on heal-myself mode. I was experiencing a lot of gas, something that I rarely had a problem with, which turned out to be SIBO, small intestinal bacterial overgrowth. I was put on a thank-God-it's-covered-by-insurance-expensive antibiotic that targets only the digestive tract, which should have worked, but didn't.

I rebooted my food intake in the most drastic way possible, following a new diet designed to control inflammatory bowel disease with real food. I was down to boiled or baked meat, cooked carrots, zucchini, and green beans, and these super-expensive mail-order elemental shakes, which I was going through by the tub-full. Despite this, my symptoms persisted. For the first time in my life, I truly didn't know what to eat.

The gas from the SIBO was so bad that my stomach contorted in different shapes as the gas rippled from one segment of my intestines to another. This was not only uncomfortable from a gas-pain perspective, but because of it I also had issues with my ostomy appliance sticking. I had a raw patch of skin that was constantly exposed to stool under my appliance, which felt like a swarm of bee stings on my waistline as I moved throughout the day.

It was a Tuesday in late February. After tying up some loose ends at work, I left in the early afternoon to go home and sleep. Besides doctor's appointments, taking time off of work for anything Crohn's related was still a rare occurrence for me. I still strived to push through despite my poor health. But today my body just needed a time-out. Despite being uncomfortable from the gas pain I managed to nap in our downstairs family room until Nicole arrived home with the boys. Hours later, after dinner had been eaten and baths had been taken and bedtime storybooks had been read, we had two soundly sleeping boys. Nicole and I retired downstairs, where she went to the office to catch up on some work on her laptop, and I went back to the family room to watch an episode of *House of Cards*.

The gas pain was big and constant. My stomach continued to move and contort as I lay on the couch with that perpetual feeling that I was going to burst. Suddenly, it felt like I did. An explosion of pain tore through my abdomen, and I let out a loud moan.

"Are you okay?" Nicole called from the next room.

I answered her only with another groan. I couldn't speak. My brain was busy trying to make sense of what could have just happened. It was pain like I had never felt before. On the pain scale of 1 to 10, I had been in a steady 3 to 4 range with all of my gas symptoms. With this sudden burst of pain, it shot past 10 to an 11. Normally the decision to go to the emergency room was something I deliberated over for hours, questioning whether or not I needed to disrupt my life and be in the hospital. But this time I made up my mind in about thirty seconds.

Nicole came in to see what was going on and found me doubled over on the floor.

"Hey, I, I need to..." It was hard to speak above a whisper. "I need to get to the Brigham."

She was stunned. "Now? What happened?"

"So much pain. Something ripped I think."

She started firing questions at me. "Should we call an ambulance? Should I wake up the kids? What should..."

"I need you to figure it out. I'm going to the car."

It took me five full minutes to get to the car. First, I slowly climbed the lower stairs of our raised ranch house. I slipped my feet into my heavy winter shoes and stepped out into the cold February night. I shuffled down our front walk, which was divided by even snowbanks on the left and right. One foot in front of the other. I finally reached the car and slowly lowered myself into the passenger seat. By the time I settled, Nicole had made it to the driver's seat. She handed me my black puffer coat, which I could only drape over me as the car's heater started.

"The kids are both passed out. It's going to be faster to get you there and back before I can get them up and dressed and in the car."

"Yes," I agreed. Speed was of the utmost importance. The pain hadn't given way at all, it was just as intense as when it first started.

The car's wheels crunched in reverse over the packed snow in the driveway. I clutched my stomach and tried not to move.

"You can just drop me off," I said.

"Right. Can you call them to let them know you're coming?"

"I'll text Hamilton."

Going to the ER at Brigham. Severe sudden gut pain. I fear something might have ripped.

For the past month and a half, Dr. Hamilton and I had been in close contact trying to hone in on what was wrong with me with all of the gas.

Dr. Hamilton let them know I was coming. Nicole was flying down the highway, which was wide open at 8:45 at night. All I remember from that drive was me doubled over in the passenger seat groaning as Nicole sped up Route 128 and down Route 9 into Boston. A trip to Brigham and Women's typically takes thirty-five minutes from our house. That night, Nicole got me there in twenty.

"I love you, Meesh. I'm sorry. I'll be okay," I said.

"I love you too. I wish I could stay with you."

I nodded. "I'll text you as things progress. It'll be okay. I'm in the best hands here."

She leaned over and kissed me goodbye. I opened the door and limped my way to the glowing red emergency sign, twenty feet away.

About forty-five minutes later, I lay in a curtained-off room in the emergency department, an IV in my arm. For the first time in my life, the narcotics they administered through the IV barely did anything to curb the pain in my abdomen.

I texted with Nicole. The boys were safe and still fast asleep when she arrived home. I told her to get some sleep herself, but to leave her ringer on.

The whole night was a blur. I got an NG tube placed and the usual X-rays. They did a CT scan of my abdomen, and from what they could see, my intestines were obstructed and there was evidence of perforation. It most likely meant surgery in the morning, and this time I believed it. A tear sounded about right to me. The pain was just so severe and constant compared to just an intestinal blockage.

Every chance I got, I asked for more pain medicine. I tried to explain to them that I wasn't someone to complain about being uncomfortable, and could they please do something more. There were people in the world that knew that if Brad Harris was saying he was in pain, then they should pay attention. But none of those people were working in the Brigham emergency department that night.

Nicole and I spoke briefly in the morning. She was going to come in after dropping the boys off at 7:00, Redd at daycare, and Cooper at preschool. Around 7:30 I talked to my boss at Cramer and briefly explained what was going on. I told him about the state of my work projects, which were fortunately in holding patterns. He was understanding, supportive, and of course, told me to not worry about work.

By 8:00, I was in pre-op, and Dr. Boyle came in bright-eyed and wearing his surgical scrubs. We discussed my situation. I knew that coming in unexpectedly to the ER meant that anyone on his team might be the surgeon. He might have had a light surgical schedule that day, but most likely he bumped other patients who weren't as complicated as I was that morning. I was so grateful to be in his care. If anyone could fix me, he could.

"So, the CT scan shows that your intestines have perforated at the anastomosis," he began. An anastomosis is the connection made during previous surgeries where the two healthy intestine segments are joined together. "It looks like you have a tight stricture there, which in turn might have caused this. I won't know until we open you up. This is going to be complicated. I'm going to clean you out as best I can, and most likely will leave the wound open so bacteria can continue to exit as you heal."

"Okay," I said, trying to imagine what that would look like. "Thank you, Dr. Boyle."

He reviewed the risks with me. I gladly signed the consent form and wished him good luck. The biggest risk for me would have been to not sign that form.

Things happened fast, and although I'd given them Nicole's contact info for surgery updates, the operating room was ready for me before she could make it in to see me. I put my wedding band in a small plastic bag for them to give to her.

The curtain was opened up and they began the usual cycle of prep for the OR. A shot of fentanyl to relax me. A paper hairnet on my head. The cool breeze of being whisked down the hall as the overhead fluorescent lights passed by like streetlamps. The pain had finally vanished as I entered the brightness of the OR. I was worried but calm. There was lots of movement around me, everything in slow motion. Cold heart monitor stickers were stuck to my chest. A blood pressure cuff squeezed my ankle. The cloud of anesthesia was thick in my head. I could see an empty part of the room on my left side. I imagined my mother standing there watching me and my broken body being prepped for what was about to come. I closed my eyes and felt her in my heart. Make sure they fix me, Ma, I pleaded. This is really bad. Those boys are going to need me.

After surgery, I was wheeled up to the ICU where I spent the next two days. I was heavily sedated, and don't remember much of anything until the next morning, Thursday, when Dr. Teeple, Dr. Boyle's fellow, entered. I had built a bit of a rapport with her back in September when I was in the hospital for my fistula surgery, and I was relieved that she was still working with Dr. Boyle.

She pulled back the covers and we looked at my stomach together. I had two bags, a lot of tubes, and a bandage down my midline, which she uncovered to examine.

"Dr. Boyle thought it would be best to give you an ileostomy here," she pointed to my right side, "and close off your regular colostomy so your remaining large bowel can rest and heal."

"Okay, so everything is going to exit through the ileostomy now?"

"Right, and it's going to be temporary. Once we get you better, we'll take it down and reconnect you. That's the long-term goal anyhow. Your labs are looking better and you're stable enough to get you out of the ICU and send you up to a regular room on the fifteenth floor.

"That's good news," I said.

"We'll get that catheter removed, too, and we're going to replace that A-line we gave you in the OR with a PICC line. Have you had one of those before?"

"A PICC. I don't think so."

"It's a long-term IV, and it'll have two lines. One we can give you meds through, and the other is going to be for TPN."

"Oh, so you won't have to keep sticking me for a new IV every few days?"

"Exactly."

I knew what TPN was. It stood for total parenteral nutrition. Dr. Hamilton and I had discussed it the previous summer as a way to bulk me up before having the surgery to repair my fistula. Back then it turned out that I wasn't unhealthy enough for insurance to cover it. Now I wasn't healthy enough to go without it.

"The TPN will provide nourishment for your body so it can heal while we give your gut a rest," Dr. Teeple continued. "To say that you've been through a lot is an understatement. You're stable, but we're not out of the woods yet."

Nicole came in later that morning. It was so great to see her. We caught up on how things went from her end. The surgery was over six hours long, and she didn't hear from Dr. Boyle until 1:00 in the afternoon.

"How are the boys?" I asked.

"They're good," she said. "Cooper really misses you. He's used to having you there all the time."

"I know. Well, maybe when we get up to the fifteenth floor they can come and visit."

"We'll see. Oh, I almost forgot."

She took out her phone and showed me a photo of Cooper's preschool class holding up a sign that said "Get Well Soon."

"You can't tell from the photo, but they all wrote on it. They gave it to me to bring in for you. It's cute!"

"That's so great!" I said.

"I'll bring it in when you get settled in a regular room."

She rounded up my belongings for the transport person. I was wheeled up to a pristine roommate-less room on the fifteenth floor. There are four pods to each floor: A, B, C, and D. Because the fifteenth floor is designated for patients in surgical recovery, the nurses on the floor become specialized in all things post-op.

"Hey Brad, I'm Cathy," she said as she started her usual intake for patients in her care. "So, the PICC team will be here soon to get your line set up. They do it right in the room."

"Okay, nice. If I get it then they can start the TPN tonight."

"Yes, I'm here 'til five, and TPN usually comes up around six. Looks like you're due for pain meds though."

She administered Dilaudid through the regular IV in my hand, and I instantly felt better.

"Once you get the PICC, we'll probably get rid of this one," she said.

"Cool," I said. "So I imagine the PICC will cut down on me needing to constantly change the peripheral IVs?"

"Yep. Definitely a bonus of having a PICC."

That afternoon, the two-person PICC team showed up. Like a pair of synchronized swimmers, they performed a well-rehearsed forty-five-minute routine of sterilizing the area, putting on their equally sterile paper garb, numbing and inserting the line on the inside of my upper arm, and doing an X-ray to make sure the line extended up my arm and into my chest. They covered the insertion site with a transparent dressing, and as Dr. Teeple explained, the end of the line forked into two lumens.

After they left, Nicole came back into the room looking somber. She had been talking to a woman outside who I didn't know. She was wearing regular clothes, so I assumed she was some kind of administrative person. Nicole turned the chair toward the bed and sat down.

"So, I have some bad news," she began. "That woman that just left, she was a social worker. Someone called DCF, the Department of Children and Families. They somehow found out we left the kids at home alone when I drove you here the other night."

"What? Are you serious? Who called DCF?" I said.

"She can't say. Honey, did you tell them?"

"Well, yeah, I told them that. I was trying to explain how much pain I was in. I told them that we'd just put the boys down and left them because I needed to get here fast. I needed to illustrate how urgently I needed to get here. I was just in so much pain and the drugs weren't covering it."

"Meesh, I know, but you shouldn't have told them that."

I was fuming. "Well fuck whoever it was, probably one of the ER nurses. Let's have her go through what I went through and see if she makes all of the best decisions."

"Yeah," she said, almost to herself, "but I should have known better."

"Don't put this all on you. I agreed with the decision that night, and I still think it was the right call. If we'd have called an ambulance, they would have taken me to Norwood Hospital, and who knows the shape I'd be in now if I went there. If we could do it over again, we'd do the same thing."

"Well, don't tell them you think that."

"What do you mean? What's going to happen?"

"She said they're going to investigate. They have to because someone flagged it. That's the protocol. She said they're going to need three references. That's the first step. Our pediatrician has to be one of them, and it can't be family members."

"How long have you known about this?"

"Since yesterday morning. Once you were settled in the ICU and out of post-op, they came and found me."

"I can't believe they would spring that on you with the shape that I'm in. Okay, well, for the references we have the Lisas for the other two besides Dr. Allen."

It was a bit of a joke between us that everyone in our world seemed to be named Lisa. Two of them took care of our kids. Our daycare provider, who we were becoming friends with outside of daycare, was the first Lisa. And the director of Cooper's preschool was the other. We had good relationships with both of them.

"Okay," she said, "that's a good idea. And I'm going to call Dr. Allen to give her a heads-up and see what she thinks. Sorry to leave you on such a down note, I needed to tell you."

"It's okay, I know. Hey, we're going to get through this. I can't believe we have to deal with this on top of everything else, but we'll get through it."

"I have to go get the kids."

She gave me a kiss and a long hug, and left.

Soon after, Dr. Boyle stopped by. He'd visited when I was in the ICU, but I was out of sorts.

"Hey Brad," he said.

"Oh hi," I said, shifting myself higher in the bed. "Well, I made it through, thanks to you."

"I'm glad to see that you're doing better. We'll get you going on TPN tonight and that should help. We're giving you the maximum amount."

He turned on the bright overhead light, lifted my gown, and began to explain his handiwork.

"So as you can see, you have two ostomies now. The perforation happened at your anastomosis, where the large bowel meets the small bowel. So, I created an ileostomy here," he pointed to the pouch on my right side, "to give the rest of the large bowel a break. You won't have any output out of this one." He pointed to where my usual appliance was, which was now just a gauze covering.

Between the two pouches was the main wound. He removed the dressing, gently lifting it up, and explained that it was sutured together, but not totally closed. Just like he had said before the surgery, this was to allow for the bad stuff to get out on its own. The discharge was just red and bloody.

"The IR drains will also help." He pointed to two plastic tubes that were inserted in my abdomen, below the appliances. "You know the drill there. We'll remove them after they stop having output."

"Quite the science project," I said.

"Yes. Well, Dr. Teeple will be on this weekend and she'll be keeping tabs on you," he said as he covered me up.

"Dr. Boyle," I said, cutting through the informative conversation by extending my hand. "Thank you."

He smiled and shook my hand. "We'll see you on Monday."

At 6:00, a new nurse came in with what looked like a bag of milk that was about as big as a family-size box of cereal.

"Hi, I'm Emily. I'll be your nurse tonight. I think I remember you."

"Yeah, I was here back in September," I said. "I remember you too."

"Looks like you've had a tough week. This is your TPN," she said as she hoisted the bag onto the IV pole and started pushing buttons on the IV pump.

"Dinnertime?" I said.

"Exactly," she said, smiling.

She primed the line to make sure the white liquid ran through, and there wasn't any air in the tubing. She cleaned and flushed the lumen on my PICC line, which had a pink sticker that read "TPN ONLY," and connected the tubing.

"This line is reserved for your TPN, just so you know. So don't let anyone put anything through this that isn't TPN."

"Got it," I said.

"This is going to run for sixteen hours, so until 10:00 tomorrow morning. The pump is going to beep in a little while, that just means I have to increase the speed."

"Okay, I'll buzz you when it beeps."

"How are you doing pain-wise?"

"If I'm due for pain meds, I'll take them."

After she left the room, I lay back in bed. I took the deepest breath my abdomen would allow and exhaled. Even with this crisis, I was relieved to be in the hospital. I was completely burnt out from trying to heal myself and figure out what was wrong with me, which is a steady backbeat in my life most of the time. Finally, I could pass my care off to the experts and be on a vacation from taking care of myself.

On Saturday morning, my dad came in for a visit. He had also been in while I was in the ICU, but I was asleep so he only talked to Nicole.

This was hard for my father. Partly because, unlike me, he'd led a life of robust health and therefore has a strong distaste for health-related complications and the stress that goes along with it. In addition to that, my mother always acted as his medical translator, and without her, he had a hard time understanding the details of what was going on with me. My mom knew how to distill down all of the complexities in a way that made sense to him. Either that or she left out the details. I guess I would never know.

"Well, this is a nice room! How are you doing today?"

"I'm good, Dad," I said as I shook his hand, which was still cold from the air outside. "How was the traffic?"

Though retired, my dad was always at odds with any kind of congestion on the roadways. Traffic was always a topic of discussion for him, and it was a formality to ask about it.

"Not too bad I guess, for a Saturday," he said. "So how are you doing?"

"I'm good." I took the next five minutes to explain everything that happened to me in the past five days. The rupture, the pain, the surgery, the ICU, the PICC line, what TPN was and how it was basically IV nutrition for me, and that I had a lot going on in my stomach region.

He appeared to be listening, but he summed it all up by saying, "So you had surgery for your Crohn's. When do you think you'll get to go home?"

"I have no idea, Dad. Probably another week? Maybe two weeks? This is pretty major."

"Well, here's something for Nicole." He reached into his shirt pocket and removed the white envelope that stood behind his glasses case. "It's money for parking. Parking is expensive, and this is something I can do to help."

"Oh, thanks Dad," I said. My dad's philosophy in his stage of life, being a retired widower, was that he could supply money when things were needed. And based on the Brigham's parking rates, this was a welcomed gift.

"Call Nicole when you get home," I said. "Cramer sent a bunch of food to the house. Isn't that nice? It's more than she and the boys can eat, so you should take some of it."

"Oh! That's nice of them."

"I know, they're great. There's a pan of seafood casserole that has your name on it."

Cramer was a family-run business, and they really helped

employees out when they were going through rough times in ways beyond HR benefits. All week they had been sending food to the house from the company's cafeteria.

He bid me goodbye after a short visit, shook my hand, and headed out.

Up until this point in our lives together, I never involved Nicole in my actual care. There were times when she offered to help, but I've always been stubborn about doing it myself. But now I had her stepping in. She brought in clothes and ostomy supplies for me, and we talked openly about the science project on my stomach. Fortunately, she was at a point with her job where her boss was understanding of our situation and gave her the flexibility she needed. She was able to visit every day and do 100 percent of the parenting with the boys, which was a lot considering that Cooper had just turned five and Redd was twenty months. So every day I would text her a list of things to bring in to the hospital. Headphones. Tea. Coconut water. Books. Boxers. T-shirts. My uniform in the hospital was the standard-issue blue hospital pants and a T-shirt.

The boys didn't come in on the weekend. The doctors felt I should wait to get a bit better before seeing them, but we FaceTimed almost every night and Nicole texted me photos of them playing at home. The colorful poster that Cooper and his preschool class had made me was taped to the wall. One side said "Get Well Soon" written in large, teacher's handwriting, but the other was what I displayed: a chaotic array of scribbles and swirls and swaths of color, kind of like a Jackson Pollock painting made with markers.

I got up and walked the halls with my IV pole as much as I could manage. The four pods of the fifteenth floor were connected by a square block, which made a natural track shape for me and other patients to walk around. I would push myself to do an additional lap every time, which usually resulted in me collapsing into bed for a nap after each walk.

That weekend my brother Steve, cousin Julie, and my aunt and uncle came to visit me. I'd recovered pretty well, as I had always done, and gave everyone optimistic forecasts. Nicole's parents came down from Maine to help her on the home front. They did laundry, cleaned the house, and her dad installed a coatrack on the wall for our winter coats.

By Monday, my belly was making digestive sounds, so they advanced my diet to soft food. I had Nicole bring in protein shake mix and juice from the juicer. It felt good to eat, even if it wasn't anything good yet. I was beginning to feel better.

That first week of March, however, something felt wrong in my belly. I began to have a strong feeling of fullness, like I had a gallon of water in my stomach, just sloshing around. It began to feel uncomfortable, and I felt nauseous. They gave me Zofran for the nausea, but I still felt distended.

I spiked a fever, which earned me a trip to radiology for a CT scan. It showed that I had developed some pockets of fluid in my belly in areas where the drains weren't reaching. Dr. Teeple came in and explained what they were going to do.

"Hi Dr. Erin Teeple," I said as she entered. This was a joke I had with her, or myself, that she was a three-named person.

After some small talk she explained the plan. "So, we're going to send you down to interventional radiology to have them extract what they can. They might leave you with another drain if they feel it's an area that will continue to produce fluid."

"Okay. I'm honestly not feeling well." The pressure in my stomach was a lot to take, and even with the anti-nausea medicine, I felt sick. For the first time in my career as a professional patient, I volunteered myself for what I considered one of the worst procedures.

"I think we need to put the NG tube back in. That's going to give me the relief I need."

"Oh, I was going to hold off on that until after you get back from IR, to see if it's really needed."

"I never thought I'd ask for it, but I need it. Have you ever even heard of a patient volunteering for one?"

"No, I haven't. I'll put an order in for it. With your experience, I'm getting the sense that you know your body better than we do sometimes."

"Okay, thanks. Back to NPO, I guess," I said.

"Unfortunately yes, but let's keep our hopes up. It won't be for long."

I indeed felt relief about thirty minutes after the tube was put up my nose and down my throat and hooked up to suction, which began rapidly removing the contents of my stomach. Later that day when the shift changed, my new nurse looked at the output of the tube and was amazed.

"Three liters! I can't believe it," she said. "The most I've ever seen in that amount of time was two."

Throughout the course of a day, the body makes two liters of stomach acid to break down food and aid digestion. It travels with the food through the small intestine and gets reabsorbed at some point downstream. Somehow my stomach alone held three liters.

In addition to the NG tube, the radiologists found two pockets of fluid that were most likely infected and the cause of the fever. So I left there with two more drains.

On the DCF front, someone was going to come over to our house to interview Nicole.

"They said that they want to talk to you, too," she said.

"They can try. I'm pretty out of it. Next week might be better."

"Okay, I'll tell them that. It'll help to illustrate the condition you're in."

"Right. Well, I'm glad we got that gallery wall up in the living room, finally. It'll help to show off our family."

About a month before all of this happened, Nicole and I put up a large number of photos in a grid on our living room wall. Two large, professionally shot photos of the boys as babies. A shot that I took of Nicole and Cooper fawning over Redd the day that he was born. Lots of cute photos of the boys together. A posed photo of Nicole's family of four where Nicole must have been about six months old; she's screaming her head off sitting on her mom's knee. There's one that my mom took of Steve and me as little kids singing "Happy Birthday" to my dad in our dimly lit kitchen. There's a shot of us at our wedding and another on our honeymoon. Underneath that sits one of my mom from the mid-1980s, her curly permed hair salty from a day at the beach, smiling at the camera through her oversized glasses. The text on her Museum of Science T-shirt says *Extinction Is Forever.* And in the middle of the whole grid there's a small black-and-white photo of me smiling back at the camera from Ryder Beach in Truro in July of 1986. Exactly one month before I was diagnosed with Crohn's.

"Yes, those photos will be the first thing she sees when she comes into the house," Nicole said.

"So if this goes well, then we're in the clear? You should open the conversation by telling them that you went to Wellesley and that I'm an Eagle Scout. That should wrap things up in less than a minute."

"I think if this goes well, which it should, they'll drop it."

"Okay Meesh, well good luck. I love you. We're in this together, right?"

"Right. I love you too Meesh."

. . .

The meeting with DCF on Friday was a success, and with the NG tube in my nose, and the two new drains in my sides, my body was able to turn things around over the weekend. By Monday they removed the NG tube and I was back to eating small meals of soft food. Going home on Friday was now the goal, but I still had some milestones to hit. The biggest one was the fact that my output was high, even though I wasn't eating anything.

They started me on DTO, short for diluted tincture of opium, which is pretty much the granddaddy of all bowel-slowing drugs. It only comes in liquid form and has a sharp bitter taste to it. Sometimes I would take it straight, like a shot. One nurse tried to mix it with orange juice, but that made the taste even worse. Another nurse tried mixing it with ginger ale, and that was the most tolerable.

After a couple of days on DTO, they added another drug to slow things down, octreotide. Fortunately, I didn't have to drink it, but unfortunately, after the second dose, it made me vomit. In the middle of the week, I spiked another fever and had another CT scan, which came back negative. They chalked it up to a drug interaction, but still, my output wasn't where it should be so I wouldn't be going home on Friday anymore.

Besides throwing up again on Friday morning from the octreotide, I felt better. I spent much of the morning sitting up and going for walks. In the afternoon Nicole came in for a regular visit with a surprise for me. She had Redd in tow.

"Daddy!" he said when he saw me, which just melted my heart.

"Hey Redd! There's my little man!"

Kristin was a young nurse that I'd had a few times. She came in to check on me and brought a Jell-O cup for Redd.

Nicole picked up Redd and put him in one of the hard plastic chairs, his feet just barely hanging off the edge of the seat.

"He looks bigger, even though it's only been a few weeks since I've seen him," I said.

"I bet," said Nicole. "Well, soon you'll be home."

I was feeling good, and ready for another walk. As Redd finished his Jell-O, I got myself situated and out of bed. The four of us, Nicole, Redd, me, and my IV pole, made our way out of the room and down the hall. At one point, Redd reached up and took my hand. It felt so good to have his tiny warm hand in mine as we made our way around the track of hallways. We did one lap together and then went back to the room.

"I talked to Boyle about signing the time-off paperwork for my short-term disability at work," I said after settling into the bed. "He's going to sign for two months."

"Two months? Wow, that's going to be tough financially."

"Well, it's 60 percent of my salary, so hopefully once the checks start coming in we'll be okay."

"Well, we'll figure it out I guess. Like we always do."

"Yeah, I'm not sure I'd take it all anyway."

"Yeah, two months is a long time," she said as she picked Redd up from his adventure walking around the room. "We should get going."

"Okay, yeah, I know there's not much for him to do here," I said.

"Buh bye Daddy!" Redd said from Nicole's arms. He leaned over and gave me a wet kiss with a "mmmwah" sound.

Saturday was one of those unseasonably warm days in New England. It was sunny out with temperatures in the mid-50s. My TPN wrapped up at 10:00, and after my morning dose of octreotide and subsequent vomiting session I had a window of time before my next medication was due to infuse. For the first time, I was completely unhooked.

"Hey so, when I go for a walk, do I have to stay on this floor?" I said to my nurse, Emily.

"No. Are you thinking that you want to go outside?"

"Yes."

"I don't have a problem with that," she said.

I got my shoes out of the closet and put on an extra robe. I grabbed my phone because Nicole was going to text me with her arrival time.

Soon I stood on the elevator surrounded by regular people and hospital staff. No one questioned the tall, thin patient that appeared to be making a break for it. The doors finally opened on the main level, and I made my way through the sunny expanse of the Brigham's lobby. I stepped into the churn of the oversized revolving door and seconds later felt the first breath of fresh air enter my lungs in two and a half weeks. The air was warm despite the bleak grayness of Boston in March. I walked the sidewalk between the Brigham's two entrances, 75 and 45 Francis Street, which were about a hundred yards apart. The warm sun beat down on my arms as I shuffled slowly down the sidewalk, with the nameless health care workers passing me by.

My phone vibrated. Nicole texted that she was almost at the hospital, so I texted back, *I'm downstairs walking between 75 and 45 Francis. You can pick me up on the sidewalk.*

She pulled up next to me and honked. "Hey, don't I know you?"

I opened the door and tenderly sat down in the passenger seat.

"You're pretty proud of yourself, aren't you?" she said.

"Yep," I said, smiling and leaning back.

It felt good to sit in the car. I wasn't going home, but this felt like a dress rehearsal. She parked in the garage, and we walked back to my room for our regular visit.

29

HEARTENING AND HEARTBREAKING

THAT NIGHT THEY PUT ME ON A HIGHER DOSE OF octreotide, which of course made me throw up again. My output was still high, and they were doing everything they could to slow down my gut. They also gave me a heart monitor attached to an octopus of EKG lines that stuck to my torso because my heart rate had been high all day. Needless to say, I did not sleep well.

The night nurse that came around and took everyone's vital signs meant business. She had no problem waking patients up to get the stats that she needed. Tonight was different. In the early morning hours, she lugged in a scale.

"We need weight," she said in a thick, demanding accent.

"Ugh," I said as I hit the button to make the head of the mechanical bed rise. I swung my legs around and planted my feet on the cold tile floor. This was a large platform scale designed for bariatric patients. I gripped the railing and stepped on.

The red 0.0 changed to 49.8.

"Okay." The nurse said.

"What's that in pounds?"

"Mmmmm. 110."

Dread dropped inside me. I hadn't weighed 110 pounds since I was a teenager. Coming into the hospital I didn't have any weight to spare, I was in the low 120s. But 110?

I lay back down in bed as the first sliver of dawn light cut across my room. This was the least I'd weighed in decades, and at three weeks this was the longest I'd ever been in the hospital. I wasn't getting better, I was getting worse. Fevers. Nuke-level antibiotics. CT scans. Vomiting. This wasn't my typical recover-from-Crohn's-surgery hospital visit. In fact, I rarely even heard anyone say "Crohn's disease" when people talked about my case.

This wasn't Crohn's, I realized. This was collateral damage from having Crohn's for decades.

It was St. Patrick's Day. The hustle and bustle of Monday mornings were always a stark contrast to the quiet and lightly staffed weekends. Dr. Erin Teeple was in early. Positive and cheery as always, she could read pretty quickly that I wasn't.

"Well, we can d/c that heart monitor. The readings are back to normal. So that will be one less thing attached to you."

"Great. When can I go home?"

"Well, maybe later this week. Your white count is still elevated, so we're watching that. And it's just going to take some more time to get your output regulated."

I felt a little better after talking with her, although what we talked about still felt very surface-level. Emotionally there was something bigger at play.

Nicole came in around noon carrying an Au Bon Pain bag.

"Hey," she said, placing the bag down and planting a kiss on my forehead.

"I got you some carrot ginger soup," she said, unpacking the bag on my tray table. "And these raspberry cheese croissants are going to be my downfall."

We sat quietly together eating, which was different from our normal upbeat conversations about my prognosis and stories about the boys at home.

"What's going on, honey," she said.

I let out a deep sigh. "They weighed me this morning. I haven't weighed this much since I was in middle school."

"How much?"

"110."

She didn't respond and I continued. "I'm not feeling good about all of this. I'm not getting better. I just..."

My throat caught and I couldn't speak. I turned to Nicole, whose eyes were filling with tears.

"One thing gets fixed and two more break. I'm sick of being sick, and I just want to go home."

"I know Meesh," she said, putting down her food and holding my hand.

Just then my nurse walked in. Sheila was one of my favorites. She was a seasoned, type-A kind of nurse who was always on the ball.

"Hey guys! Hey Nicole. How's everybody doing today?" she said.

Nicole was able to shift into some friendly small talk, but then the conversation turned to me.

"I'm not doing good," I said, losing the fight to the lump in my throat. I looked over at Nicole and again she had tears in her eyes.

"I think I need to talk to one of the doctors. I want to know if I'm ever going to get better. It seems like one thing gets fixed, and two more things break. Like, I'm not strapped to the heart monitor anymore, but now my fucking white count is up again."

Sheila knew my situation was bad, and that knowledge had finally caught up to me. "Okay, I'll talk to them and someone will come and see you."

"Thank you. I know Boyle's in surgery today, and Dr. Erin Teeple has already been by."

"It's okay, I'll get one of them. I'll get back to you," she promised.

She left, and Nicole and I continued.

"I'm just at the end of my fucking rope. I've been in here for three weeks," I said.

"I know honey. This will be good to talk to someone."

I moved over in bed and secured all of my lines and tubes, and she climbed in next to me and we both held each other and cried together. We were both at a low point. While I was stuck in the hospital dealing with my failing body, she juggled everything outside of the hospital. She was working and taking care of the kids and finding coverage for them when she needed to be in the hospital with her critically ill husband.

An hour later one of the residents that I was becoming fast friends with, Laura, came in. Like the other residents, she was young, but she had something else to her. Like she was meant to do this kind of work. She had a great mix of medical talent and bedside manner.

I explained how I felt to her, even though it was a lot to put on a young doctor, but I was at a loss for what would happen to me. At this point, I was full-on crying. My body was in chaos, and I became really sad about it for the first time in my life.

"So, my question is: am I going to get better? Am I ever going to go home, to my kids? Have you ever seen someone sick like this, in the same way that I'm sick?"

Laura was patient and calm as she talked. She said that I would get better, but it was going to be a longer road to recovery than we had thought initially.

"The good news is, you're out of the danger zone that you were in when you arrived. We just have to roll with the punches here. And yes, we've seen patients like you before. My hunch is that if anyone can get through this, you can."

"Yeah, but my weight. It's so low. I thought the TPN was giving me the maximum amount of calories I could get. And that's going right into my bloodstream."

"It is, we have you maxed out on TPN. But your body is using all of that nutritional power to try and heal itself before it adds weight. Believe me, it's making a difference."

She went on and instilled confidence in both of us. It was what I needed to hear. I knew I was where I needed to be, and that I was going to get out and back to my normal life.

"Okay," I sniffled. "Thank you so much for the talk, Laura."

"You bet," she said.

Nicole turned to me after she left.

"I think that was really good, you know? To get everything out in the open?"

"Yeah, that's what I needed. Probably what we both needed."

"Totally. I know it's not easy for you to be vulnerable like that honey. But it's heartening to see. Heartening and heartbreaking all at once."

"I love you Meesh, you're my favorite."

"You're my favorite" was something that Nicole and I said to one another since before we were married. It was our unique way of saying "I love you" to each other without saying the same three words everyone else used. When we got married, we had the initials YMF inscribed under our wedding bands.

"You're my favorite too, honey. I'm sorry but I have to go and get those boys of ours."

"I know, okay. I love you."

"I love you too, Meesh."

After she left, I sat in bed alone. The release of having all my emotions come to a head like that allowed me to see things differently. Up until this point I had laid back and let everyone else take care of me, my in-hospital vacation from dealing with my chronic illness. But now the vacation was over. It was time to push myself. It was time to get involved and fight.

To kick off my newly formed disposition, I pulled myself out of bed, unplugged the IV pole from the wall, put my earbuds in, and hit the hallways for a walk. There was only one song to play for this occasion. "Eye of the Tiger" by Survivor. The opening guitar licks put a smile back on my face. I did about six laps, two more than usual, passing all of the people wearing green for St. Patrick's Day.

As I walked, I reviewed everything in my head. I was vomiting from the octreotide so hard that it sprayed out of my nose. I was in a perpetual cycle of CT scans. I either needed one, had one scheduled, was waiting for the results of one, or was starting a new antibiotic based on the test's results. But, I also took stock of what I had going for me in the hospital. Nicole and I were able to spend time together every day, which was really nice compared to our day-to-day at home, where we would constantly be interrupted by the kids. It felt like we had these little day dates with each other where we caught up on what was happening at home and in the hospital. Another thing I had going for me was that I felt like I was in the right place. I had full confidence in my team of doctors. And, I reasoned, the drugs weren't bad either.

Back in my room, Sheila was waiting for me.

"You're due for your pain meds," she said as I plugged my IV pole back into the wall, and climbed back into bed.

"Hey, thank you so much for getting Laura."

"Oh, she came by already? That's great! Did you guys have a good talk?"

"Yes, that was just what Nicole and I needed. I feel better, mentally at least. Nicole does too."

"Oh good. I could tell that you guys were in rough shape this morning. That's not like you."

"Yeah, I know. I just don't think I realized how sick I was when I came in here," I said, almost to myself.

Sheila was such a good example of why nurses are so important. They're the glue of the hospital because they're in the unique position of seeing things from all sides and making connections. Nurses understand what the doctors are doing because they see similar patients all the time. Through conversation, they get to know the patients and their families, and they know how to negotiate the hospital politics and what to expect from each doctor's approach.

"Okay, time for pain meds. How do you rate your pain?" Sheila asked routinely.

"About a five."

"Got it," she said as she recorded it in the computer, and began the ritual of administering my IV pain medication, Dilaudid. Stop the infusion. Scrub the entry point with an alcohol wipe. Flush the line with half of a saline flush. Connect the syringe filled with a small amount of clear liquid. Depress the plunger. Then flush the medication through with the remaining saline.

Three. Two. One. All at once, a wave of euphoria quenched my body, like a platonic orgasm. It's a wringing feeling that starts in my forehead and temples, moving down my body until it exits through my feet. Relaxation followed, and just like the oxycodone I'd had as an outpatient, I felt a palpable sense of well-being.

Sheila left, and I lay back in my bed. If there was a thin silver lining to everything that was going on with my body, the rush of Dilaudid in four-hour intervals was something I had going for me. I started to look forward to it. Some nurses would administer it slowly because some patients didn't like the feeling of it. I always told them to flush away.

30

THE VAC

STAYING TRUE TO THE WHACK-A-MOLE NATURE OF MY current condition, they finally stopped the octreotide only to have an issue arise with the midline incision. For a few days, the nurses and I noticed that the gauze used to dress it was getting wetter and wetter. Then it started having a discharge to it. It got to the point where the gauze dressing wasn't cutting it.

Diane, my ostomy nurse, had been in and out since I had been in the hospital. I could handle one appliance on my own, but two of them plus the midline incision was a lot, so she helped when she could. But now things were getting complicated.

She came in, raised my bed, and asked the nurse to give me my pain meds.

"It's going to be better if you're relaxed," she said to me.

"Hey, I'm not going to argue with that," I said. Inside I welcomed the rush of opioids every time. I wasn't squeamish about the science project on my stomach, but most people would be.

As usual, she and I changed the dressing together and talked through everything. It was always important for me to understand what she was doing, and why she was doing it. She turned to me after fishing through her giant duffel bag of supplies with something in her hand.

"So, this is a fistula pouch. It's like a small ostomy that we adhere over the wound. Everything can drain into it. The doctors will want to measure the output, I'm sure."

"Wow, I didn't even know this kind of thing existed. I wish I'd known about these last year when I was dealing with the fistula. I never even thought to ask you about it."

"I know, that's too bad."

"Oh well, that's my independence working against me I guess."

I was in more pain with this new development, so they increased the Dilaudid. After Diane left, I spent most of the afternoon feeling drugged. Like the feeling you get when you're drifting off to sleep. I kept having daydreams and then would realize it wasn't real. The mix of colors on the get-well-soon poster sprang to life in the late afternoon light. It seemed that every time I looked at it, it was a different poster. Like I had never seen it before and could just fall into it.

Dr. Boyle came by later and examined Diane's handiwork on my stomach.

"It'll take a couple of weeks before we can tell if it's actually a fistula. It's going to take some time for everything to settle down and sort out."

"Are you saying that I'm going to be here for another two weeks?"

"It's hard to say exactly, but I would put you in the sixth or seventh inning here at the Brigham. This is a slow and steady race."

"And bumpy," I added.

"For the time being, I'm going to have Diane and the ostomy nurses continue to pouch this. That will take care of the leakage," he said. "There's a treatment we have that's been successful in wound healing, it's a wound vac. How it works is you cover the wound with a special adhesive and there's a tube that goes on it, and we hook that up to suction. That draws off the excess fluid and discharge and every-thing heals faster."

"Faster sounds like a good plan to me," I said.

"Good news honey!" I exclaimed on the phone the next morning. "It's pus!"

"What's pus?"

"The output into the fistula appliance. It's not ostomy output, it's an exact match to what's going into one of the IR drains."

"Oh, that is good news! So it's not a fistula then?"

"Nope," I said as I adjusted myself in bed. "In celebration of this, I propose that you bring in sushi for lunch."

"Are you serious honey?"

"Yes."

"Well, I can gladly make that happen."

Two hours later Nicole arrived carrying a white paper bag containing our usual order of sushi.

"I never thought you'd be so excited about pus."

"I know, seriously."

The black sushi takeout containers sat in stark contrast to the beige hospital surroundings. It felt good to eat something that felt so much like our regular life. I had sashimi, and Nicole ate a mix of maki rolls. The nurses laughed at how we smuggled in this contraband, which was technically within the guidelines of my current diet.

With everything good came something bad. That night two unusual things happened. One was another fever, surely keeping me in my CT scan cycle, and the other was that my regular ostomy on my left side became active. This wasn't something that should have been physiologically possible because it had been sealed off during the surgery a month ago. It was like that trick the magicians perform when they take a handkerchief and insert it in one ear, and it comes right out the other side. It seems real, but you know it's not possible.

But, sure enough, here it was making a mess. The nurse and I ended up putting an appliance on it. It was unclear to everyone what was really happening underneath the surface of my abdomen. Because of my fever, an order was put in for blood cultures to test for a blood-stream infection.

A resident that I didn't know was on that night, and at two in the morning there wasn't anyone else around to help her with the blood draw. She took a batch of labs from my PICC line, easy. But with blood cultures, you need them from two separate sites.

I could tell she lacked experience drawing labs by the way she clumsily organized the supplies on my bed. Most people have a solid routine for the things they do frequently, and she didn't have one. I could tell she was nervous. Had she ever drawn blood before? I had no idea.

With the bright overhead light beaming down over us, she approached my arm timidly with the needle. For anyone that's ever had blood drawn, you know that you have to commit to the vein with a quick jab, kind of like throwing a dart at a dartboard. That's how the needle gets in. This resident moved the needle toward my arm apprehensively, in slow motion. The needle was sharp, but I questioned whether it would puncture my skin at this speed. Somehow she got it, and the containers were filled, but it was the most timid blood draw I'd ever had.

I reached the one-month mark in my stay at the Brigham the day I was slated to have the wound vac set up with Diane. Unfortunately, the output from my midline incision switched from pus to ostomy output, which meant it was definitely a fistula, but there was hope that this vac system would heal it anyway. From what I understood at that point, it was a fairly new technology for healing wounds fast. There was a seal made around the wound, and then a light suction pulled the moisture, or in my case the output from the new fistula, out and away from the wound. This would make the wound shrink faster over time.

I was happy to learn that two of my favorite residents, Laura and Ian, were going to be helping Diane with the vac dressing. Laura was the resident who talked Nicole and me out of the dark place we were in the week before, and Ian was the chief resident.

The procedure was done right in the room, and it was pretty much a longer version of a regular dressing change. I sat back and watched them as they constructed a border barrier around my kidney bean-shaped wound. A foam cutout went over the middle part of the wound, and everything was covered with an adhesive clear plastic covering called Tegaderm. A tube came out of the middle, and it was connected to a suction machine. All in all, it took them an hour to cut the pieces and put it all together.

"Okay," Diane said, "that should last about three days."

"Okay cool. I'm really curious to see what it's going to look like then."

"These vacs work wonders," Ian said.

So now I officially had three exits for my stomach. The ileostomy, the vac which drained into a glass container on the wall, and the original colostomy site which surprised us every few days with output.

That night, Nicole brought Cooper in to see me. He wore his blue Superman shirt and a huge smile on his face. He lit up when he saw me.

"Hi, Daddy!"

"Hey! Super Coop! How's it going?"

Nicole made the visit special by giving us time alone for a while by going downstairs to the Au Bon Pain for another raspberry cheese croissant. I had Cooper climb up next to me so we could play with the mechanical bed together. Head up. Legs down. Legs up. Head down. For a five-year-old, this was amazing fun.

"Up!" he said, and we went up.

"Down!" he said, and we went down.

"Hey man, how's school going?"

"Good. Up!" he said, and we went back up.

Nicole returned and announced that it was time to go. It was hard to pry him away from the amusement park ride of my bed, but he eventually climbed down after giving me a big hug.

"I love you Daddy!" he said and gave me a wet kiss.

Later that night, Nicole and I talked about the visit.

"Cooper seemed to do okay today, seeing me in the hospital," I said.

"Yeah, I thought for sure he was going to ask what that stuff in the vac container was, but he didn't. He really is your kid."

"Yeah, I guess he keeps that stuff to himself," I said.

"No, I mean he's not fazed by any of it."

"Oh yeah, that's my boy," I said.

Over the years I'd developed a heightened sense for moisture on my stomach. A feeling of cold wetness on my abdomen meant that my appliance was leaking and needed to be changed right away. The day after they installed the wound vac, I felt it. I looked down and saw that my blue hospital pants were wet with a brown stain. I pulled up my shirt and pulled down my pants to investigate, and found that the vac seal had broken, which had caused the leak. So much for three days.

Ian and Laura came back in, and for the next hour created a new seal for the vac. The first time around they had hooked me up to a portable vac, so I could attach it to my IV pole and get up and around. This time they tried somewhat more of a custom approach and hooked me up to the suction on the wall.

Despite not being on the octreotide, I was still battling nausea for most of the day and then throwing up. It became a clear cycle, and the nursing staff closely measured and monitored what was going through me in both directions.

My father came in for a visit on Thursday. Typically, he would come in for a fairly short time where I would give him a high-level update, and he would sum everything up with the same confident conclusion: "So, you're progressing." Depending on how much energy I had I would either lie and tell him yes or go into a longer explanation of why not. Then he would go on to report the things going on in his world, like if he got an oil change for the car or maybe something about the house, or what he had for dinner at a restaurant the day before.

When he entered that day he was shaking his head with disgust on his face. I've seen him with this look before; he was rattled about something.

"Uh oh," I said. "What's up, Dad?"

After shaking my hand with his cold palm, he stood at the foot of my bed, not having taken off his jacket yet, and launched into his story.

"I had an appointment with my dermatologist this morning. Dr. Reed. Well, I just found out that I need surgery on the top of my head. He said it's called Mohs surgery." He scoffed, again shaking his head. "That's all I need at my age!"

I've found that when people say outlandish things to me, my natural response is to not respond. Just let it slide by and give it some thought later on. Like here, where my seventy-nine-year-old father, who has lived an almost entirely healthy life, complains about a single medical procedure to his thirty-seven-year-old son who, aside from having Crohn's disease for most of his life, has been in the hospital for a month and at the moment is physically tethered to the hospital itself via the suction machine on the wall.

"That stinks, Dad. What's Mohs surgery?"

He went on to explain roughly what the skin surgery would be, basically an outpatient procedure.

"Anyway, how are you?" he said.

I went on to give him my update, and he gave me his report on everything else at home.

"Here you go," he said before he left, handing me an envelope containing a few twenty dollar bills. "For Nicole, for parking."

"Thanks Dad, we really appreciate it." He gave me an envelope every time he came in, which did help. The fact was, we'd spent close to $300 on parking in the past month alone. This was my dad's way of helping out.

Shortly after he left, the vac failed once again. "Oh fucking A!" I said as I hit the red buzzer for the nurse to come in.

"Yes?" It was Mary, one of the PCAs, poking her head in with a smile. Patient care assistants take vital signs, empty bedpans, or in my case cylinders of output, and help patients get washed. There were two that usually worked through the day, Mona and Mary. They were both so nice and helpful. This time it was Mary answering, most likely because my nurse was helping one of her other patients.

"Hey Mary, can you have Emily come in here? This thing is leaking. Can you hand me some of those white washcloths?"

She gave me the washcloths so I could clean and dam the leak.

"That was your father?" she asked as we waited for my nurse to come in.

"Yep, that was him."

"Such a nice man," she said, smiling.

I let her words sink in as I frustratedly tended to the leak in the dressing, thinking about him. Mary would see him as a nice man, always chatting with the nurses and telling his life story. Coming in every few days to visit with his sick son. But the nerve of him complaining to me about his health right now. His voice rang in my head: "this is all I need at my age." Why would he say that to me?

"No," I said, quietly seething in my bed.

"What's that hon?"

"No, he's not a nice man. He's a weak man."

Mary watched me now, her face concerned, unsure how to respond.

"There's this Buddhist saying that goes something like, 'the strong man is brave at the sight of his own blood; the weak man faints at the mere sight of another's.' He is the weak man."

"Mmph," was all Mary could say.

Emily, my nurse, came in. "Hey, I paged Laura. She should be by soon."

"Okay, thanks," I said to her.

They left, and instantly I felt bad that I'd vented so badly to Mary. She didn't deserve that kind of explanation of my father. He was a nice man, he just couldn't handle a lot. Still, I wish he could realize who he was complaining to. What I'd discovered about him in the two years since my mother had died was that everyone naturally loved my father. Strangers were drawn to him as if he gave off some kind of pheromone. He was outwardly happy and positive and had his life story down pat to a two-minute elevator pitch. It was remarkable to hear him pridefully list off all of his headlines like a well-crafted resumé.

I'm a widower, I live in Medfield, yep, the same house for the past forty years. Brad, he's the artist. He works for Cramer Productions in Norwood. He and his wife Nicole have two boys, Cooper and Redding. Steven, he's my other son. I've always called him Steven, never Steve. He's in finance, works for Boston Consulting Group. Anyway, he and his wife just bought a house in Wayland. My wife Sally, she died from multiple myelonomia...

So, I understood where Mary was coming from, or at least I was beginning to. For me, this all tied back to that first appointment I had with Dr. Flores, almost thirty years earlier. A ten-minute walk across the street to Children's was enough for Dr. Flores to always ask about him. People just love my dad. He is who he's always been, and I began to understand him for the first time.

An hour later, Laura still hadn't shown. I lay patiently and awkwardly in my bed with a patched-up science project on my stomach. Emily paged again, and another hour went by before she showed up. Two hours, waiting.

"Hi, I'm sorry it took so long to get up here," she said when she arrived.

"That's okay, you must have a lot going on," I replied.

"Yeah, sometimes everything happens at once, and I knew I'd be here for a while changing this. I got everyone else taken care of so I can totally focus on you."

"Is anyone else coming?" I asked.

"Nope, just me this time."

"Okay, well let me help. I'm a graphic designer by trade, so this crafty stuff is right up my alley."

It still took us over an hour to get the new vac seal established. I cut out all of the barrier shapes to match the border of the wound, and she worked on the filters that covered it. It felt good to help and be involved.

After she left, I texted with Nicole about the boys. She told me that at least once a day, Redd points to the gallery wall and says, "Daddy."

"It melts my heart," she said. "Every. Single. Time."

She passed the phone to Cooper, and we texted back and forth the way five-year-olds do: Random emojis. Back and forth for about three full screens of random emojis.

It takes about a week in the hospital to realize that the beds suck. But typically, by the time I would start being uncomfortable at night I would be getting discharged. At this point, I had not only been in the hospital for a whole month, but I also had to keep up with the bags, tubes, and drains on my abdomen that needed to be positioned just right so I could sleep.

I explained this to Sheila one morning, and she asked, "Have you ever had anything for sleep?"

"Nope. Insomnia is one thing that I've never had a problem with."

"Well if you want," she continued, "I can ask them to write you a prescription for something. Getting a good night's sleep for you is important in the healing process."

"Okay, I'm interested. What kind of stuff are we talking about?"

"We could do Benadryl or Ambien," she suggested. "I'll talk to them and they'll put you on something that won't interfere with the other meds you're on."

They started me on Ambien, and I was on it for about a week. It helped me to get to sleep, but I still had trouble waking up in the night. I'd get woken up for vital signs twice every night, and I couldn't get back to sleep. So next was IV Benadryl.

That night, my nurse was Jian. She was a middle-aged Asian woman with a thick accent. She was super friendly and awesome.

I had been feeling nauseous all day, which was pretty much how I felt every day at that point. When I couldn't take it any longer, I vomited the contents of my stomach into the pale pink hospital basin. I hit the buzzer for Jian to come in.

"Hey, wow, that's a lot," she said, lifting the full basin from my hands. She took note of the measurement on the basin before emptying the contents into the toilet. "Two liters."

"Whew! I feel like a million bucks after off-loading that!" I said with enthusiasm.

"Do you want this back?" she said, holding out the cleaned pink basin.

"Nope, I have nothing left to give."

"Are you ready for sleep?" she asked.

"Uh, why, am I due for pain meds?"

"Yes, and I have IV Benadryl to help you sleep."

"Okay, can you help me get ready?"

She brought over a pink kidney-shaped pan and I brushed my teeth and rinsed while she prepped the drugs.

"What's your pain level?"

"Eh, about a four."

Jian and I chatted as she first administered the Dilaudid. Anticipation. Euphoric wave. Relaxation.

"Okay, now the Benadryl," she said as she screwed on the second syringe, followed by a flush of saline.

The standard over-the-counter Benadryl takes time to kick in as it enters through your digestive system. It's a whole different experience when it infuses directly into your bloodstream. It's like drinking six beers in ten seconds, and all of a sudden I'm sluggish, like I was underwater, and my head weighed a thousand pounds. It was similar to getting knocked out before surgery.

"How you feel?" she said after organizing her things.

All I could muster was, "Okay Jian, good night."

She turned down the lights as she left the room, I closed my eyes and fell into a deep sleep.

. . .

The next few days were more of the same. I felt nauseous all day, would vomit in the evening, and feel better. So it wasn't that I was sick, but just that there was so much in my stomach that evacuating it felt great.

The vac's promise of holding for three days never came through. It only ever lasted twenty-four to thirty-six hours before it leaked. It didn't matter who was officially doing the dressing change, Ian, Laura, or Diane, I always contributed. Each time we tried something different, trying to learn about it. A different positioning, a different cut of the materials, or different types of supplies. Nothing seemed to work for my wound, but our hope that the next change would be the right solution never faded. If nothing else, I was getting a lot of practice changing it.

Rumors started to fly that I would be able to go home with the vac. They had a portable vac that I had been using so I could get up and walk around, and not be stuck in bed with the vac connected to the wall suction. And because I had become so adept at changing the system, they felt pretty confident that I could do it at home with assistance from visiting nurses.

Dr. Boyle came in on Thursday morning, April 3, to have a conversation with me.

"I think you're in good enough shape to send you home tomorrow if you think you can handle everything on your own. Laura and Diane have been quite vocal about how involved you've been in crafting the vac dressings."

"Yes, I can handle it. I really want to get out of here."

"Okay then, we'll get you slated for tomorrow morning. We'll get you set up with the visiting nurses. They'll train you on how to infuse the TPN, that can be done as an outpatient."

"Okay, awesome. Thank you so much. This is so great!"

"Okay then," he said, and we shook hands.

The rest of my day was filled with making arrangements to go home. Everyone was so happy for me. I rested up and got my final dose of my nighttime drugs to get me off to sleep.

Friday was busy. We did a vac change in the morning, and Nicole drove in for the last time around three in the afternoon. We packed up my room and went over all of the discharge paperwork. By 4:00, the transport person wheeled me downstairs. I still had my hospital pants on, but it felt great to be in the lobby of the Brigham, surrounded by civilians going about their daily business. I was wheeled outside through the large revolving door, and then the smell of fresh cold air tinged with car exhaust filled my nostrils. Outside felt wonderful.

Nicole had pulled the car around and was waiting for us by the curb. The transport person helped me with the vac and tubing, and then I was back in our car. I looked back at the boys' empty car seats as Nicole unloaded the boxes of supplies in the trunk. Then she sat down in the driver's seat, and leaned over and kissed me.

"Well, Meesh," I said. "I'm in better shape than when you dropped me off."

She laughed. "Let's keep it that way."

"Deal," I said.

"Wait until you see how clean the house is."

"I bet it's like you were nesting again," I said.

"Yup. And I have another surprise for you. We're going to pick up the boys on our way home."

"Okay, awesome," I said and settled back in the seat.

Our normal schedule with picking up and dropping off the boys was so foreign to me at that point that I didn't realize our drive home would align with getting them. We picked up Redd first, at his family daycare. I stayed in the car, parked in the driveway, and when Nicole brought him down, I unrolled my window.

"Daddy!" he exclaimed as he reached in to hug me.

Nicole buckled him into his car seat behind me, and we set off to get Cooper at preschool, less than a mile away.

"Redd can stay in the car with me," I said. "That'll be easier."

"Okay. I didn't tell Cooper that you're coming home today so this will be a nice surprise."

"You didn't tell him this morning?"

"Well, no. You've just been so up and down that I didn't want to disappoint him."

"Yeah, that makes sense," I said.

I sat and conversed with Redd, a one-word call-and-response conversation with pointing.

"Redd, who am I?"

"Daddy."

"What's this?"

"Car!"

"Oh look at that, what's that?"

"School. Boopa school."

"Right, Cooper's school."

After a couple of minutes of talking, Cooper came bounding around the corner of the building and down the walkway. Seeing him with his messy blond hair in his red jacket coming down the hill was therapy for my heart. Nicole must have told him there was a surprise in the car because once he saw me his face split into a huge smile. I opened the door and gave him a big hug.

"Daddy, you're here!"

"I know buddy. I'm home!"

We arrived home, all four of us, and at 7:00 that night I had my first outpatient appointment with the visiting nurse. Nicole had the house spotless for me, and she had moved our dining room table over to the wall. Before we knew it, it was a hill of hospital supplies.

The nurse arrived on time. She was a thin woman in her fifties with a German accent. She quickly unpacked and transformed the supplies into a TPN workstation. By that point in my hectic day, I was absolutely exhausted from the travel and wasn't up for the TPN DIY course that she had planned. I made it through and was finally hooked up to my bag of TPN, which hung from a portable IV pole. Someone would be back tomorrow for me to do a trial run to make sure I could do it myself.

After I took my pain meds, I dragged the wound vac and IV pole through the living room, where the medical supplies were beginning to overtake the kids' toys, over our hardwood floors in the hallway, and into our bedroom where I collapsed into our flat, comfortable, non-mechanical bed.

31

BOOMERANG

THE VAC FAILED AT 5:00 THE NEXT MORNING BECAUSE THE portable vac wasn't working properly. Nicole was the only one there to help me and unsurprisingly she proved to be a solid assistant. I sat in our living room chair with my legs on the ottoman, with big absorbent bed pads all around and underneath me, and Nicole and I worked together to get the seal on the wound down. It took us three hours, but we finally got the vac working and the whole dressing reestablished.

Three hours after that, the dressing leaked again. Laura had given me her number, and she and I texted back and forth to troubleshoot and find a new fix. I told her what went wrong, and texted photos, and she would send me drawings back of how I should construct a solution with the supplies I had on hand. I hadn't been home a full day and I was already using lifelines for help.

By Sunday, frustration was growing. The vac never lasted three days. In reality, it was only lasting twelve hours at most, and visiting nurses weren't outside-of-the-box thinkers like Team Diane/Laura/Ian/Brad were. Nicole was my assistant almost every time because leaks and breakdowns of the dressing happened during odd hours when the visiting nurses couldn't come.

I was on a liquid-only diet ever since they figured out that the fluid exiting through the wound site was a fistula, and for the past week and a half, I had been consistently vomiting two liters of fluid a day.

"I hate to say it," I said to Nicole, "but I'm pretty sure everything I'm drinking is coming back up eventually."

"Really, you can tell?" Nicole said.

"The thing is, I always feel so much better after I throw up. It's always two liters. Then, when I start drinking again I get that water balloon feeling in my stomach right away."

"Can we talk to them about that on Friday? Who's going to be at the appointment?"

"It's Diane, a clinical person from the wound vac company, and hopefully Laura. Boyle will come in at some point for probably ten minutes or as long as we have questions for him."

So it went for the rest of the week. My motto was *one day at a time.* Nicole and I battled the wound vac dressing. I fumbled through doing my TPN by myself, which after a couple of days I got the hang of with the help of the visiting nurses. That was easier because it was something we could schedule and plan for. More and more I realized that being in the hospital was a luxury. I really did need people to care for me so I could rest and heal. Taking care of myself was exhausting.

But as hard as it was, my soul was nourished by being able to see the boys. Redd had changed so much since I had last seen him, as toddlers do at that age. I couldn't get on the floor and play with them, but just being home and seeing them in their environment made me feel human again. Like a dad again.

Friday finally came, and Nicole and I loaded up a box with vac supplies and headed in to the hospital to meet Diane and a rep from the company that made the vac system. All in all, the vac had shrunk the wound a visible amount.

I met Diane in the clinic at 45 Francis Street, the same place where we would have our annual ostomy appliance appointments. The vac rep resembled more of a sales guy than any kind of clinician, and I was a little worried that he wasn't going to be able to stand the sight of my wound, which had all the gore of a horror movie.

The rep was full of confidence. I figured he can be as much of a know-it-all as he wants if he can get a good seal. I sat back and let him work his magic.

"You look tired," Diane said.

I sighed. "We're at our wit's end. I mean, if we can figure out the vac, that would make things easier. But even so, I'm exhausted all the time."

"I can tell," Diane said.

"But on the other hand, it's good to be home with the boys."

It took the usual hour to construct the dressing. Dr. Boyle came by in the middle of it to examine the wound. He was concerned mostly about my continued vomiting and left the wound care to the experts.

Once the wound was sealed and the vac was running, Diane and the rep began cleaning up the area. The rep was clearly proud of his contribution to this tough situation, but that was short-lived.

"Um, you guys," I said. They both stopped their cleaning and turned to me. "It's leaking."

All that effort for less than five minutes of wear time. Diane left for a minute because she had other patients to see, and she was able to have her colleagues cover those appointments for her so she could focus on the task at hand. They took down the failed dressing, and we put on a new one, which also failed. Finally, on the third try, we were able to get a successful seal.

I was wiped out from the session, which by then was pushing three hours, and from my week at home. I felt my typical late-afternoon pangs of nausea as Diane left to consult with Dr. Boyle. Nicole and I were visibly exhausted. The vac wasn't working. My wound needed some kind of new approach altogether, and on top of that, I kept vomiting. Diane and Dr. Boyle both came into the exam room, and as a group, we decided that it would be best if I was admitted back to the hospital. It felt like it was the right decision.

"I'm going to come over when you get settled, and we're going to do something else," Diane said.

Diane would later tell me that the appointment that afternoon was a low point for her. She left the exam room, went to the kitchen, and bought a candy bar out of the vending machine. She sat down at the table alone and ate it, feeling completely defeated.

Transport arrived to wheel me over to the hospital side of the building, and up to my home away from home, the fifteenth floor. Nicole walked alongside us as the transport person navigated the labyrinth of white corridors connecting the two hospitals. Finally, we reached a bank of elevators. We hit the up button and we waited.

"Fuck," I said.

"What is it," Nicole said, alarmed.

"Another leak."

There wasn't anything I could do except try and dam the leak with my T-shirt. What was Diane going to do differently this time? I began to crave the small consolation prize I had coming in the form of IV Dilaudid. If I had nothing going for me, I still had that. For the past week, I'd gotten along well taking oxycodone orally, but now that I was back I could feel that rush once again.

As soon as I got settled in my new room, Diane appeared in the doorway.

"You found me," I said.

"I found you," she said.

"What are we going to do?"

"We"—she paused as she opened her bulky bag of supplies—"are going to do it the old way. No more vac."

"Really? There's another way?"

"Yes there is. We're going to pouch it," she said, showing me a pouch that looked like an elephant trunk.

In a fraction of the time that it took to construct the vac dressing, we simply put a large fistula pouch on the wound. It was done in less than twenty minutes.

Before she left for the weekend, she gave me her home phone number.

"I've only ever given this to one other patient before in my whole career. If you get into a jam this weekend, call me and I can talk you through it."

"Oh my God, Diane, thank you so much."

I don't remember if I called her or not that weekend, but just having her number and knowing that she was a lifeline for me meant everything.

I granted myself a vacation for that first weekend I was back at the Brigham, reveling in the fact that I was back to having care at my disposal. The nurses took over control of my pain management, TPN, and general care. I was able to rest both physically and mentally.

Up until this point, I'd had a few different roommates. There was a Latino man who'd only been in the hospital for a few days and had constant visitors. At one point he had a dozen relatives in at the same time, all of them on his half of the room. They kept spilling over to my side through the drawn curtain, and the kids used the bathroom despite the *Restroom for Patients Only* sign.

After him, there was an older man who'd come in with intense abdominal pain. He'd been in sales; a ton of bravado and very over-friendly. He was the stereotypical never-been-sick-a-day-in-my-life kind of guy, and here he was stuck in a hospital bed waiting for test results. I remember at one point he and his wife were talking about sending flowers to the whole nursing staff because they were so wonderful. All that positive energy conked out when they learned that the reason for all of his pain was that he had a tumor the size of a football in his ribcage. Watching this man and his wife weather the storm of illness grief for a week was heartbreaking. Finally, with a treatment plan in place they sent him home crying. He didn't want to have another pain episode like the one that brought him into the hospital. I hope that guy made it through okay. After he was discharged our paths never crossed again.

The weekend I returned to the fifteenth floor, my roommate was a mean old man. I could tell the nurses were doing everything they could to keep their cool around him. He yelled and swore at everyone. He thought everyone was against him. He was post-op for something and was completely skeptical about every recovery treatment that the hospital staff had for him. At one point when he was clearly in pain and his nurse offered him Tylenol, he exclaimed, "Oh what kind of pills are you trying to shove down my fucking throat now!" His wife came to visit, and he railed at how the hospital was torturing him. I commiserated with the nurses, who dealt with him in a professional manner. After he was discharged, I was able to piece together the full story. He was in his seventies, lived in New Hampshire, and this was his first time in the hospital, ever. This guy probably hadn't even set foot in a pharmacy before. What appeared to be rage and anger was really just the manifestation of this man's fear. He was just afraid. He was in a foreign place with strangers in white coats or scrubs taking care of him, and on top of that, he was in pain. He had no trust in the medical establishment because he had lived such a healthy life that he'd never needed it before.

I thought of my dad and his rant about his minor skin surgery. Similar to the old man and the sales guy, he'd rarely been sick in his life. He'd had a brief stint in the hospital about fifteen years earlier when he had his prostate removed, or as my dad would always mispronounce it, his *prostrate*. Living a healthy life was as foreign to me as the hospital was to these men. I could barely imagine the luxury of health. Not knowing what severe pain was like. Not needing to take pills in the morning and at night. Having a belly that just worked and wasn't a lemon. The result was that I had experience in health care environments. I knew the system and the procedures and maybe I took my knowledge for granted. My dad was twice my age but only had an ounce of the experience I had with being sick. He was scared, and I realized then that instead of begrudging his inexperience I could help and comfort him.

After the angry old man was discharged on Monday morning, I didn't have any more roommates. Labs came back that showed I had klebsiella, which was an antibiotic-resistant bacteria that guaranteed me a single room from then on due to the risk of passing it on to other patients. Hospital staff had to put on yellow smocks when they entered my room.

Dr. Boyle came in that morning, scoffing at the yellow gown procedure. I could tell he was against the protocol but tempered his opinion. He was here to discuss a plan moving forward.

"Hi Brad, how are you feeling?" he said as he adjusted the smock's sleeves.

"Well, the weekend of rest was exactly what I needed. That was a lot being home. Too much. I should have just stayed here..."

"Hold on," he cut in. "You were the one who wanted to go home. I made the arrangements so we could try it, and here we are."

Dr. Boyle was swift at giving me a dose of tough love when I needed it. It didn't happen often, but it was always effective.

"Okay, yes. You're right. I'm understating the fact that it was great to be home with the kids. In a way, it was a break that I needed."

As we talked, he examined my belly and Diane's handiwork, which had held all weekend.

"This pouching system has held longer than any of the stints I had with the wound vac."

"Yes, the wound vac is a thing of the past."

"Okay, that's good news."

"Now, the GI team is going to get involved because I have a theory as to why you're vomiting so frequently. I think you have a rare condition called SMA syndrome. That stands for superior mesenteric artery syndrome. Your mesenteric artery is right below your stomach," he said, making a "c" shape with his palm facing up over his midsection.

"In patients like you, who have lost most of their body mass due to being so sick, the artery presses down on the jejunum, which is the first third of the small intestine, and the weight of the artery on the intestines makes it impossible for anything to pass through. Your stomach, and everyone's stomach, makes two liters of stomach acid every day to digest the food that you'll eat. In a normal person that acid is reabsorbed downstream, and that cycle continues."

I could see where he was going. "So basically, all that stomach acid is trapped with nowhere to go, building slowly over the day. And that makes sense because I've been vomiting two liters each day."

"Exactly," he said. "It's a rare condition, and with your low body mass, I think it's going to prove my theory correct."

He was certainly right about my body mass. Before my intestines ruptured, I was operating about twenty pounds underweight. At 6' 2", my weight was in the low 120s. That morning, I still weighed 110. All of the nutrition I was getting via TPN, about 3,500 calories a night, my body was using toward wound healing. I was downright skeletal. When my stick-thin legs would reveal themselves from underneath my hospital pants, I did my best to censor them out. I would avert my eyes and tell myself that they weren't my real legs. I couldn't be that thin. I avoided looking at myself in the mirror as I washed in the chair with the hospital's cleaning wipes. I could see my body, but I also wasn't seeing it.

"The GI team will be by later today to explain the solution," he said.

Now that it was Monday, everyone had returned from the weekend. Ian and Laura came by. Diane came in and we did an appliance change, which was now three pouches. One for my colostomy, one for my ileostomy, and a large wound pouch that, with a little help from other adhesives, was able to cover my wound on my midline.

Later that day, Dr. Hamilton arrived.

"There he is," he said as he extended his hand toward me.

"Here I am. Now there's a sight for sore eyes," I said as I shook his hand.

"So tell me, what's been going on?"

Dr. Hamilton seemed a little skeptical about the procedure I was lined up for, and I quickly learned that he was pretty much out of the loop about my saga. He wasn't aware that I was still in the hospital since that surgery at the end of February.

"I'm guessing that you've stayed away for jurisdiction reasons," I said.

"Pretty much. I know you're in good hands being in Dr. Boyle's care. I still need to catch up with him, but I figured I'd come and see you first."

He went on to explain the procedure I was now scheduled for. They were going to put a G/J tube in, which is a tube within a tube that gets inserted into the left side of my stomach.

"The outside tube will stop in your stomach, and we'll be able to hook that up to suction to pull out all of your excess stomach acid which you've been throwing up. The inside tube will extend down into your jejunum, the first part of your intestine. They'll get it in past the tight spot by the mesenteric artery, and we'll be able to start feeding you through the tube."

"Wow, that sounds like quite the contraption," I said.

"Yes, well we think this is going to be a good solution for you. Interventional radiology will be doing the procedure. They'll be able to place it and check with an X-ray to make sure it's placed right."

I thanked him, and he left to find Dr. Boyle.

32

THE CIRCUS

The next day, the science project I had on my stomach was expanded with the addition of the G/J tube, which stuck out about halfway between the center and left side of my stomach. Proof of its success happened later when I realized that the slow build of nausea I had grown accustomed to wasn't happening, and I didn't vomit for the first time in about a month. Everything in my stomach was all being sucked out from the G part of the G/J tube, through a long tube that drained into a large glass beaker on the wall. I could have the nurse pause the suction and cap off the tube when I wanted to get up and walk around. If I was off for a long time, say an hour, there would be a lot that the tube pulled out upon hooking it back up to suction.

Despite everything I had been through up to this point, the G/J tube disappointed me. The fact that my body was reliant on this equipment and was so far from its normal function made me sad. Not crying sad, because the steady influx of opioids held me in a steady positive state. I just had this awareness that I was a million miles away from a regular healthy person or even the version of healthy I'd been for most of my life living with Crohn's. The only solution was to somehow gain weight, which has always been one of the single hardest things for me to do.

Each nurse had a different theory on how to snake the tubing up and around me. Some would simply leave it dangling and only adjust if there was a problem. Others would walk in at the beginning of their shift and reset the tubing to their liking. For example, behind my head, across the top of the bed, and into the beaker from there.

One of the first nights, I vomited because the G/J tube wasn't set properly. The night nurse didn't know what was wrong, but in the morning Dr. Erin Teeple explained that it was set to a slow rate, and should have been increased.

"And, even with the increased rate, the nurses can extract more manually if they need to," she explained. "I'll let them know."

Almost everything I had attached to me had its own personality and temperament and needed to be dealt with in a unique way.

Around that time, I began receiving a steady stream of cards from my colleagues at work. They were all the same size and were mailed to the house. Later I would find out that my friend Sarah set up a card station in the office. People could stop and write me a letter, and they would get mailed out each day. So when Nicole arrived each day, she would have three or four cards for me. Some were simply Get Well Soon cards. Some would be little brain teasers or have other fun things written in them. All of them were heartfelt and made me feel supported.

Outside of the hospital, people were stepping up to help us. Cooper's teacher at preschool offered to start picking him up in the morning two days a week, which was so unbelievably kind and helpful. It helped Nicole because then she only had to drop Redd off at daycare in the morning. And more importantly, it was special for Cooper. Getting picked up by his teacher and riding to school in her minivan was a big deal for a five-year-old. So that was a win-win.

My brother Steve and sister-in-law Katie were enormously helpful. They would watch the boys for Nicole at home on weekends and take them places. Cramer meals continued to arrive as well as food from Nicole's work, neighbors, family, and friends. People sent us gift cards to restaurants so Nicole wouldn't have to cook.

Friends and relatives from afar sent us care packages. Nicole's parents continued to come down from Maine just about every weekend, which gave Nicole time to visit me in the hospital. New friendships were formed from the crisis, especially Louise, who was a Canton mom with two girls that were about the same age as the boys. She watched them a bunch of times so Nicole could come in and see me.

At the beginning of the week, after the new G/J tube was placed, they began giving me nutrition called tube feeds. This was my main hope to resolve the SMA syndrome, because the J-tube bypassed the compressed area at the bottom of my stomach, and deposited nutrients right into my intestines. They began on Tuesday in a small introductory capacity, which went well.

On Wednesday they increased the volume. I was still on TPN for sixteen hours a night, but the tube feeds were considered a more effective way to nourish me because my body would be absorbing it naturally, like food. It was then that I started getting sick. Wednesday's tube feed supplement brought on nausea and eventually vomiting. Lab work showed that my white count was elevated.

Thursday I continued to decline. A CT scan was scheduled to find out if something obvious caused the infection. If there was a pocket of fluid in my abdomen, they could simply put a drain in and that would take care of it. Dr. Boyle came by in the middle of the day.

"Hi Brad, how are you feeling?"

"Ugh, not great," I said, not even attempting to sit up higher in bed as I usually did when doctors entered my room.

"Well, let's have a look," he said.

I pulled up my T-shirt to reveal the cacophony of medical appendages on my abdomen. The G/J tube now sprouted out above the three pouches that occupied the entire south side. Dr. Boyle moved around the perimeter of all of this, barely finding spots to put his stethoscope as he listened to what was happening inside.

"We just don't know why your belly is so sick," he said softly. He was just as puzzled as anyone at this point.

"I just really feel like crap now. Yesterday and today."

"Hmph. Well, it's strange that you've vomited again because the G/J tube should be taking care of that. I think that the antibiotic we have you on may be contributing to this."

"Okay, that would make sense, I think," I said.

"I'm going to have them cut that out, and we'll just keep at it, Brad."

I thanked him, and he left.

Nicole had acquired tickets to the circus that Thursday night from a neighbor. She took Cooper and Redd, and Steve and Katie joined them as well. She called me on the way home.

"How are you doing, honey?" she said over the phone.

"Not good. Not a good day at all. I vomited again. Boyle thinks it might be the antibiotic they put me on. I don't know, I guess they're sending me for yet another CT scan tomorrow. Whatever. How are you guys doing?"

"Pretty great. I left at intermission with Redd but Cooper's still with Steve and Katie. Cooper had a ton of those great belly laughs. He really enjoyed the clowns."

"That's awesome," I said.

I had my own circus to deal with on my stomach, but on top of being sick, I was getting homesick again. I missed Cooper with his shaggy blond hair and his young observations of the world. I missed little Redd with his big brown eyes and his ever-evolving vocabulary. Dilaudid had the power to lift my spirits, but my situation kept bringing me down.

It was the last Friday of April, the 25th. Eleven years to the day when Nicole and I met for the first time at The Green Briar bar in Brighton. With Cooper being born on Valentine's Day, we had decided that February 14 was his day, and we would celebrate our Valentine's Day on the day we met from then on. If it fell on a workday, we would take the day off and spend it together, or if it fell on a weekend we would plan a special date. This year would be very different.

Feverish and feeling ill, I stayed in bed, except for the CT scan in the middle of the day. When I returned, one of Diane's colleagues helped me change the appliances and dressings on the science project. Unfortunately, it only held for a few hours, and by about 4:00 it was leaking. Halfway through the second change, which my nurse helped me with, I got the sense that something was brewing. Doctors were swarming around in the hallway outside, discussing my case.

Dr. Erin Teeple came in during the appliance change to talk to me.

"Your CT scan didn't look good. It looked pretty bad in fact, so we need to put you on high alert this weekend. We're sending you down to the ICU."

I was only half paying attention to her because I was focused on finishing the appliance change. Even without the wound vac it still took about thirty minutes to change out everything. Supplies were scattered around the room as a couple of PCAs came in and began packing up my belongings. My clean clothes on the shelf by the window were put into bags. My shoes and the outfit I wore into the hospital were taken from my closet. The get-well-soon poster from Cooper's class was taken down off the wall. Things were moving fast.

A few minutes later, we wrapped up the appliance change with a tight seal, and I called Dr. Erin Teeple back in. I felt sick, but not go-to-the-ICU sick. She came back into my room with another surgeon and stood at the end of my bed as the scurrying of nurses around me continued.

"Let's hold on a second," I said with my hand raised in a stop signal. "Can you explain to me again what's happening?"

"Absolutely," she said in a serious tone. "The CT scan revealed that you have gas in your liver. Now, for anyone else that could mean several things. But, your white count is also up to 22, and you also have an elevated lactic acid count. Lactic acid is the stuff that fills in your muscles after you work out. We're worried about the combination of those two things, the high lactic acid level, and the gas in your liver. It most likely means that you have necrotic bowel."

"What's necrotic bowel?"

She paused before continuing. "Dead bowel. It means that part of your intestines are essentially dead inside you. And they're poisoning you."

"So, what would that mean?" I asked, bracing for impact because this did not sound good.

"That would mean that we would surgically remove most of your remaining intestines. It would mean that you would be reliant on TPN for nutrition for the rest of your life."

Now she had my attention.

"Normally someone with a CT scan like this would be going straight to the operating room. But..." She paused and I could tell that she read the opposition on my face. "You don't look like your test results. You're not in a lot of pain, are you?"

"No. I feel like crap, but the pain is about the same as it's been," I said confidently.

"See, typically if you had necrotic bowel you would be in a lot of pain," she said, reasoning with herself. "And you're someone who has experienced something close to this when you came in here with a ruptured bowel."

"Yeah, when I came in here I was in a world of hurt. I'm definitely not in that kind of pain."

"Right. The other thing that could cause all of this would be the tube feeds. Your body could be reacting to them because we've ramped them up so quickly to try and put weight on you."

"Now, that makes sense," I said. "I didn't feel like this before I was on the tube feeds."

"Regardless, we need to send you to the ICU to get you stabilized," she said. "I'm on all weekend, so I'll be following you."

By now, all of my belongings were loaded into white plastic bags and packed tightly around me in the bed. I texted Nicole, who would have been on her way to pick up the boys. *I'm going to the ICU. Dr. Erin Teeple is going to call you.*

This felt wrong. I felt awful, but I knew my body better than anyone. I was 100 percent sure that the tube feeds were the cause of this, not dead intestines. I'd show them.

The transport person arrived and wheeled me out into the hallway. Rolling past the nurses' station I saw Jian and some of the other nurses I had grown to know over my time there. They looked grave, but waved and wished me well.

"I'll be back!" I declared as they wheeled me by. I was Babe Ruth pointing at the bleachers, calling his shot. I raised my hand in the air, determinately pointing at the sky. "You'll see, I'll be back before you know it."

· · ·

Soon I was down on the eighth floor in the ICU becoming acquainted with my nurse, Nathan. I liked him instantly.

"I'm on all night, it's just you and me."

"Oh really, you don't have any other patients?"

"Not in the ICU. It's one nurse to one patient."

Nicole found coverage for the boys, and by 8:00 she had found me. She stayed for about an hour, and we just talked like we always did. I caught her up on the details of my turbulent afternoon, and soon we said goodbye.

"Happy Day-We-Met Day, Meesh," I said.

Despite everything that had happened that day, I got a smile out of her. "Happy Day-We-Met Day. I love you."

She kissed me goodnight and left.

All the while Nathan had been in and out of the room, monitoring the wall of machines that were hooked up to me. After Nicole left he turned back to me and struck up a conversation once again.

"That was your wife?"

"Yep," I said.

"Boy, she's great. You really hit the wife lottery with that one."

"Ha! Tell me about it. She's the best."

"Are you ready for bed?"

"Yep, can I brush my teeth? It's kind of my favorite thing to do lately."

Nathan had this fancy way of draping towels around me so I wouldn't make a mess. He made me feel like I was at a day spa, not the ICU. I loved brushing my teeth because I'd been NPO for the past couple of days. Not eating or drinking anything all day goes against basic human nature. The process of brushing my teeth, mostly the rinsing, was such an incredible feeling. Swishing cold water around in my mouth was as close to drinking as I could get, and I savored every second of it until my small plastic cup was empty.

He gave me my dose of IV Benadryl, and I was off to sleep.

That night in the ICU, I experienced what it truly means to be nursed back to health. ICU nurses are like the Navy SEALs of the nursing profession, and Nathan was no exception. He kept tabs on me and gave my body everything it needed when it needed it. Labs were drawn frequently and adjustments were made. He even placed a catheter in me, a procedure that nobody ever wants to experience while awake. But with my request for the maximum amount of sedation they were able to give me, it was successful.

By morning I felt better. Before Nicole was able to make it in the next day, I announced to my new nurse on the day shift that I wanted to take a walk. I did this for two reasons. The first was that I really was feeling better and felt like taking a walk. I hadn't been out of bed in about two days, and I wanted to get up and out. The second was that I wasn't kidding when I told the nurses on fifteen that I would be back. Walking around was going to be my ticket out of the ICU. Being up and about was the most visual way of showing everyone that I felt better.

Seeing as the ICU had that 1:1 patient-to-nurse ratio, I had my nurse walk around with me. She was very apprehensive because, after all, I was technically in intensive care here. On top of that, I had a ton of gear to wheel around with me. But, I convinced her to do four laps around the track, which was the same layout as on the fifteenth floor, before returning to my room. That was about all I could do considering the pain the catheter caused me. Catheters are comfortable when put in when you're under anesthesia and relaxed. When they are placed awake, they never sit right.

When I got back to my room and settled into bed, Dr. Erin Teeple came by. She examined me, and then walked over to the wall and removed her yellow smock, which everyone still wore around me for the klebsiella. It was Saturday, and she was wearing regular weekend clothes, a blouse and jeans. I could see her take a breath before she turned once again to face me.

"Well, things are looking much better," she said with a smile.

"Yep, looks like I dodged that bullet. Must have been the tube feeds after all. Can I go back upstairs now?"

"Your labs are still a bit of a mixed bag, so we have to keep you down here for today. Let's talk about it tomorrow."

"I don't think they're used to having a patient like me that wants to get up and walk."

"True," she said with a smile. "Most people in the ICU can't do that."

Nicole came in for the day; the boys were with my brother. We were watching *The Wizard of Oz* on the hospital's free movie channel when Emily and Sheila, two of my favorite nurses from fifteen, came down for a visit on their lunch break.

"Hey guys!" they said.

"Oh hey," I said. "You found me." I was so happy to see some familiar faces.

"We heard about what happened yesterday," Sheila said.

"How are you feeling?" said Emily.

"Definitely better. Yeah, I'm proving to these guys that I don't belong here. I did four laps this morning."

"You did?" they said, surprised.

"Yep. You should see the looks I get when I say that I want to get up and walk again."

They laughed. "Yeah," Sheila said, "it's totally different down here. They're used to caring for burn victims and people who are completely unconscious."

"Yeah, not patients that can get up and walk," Emily said.

After a brief chat, they wished us well and went back upstairs to fifteen.

"Those nurses sure do love you," Nicole said.

The next day, Dr. Erin Teeple and the residents were in early. My labs were back to normal, even my white count had normalized.

"Today's plan is going to be to discharge you from the ICU, and we're going to be giving your gut a rest for the next few days," she said. "So you have a boring week ahead."

"Boring sounds great," I said. "I'll take boring."

I had the catheter removed, and later that day was discharged from the ICU. I was back on fifteen. And when they wheeled me past the nurses' station, I closed the loop on my prediction.

"I told you. I told you guys that I would be back."

They all laughed.

Emily was my nurse, and all of the other nurses came to see me for a visit when they arrived for their shift. Jian in particular was so glad to see me.

"You were right! You said you would be back and here you are!" she said with a big smile on her face.

I was becoming a legend on the fifteenth floor.

33

OBSESSIONS

MY PLAN FOR THE FOLLOWING WEEK WAS REST AND recovery. Boring, but that was okay. Boring sounded beautiful.

But it meant going back to NPO. Nothing by mouth. Even given what I had just been through, this was difficult. When I wasn't visiting with someone, walking, or napping, I craved food. I would binge-watch the Food Network, salivating over meals being cooked and plated and eaten. Their show *The Best Thing I Ever Ate* aired regularly, with the Food Network celebrities and renowned chefs visiting different parts of the world and reliving the pinnacle of eating in their life.

But it wasn't just food. Drinking was equally compelling. I watched each commercial break in desperate anticipation of an orange juice ad where a glass pitcher of orange juice was poured toward the camera, as if pouring it into the viewer's mouth. And every time I would open my mouth, a willing receiver of this ice-cold, sweet orange juice fantasy.

Nostalgia kicked in, and I began fantasizing about my favorite food experiences. The meals my mother made in my childhood came to the forefront. I mentally transported myself to our old house on

Charlesdale Road, the four of us sitting in our assigned seats in our small kitchen as I dove into the classics. Spaghetti and meatballs with Prego sauce. Lasagna. Tuna casserole. Meatballs cooked in Campbell's mushroom soup for sauce over mashed potatoes. Friday night was pizza night, and I would drive to Royal Pizza with my father, the pizza boxes warming my lap on the drive home through a cold winter's night. On Saturday nights when my parents would go out, my mother would make dinner before the babysitter arrived. It was always Kraft mac and cheese and stovetop hamburgers, the greasy smell enveloping the entire house.

One scene taunted my unquenched thirst. It was summer vacation during middle school. My friend Seth and I would get dropped off at the baseball field across town, where we would play home-run derby. It was blazing hot and we were never smart enough to bring water bottles. On the walk home, we would stop off at Duffy's, a small convenience store in the center of town. Sometimes we would get Slush Puppies, but in this mirage, it was an ice-cold can of orange soda. Orange Crush, Sunkist, or Fanta. We pay at the register and carry our purchases out of the air-conditioning and into the heavy humid heat. I crack open the tab on the cold soda can, which is already sweating with condensation. I hoist it over my head and the carbonated sweetness flutters into my mouth. I polish off half of the can in the first swig. The hallucination repeats in my mind, over and over again as I lay there in my hospital bed. The taste of that orange soda flooding in and healing the dry curl of thirst in my mouth. What would that be like right now? I would give anything to be there again.

Instagram was another outlet. Hashtag anything I could imagine, and photo after photo of the real thing would materialize on my screen. #italiansub #lemonade #cheeseburger #frenchfries #spaghetti #arnoldpalmer #delicious #coke #pizza #craving #food #dinner.

By Thursday, Dr. Erin Teeple gave me the green light to start a small amount of clear liquids again.

"Can I have something right now? Can I have a popsicle?"

"Yes you can. Let me see if I can get one for you," she said.

I'd made it. I couldn't believe it. She left the room briefly, returning with what would be my own personal episode of the Food Network's *The Best Thing I Ever Ate:* a hospital popsicle.

"I'm sorry, they just have one flavor left."

I tore the wrapper off like a rabid animal. Orange. Just what I was hoping for. I quickly slipped it into my mouth, like I was extinguishing a fire. Euphoria ensued.

The days that followed bore a new favorite drink. Because the Brigham is renowned for weight-loss surgery, they have a steady supply of sugar-free Crystal Light packets in lemonade or iced tea flavor. In a stroke of genius, I combined them to make an Arnold Palmer.

"A third option!" I said to Dr. Erin Teeple as I raised my Styrofoam cup of light brown deliciousness as if I were Arnold Palmer himself. She didn't share in the celebration of my invention and instead looked at me like I was a mad scientist.

"So, we're going to try the tube feeds once more, this time at the slowest speed possible," she said.

"I'm good with that plan, as long as we take it really slow," I said. I was apprehensive, but I was desperate to put on weight somehow.

Every night the no-nonsense night nurse made her rounds. When she came into my room at any hour, I knew I would be up for a while, as she took my vital signs and insisted on emptying all of my various containers. I would fight with her about the fact that my ostomy did not have to be emptied, and that I just wanted to get back to sleep.

"One more thing," she said as she left the room.

I knew what was next even before I could hear the squeaky wheels of the bariatric scale growing louder in the hall. It was time to get weighed.

Like a comic-book villain, the night nurse's silhouette reappeared in the doorframe. Dread filled me and I felt like I was ten years old again, standing in my old downstairs bathroom with the cold tile floor underneath my feet. I knew my weight was really low.

I stood up and adjusted all of my lines, and absently checked the border of the appliances on my stomach to make sure everything was leakless as the PCA zeroed out the scale. When the red 0.0 appeared on the digital screen, I stepped on, holding the side rails for a moment to balance before letting go. The scale read 46.9, in kilograms. The PCA tapped a button on the scale and it converted to pounds. One hundred and three pounds. At 6' 2" tall, my weight was almost down into the nineties.

Speechlessly, I lay back down in bed. The PCA left and closed the door. Never, in my adult life, had I weighed so little.

"This is bad," I said out loud to my dark, empty room.

I clicked my buzzer to call in my nurse. Maybe, I hoped, it was time for pain meds.

34

HOME

THE TUBE FEEDS COMMENCED AFTER THEY HAD STARTED me back on clear liquids, this time at a snail's pace. But, just as before, I became sick from them.

Despite this, I had improved in one important area. For the week that I had been back from the ICU, we had been slowly tapering the suction from the G-tube. Little by little, we hooked it up to gravity. This meant that instead of having a machine mechanically siphon out the fluid, it now drained naturally into a bag. After a week, I no longer needed the suction.

Dr. Boyle came by on rounds and announced that it was time for a family meeting. He had a new plan on how to move forward, and wanted to get all parties involved together to talk. We met on Wednesday, right in my room. It was Nicole and myself, Dr. Boyle, Dr. Erin Teeple, and Amanda, who was the dietician in charge of my TPN.

"So," Dr. Boyle began, "the new plan is to send you home. You've proven that you no longer need the suction, and seeing as the tube feeds haven't worked, we're going to keep you on TPN. You'll put on weight gradually, probably a pound a week."

As he spoke, I did the math in my head. I didn't need the suction machine anymore. I know that I can do TPN at home as an outpatient. I'd been leading the appliance changes myself with the nurses assisting. Pain management can easily happen at home. I slowly began to realize he was right. I could go home.

"I thought you said that TPN wasn't ideal for nutrition," I said.

"Well, it isn't, but for a patient in your circumstances it's all we have," he said.

Amanda chimed in. "As long as it's monitored correctly, TPN will definitely give you the nourishment you need."

Dr. Boyle continued. "Normally we would send you to a rehab instead of home, but Diane has stressed to me that you're independent enough to take on the appliance changes yourself."

"Yes. Yes definitely," I said. "She and I make a good team when it comes to taking care of all of this." I made a circular motion over my abdomen.

Dr. Erin Teeple chimed in. "You're going to also have to track your I's and O's every day." I's and O's were short for inputs and outputs. The nurses had measured everything that came out of me and subtracted what I had taken orally to come up with a number each day. For a normal person, this would be easy. But I had several orifices at this point. On one side of the equation was my oral intake, which was just a small amount of clear liquids at this point, so I would measure everything I drank. On the other side was everything else. I had the G-tube, which pulled stomach acid out into a circular bag that needed to be emptied a couple of times a day. The appliance area was a three-part delta on my lower stomach. On my right side was the ileostomy, where theoretically everything should empty into. But, in the middle was the elephant trunk fistula pouch, which covered the midline wound and several tiny fistula exits. On the left was the colostomy bag, which from a physiological perspective shouldn't have any output, but a sinus connection must have formed somewhere in my intestines and found its way to that segment of large bowel, so it also had to be emptied. Finally, I would measure my urine output. It was complicated. But doable.

I thanked everyone and felt good about the plan.

By then, I was able to be completely untethered from machines for brief periods through the middle of the day. That week, temperatures went up into the low sixties, and Nicole and I would go for walks outside. It was only then that I realized how deprived I'd become, stuck inside the sterile environment of the hospital for so long. Inhaling the warm fresh air was intoxicating. One time we walked down a small road behind the Brigham and walked by the kitchen. The rich aroma of food being cooked filled my nostrils and made me almost dizzy. I hadn't eaten actual food in over a month.

Discharge day came, and soon I was home. Home with Nicole, and home with the boys as soon as they were done with their days at daycare and preschool. The feeling of not being in the hospital was indescribable. The start of all of this had been in the cold grayness of February, and now it was May. The world around me was springing back to life. Flowers bloomed and the trees were once again a rich green. It felt like color therapy for my soul.

Small, everyday things continued to be highly pleasurable, visceral experiences. Washing my hands under the warm running water of the bathroom sink instead of hand sanitizer. The smell of food cooking in the kitchen. Soft rugs and warm hardwood floors under my bare feet. Inhaling the fresh air outside into my lungs and having the warm sun saturate my skin. The most ubiquitous parts of life had become the most important. Like the rest of the spring landscape outside, I felt like I was blooming.

This time, I really felt that the winter was behind me, and I was strong enough to stay home.

Being with Nicole and the kids was as enriching as it was before.

Nicole said that after picking them up from daycare and preschool they were talking about me in the backseat. Cooper, who was under the impression that I would be looking different upon returning home, gave Redd a warning.

"I have some bad news for you," he said, leaning toward Redd from one car seat to the other. "Dad might be a little fat when he gets home. You might not recognize him."

Nothing could have been further from the truth.

Every week, the hope was that I would put on a pound or two via the daily sixteen-hour infusion of TPN that I maintained, preceded by a one-liter infusion of IV fluids for hydration. Eating was still not on the agenda, and I was allowed to drink only in small quantities for comfort. Because much of what I drank ended up being sucked out of my stomach via the G-tube, I flushed my pain meds into the J-tube, which went directly into my small intestine. Liquid pink oxycodone that was probably flavored provided quick pain relief in four-hour intervals.

As if I were coming full circle with my mother's method of tracking my weight as a kid, I taped a lined sheet of paper to the bathroom wall to record my I's and O's. A blue Bic pen hung from a string that was taped next to it. Each day, I would track the volume of output that exited through my various orifices on my torso, as well as how much IV fluid, TPN, and other liquids I drank. Plus my temperature and weight. I would add everything up at the end of the day. Every week, Nicole would take my lined sheet of notebook paper, now filled front and back, and input the totals into an Excel spreadsheet.

Her spreadsheets quickly became famous with my care team, which consisted of Diane, Dr. Boyle, visiting nurses, and Brooke, who was my outpatient dietician that managed the nutrients that went into my TPN and my cheerleader for gaining weight.

Even though I had been discharged, and Dr. Boyle was a surgeon, he remained my primary doctor. He knew what to prescribe for meds, ordered my TPN and consulted with Brooke, reviewed my weekly spreadsheet of I's and O's, and was on top of what I was and wasn't taking in orally.

Diane was my main point of contact with all things ostomy and wound-related. On one hand, I never would have made it home if I wasn't such an independent and involved patient. On the other hand, I never would have been able to stay home if it wasn't for Diane's willingness to always be on call for me. We would email and brainstorm over the phone. I would send her photos of my wound, and she would fit me into her schedule if I needed to be seen. Of course, there are visiting nurses that qualify for ostomy and wound care, but they are really for patients coming home with a new ostomy who just need to learn how to do a regular change. My situation was complex. I needed an expert, and Diane was it.

I also had visiting nurses to come and check in on me. They would help me with appliance changes, order my medical supplies, help with any infusion issues, administer any special medications, and change the dressing on my PICC line, which was the long-term IV I'd had in my arm since February.

The first week was gorgeous outside. Whenever I could, I sat on the deck overlooking the backyard. A large canopy of trees gradually thickened with leaves as the cherry blossoms from the cherry tree fell silently to the grass beneath. I lay back in one of our plastic Adirondack chairs and breathed all of this in, as a portable IV pole next to me dripped fluid through my PICC line. I dozed off to the sounds of birds chirping and the drift of a gentle breeze over me until the IV pump would start beeping, indicating the end of the infusion.

By five or six o'clock, I would hook up to TPN, a process that took about fifteen minutes. First, I used syringes to add a few vials of vitamins to the large white bladder bag of TPN. Then I would spike the bag with tubing and prime the line with TPN, making sure all of the air bubbles were out. TPN is peculiar. It looks like milk and smells like vinegar. I used a quarter to twist the lock and securely attached the line to the pump, which lit up with a green eight-bit LCD screen that resembled a Nintendo Game Boy more than a modern medical device. It took the pump about a minute to boot up and scroll through screens of information about the infusion, and another minute to run through the same screens after I started the pump. I would flush my PICC line, being careful to always keep the end point clean by scrubbing with alcohol wipes, and connect the TPN line to the PICC lumen. Then I would start the pump.

"You're on," I would say to myself, imitating Paul the infusion nurse from my Remicade days.

Once I was up and running, I put the three-liter bag of TPN and the pump in a small backpack so I could move around the house. The pump burned through one and a half nine-volt batteries a night and would beep loudly when it ran out of power and needed a new battery, waking me up in the middle of the night. I also had my G-tube bag that I carried around with me constantly, which extracted my stomach bile and anything I drank.

All was going well at home, until the eighth day. It was Saturday night, and Nicole and I watched some TV together before going to bed. I had felt good all day and had done everything to plan. But once I lay down in bed that night, I started to feel weird. It was like my body didn't like being horizontal all of a sudden. My head felt hazy, and I began to get cold. I tried to ignore it, and I finally fell asleep. I woke in the middle of the night feeling incredibly hot and sweaty. I finally decided to take my temperature: 103 degrees.

35

THE HICKMAN LINE

BACK TO THE BRIGHAM ER I WENT. THIS TIME I WAS diagnosed with sepsis. Somehow, my PICC line had given me a bloodstream infection and needed to be taken out.

I had expected the removal of the line to hurt because there was always a level of pain involved in pulling things out of me. Drains, catheters, and NG tubes were always uncomfortable coming out. The PICC line proved to be an exception, sliding smoothly out of my upper arm like a long strand of spaghetti. The ER doctor that removed it cut off the tip of the line, and secured it in a sterile container so they could test it for infection.

Still emaciated, I panicked about my weight.

"Without the PICC line, how am I going to get TPN?" I asked her.

"I'm afraid you won't be getting TPN for the next few days," she said in an apologetic tone. "We need to wait until your blood cultures come back negative so we know the infection has cleared. The good news is that your CT scan is negative, so we're sure that this is the problem. You're presenting a classic case of sepsis."

I was admitted, this time under the surveillance of the infectious disease team. Once my blood cultures were clear, which took at least forty-eight hours, they could give me another PICC line and send me home.

Transport arrived to take me up to my room. As we were wheeling out of the ER, we saw Ian in the hallway. He was the chief resident and had helped me a lot with the wound vac.

"Oh man, hey Mr. Harris," he said, coming over and shaking my hand.

"Hey, there he is. I'm back in for sepsis."

"Well, I figured you'd be back fairly soon."

"Wait, what do you mean? I was doing so well at home," I said, a bit confused at his unsurprised reaction to seeing me back in the hospital.

"Well, with cases like yours it usually takes a few times before you're home for good. Line infections are common with the amount of TPN you're on."

"Yeah, I can't help that at this point," I said.

"Right, but just try to be as careful as you can," he said. "Keep everything as sterile as possible. The thing with TPN is it's a really high risk for blood infections because TPN is literally food for bacteria if it gets in your bloodstream. The higher the dose you're on, the higher the risk of infection."

"Ah, gotcha. Okay man, well it was great running into you. They say that fifteen is full right now, so I'm going up to the tenth floor instead. I'm kind of bummed about that."

"Well, hopefully, they can get you up to fifteen for at least part of your stay. Everyone knows you up there."

My stay was smooth sailing this time. There was a clear path to fixing the problem, which was to put me on heavy broad-spectrum antibiotics through a regular peripheral IV. The infectious disease team would continue to monitor and test my original blood cultures, which gave them more clues as to what type of bacteria the infection was. So over time, they could narrow in on the antibiotics to get something that specifically targeted my infection and not all types of bacteria.

Even though I wasn't on fifteen, the nurses came down to visit with me on their breaks when they heard I was back in the hospital. I told them how wonderful it was to be home, about the differences with the outpatient TPN system, and all about my unquenchable thirst. They said I looked good, and that my face was finally filling out, which meant I was putting on weight.

If there was an opposite to the quick-thinking, quick-acting prowess of a seasoned surgeon like Dr. Boyle, it was the infectious disease team. They were a completely different breed of doctors, so much so that I couldn't believe they were employed at the same hospital. They were slow and measured and relied heavily on data and consultations with other teams of doctors before reluctantly making a unified decision. If the Brigham was an old Western movie, Dr. Boyle would be the Clint Eastwood character, out in the middle of the tumbleweed town, single-handedly knocking off the whole band of marauders that surrounded him with his trusty sidearm. The infectious disease team, an entire gang of cowboys, would be the slow and reluctant snipers on the roofs of the town, carefully calculating a single precise shot on a single bad guy.

While the original plan was to set me up with another PICC line once my infection cleared, the infectious disease doctors felt strongly about one thing: that I should not get another PICC line. They showed me data and gave me information on an alternative kind of line called a Hickman.

"Both a PICC and a Hickman line lead to the same place," one of them explained. "The central artery near your heart. The PICC, as you know, goes in through the inside of your upper arm." He held up his arm and pointed to his inner bicep to show the insertion point of the PICC line.

"The Hickman goes in here," he said, pointing to his collarbone. "It travels under the skin for a bit and hooks around the collarbone, and in that way. We can put a wider line in that vein."

He went on to explain that the risk of infection is lower according to studies. Based on that and the conversation I'd had with Ian about how I need to be meticulous about keeping everything clean, I decided to go with the Hickman line.

I had a few visitors during my stay. Nicole came in every day as per usual. My brother and my cousin Julie stopped by, and of course my dad. The day he came in was a sunny day in the high sixties, and I was able to indulge in my new favorite activity: being able to go outside. I had an infusion of potassium running, which always took forever to infuse because it had to go in so slowly. So, my dad, my IV pole, and I headed for the elevators.

"I know where to go," I assured him. He was a little skeptical but willing to play along. At this point, he deferred to me with anything Brigham-related.

I took him to this nice spot in the back of the hospital where there were circular benches to sit on. It was pretty close to the main tower elevators, so we weren't actually that far away. Surrounded by other people and hospital workers on their breaks, my dad gave me his usual report of how everything was going at home.

"I was thinking, it's been two years this week since Mom died," I said.

"Oh yeah? Seems like longer."

"You're doing good though, Dad."

"Well, I really like being in the house. I've decided I'm going to have a painter come by and give me a quote to repaint some of the..."

Out of nowhere, my arm erupted in pain. It felt like it was broken all of a sudden. I let out a loud groan and a hiss as I rose to my feet and started moving my body as fast as I could with an IV pole toward the hospital doors. I knew my dad would follow me. I just needed to get back to the tenth floor and find a nurse. My nurse or any nurse.

"What's the matter?" my dad said when he caught up.

"I don't know," I said through gritted teeth. "My arm just started hurting. Really bad." By now we were waiting for the elevator as more people filed into the elevator bank area. I saw my Dad watch the elevator numbers with worry. I closed my eyes and did what I always did in situations like these. I started counting.

If I could make it to thirty, an elevator door would open. One. Two. Three. I made it to twenty-one and heard the ding of the elevator and opened my eyes. Then I was in the elevator. The round 10 button lit up around my index finger, which was connected to my throbbing arm that was surrounded by perfectly healthy, pain-free people filing into the elevator, pushing other buttons for the floors they wanted to go to. If I counted to 100, that would be enough time for the elevator to make all of its stops between the lobby and the tenth floor. I'll make it, I told myself. One. Two. Three...

When the doors of the elevator finally opened, I flew out of it, my IV pole gliding beside me and my father behind me. Luckily my nurse was in view when I rounded the corner to the nurse's station.

I explained my pain to her, and she knew right away what the problem was.

"The saline is out," she said as she pushed buttons on the pump on my IV pole. "There's a bit of overfill left in the bag, that'll hold you while I run and get another bag."

Relief came with those first drops of saline into the line that entered my veins. As she hooked up a fresh, full bag of saline, she explained what happened.

"As you probably know, potassium is pretty strong stuff."

"Yeah, I know it's hard on IVs. It seems to wear them out more quickly."

"Right. It gets mixed with saline in about a 1:4 ratio, sometimes higher. When the saline ran out, you were getting an undiluted dose of potassium, which caused the pain."

"Man, I can't believe how much that hurt."

"Okay, you're back up and running."

My dad stood patiently nearby, and I motioned for him to follow me back to my room.

"It's okay Dad, it was the potassium they're giving me."

"Ah jeez. Are you okay now?"

"Yep, I feel much better. Let's just stay up here. What were you saying about the house?"

They placed the Hickman line on the fourth day under general anesthesia. In addition to the normal covering that went over the line on my chest, there were a few other incision scars in the area where they had tried to put the line but for some reason were unsuccessful.

Nevertheless, I was able to get TPN that night. I was up and running again, only having missed three nights.

Before I left, Dr. Boyle visited me to see how the science project was going. After examining my abdomen with an approving nod, his attention turned to the Hickman line.

"This thing is kind of awesome," I said. "My arms are free without the PICC line, and the nurses tell me that the wider line is like a highway compared to the PICC line."

"Just be careful," he warned, pointing first to the Hickman line's insertion point at the top of my chest, and then down to the end of the line that hung down over my stomach. His pointed hand went back and forth without words needed. My abdomen was obviously a hotbed of bacteria from the delta of outputs, and now I had an IV line that dangled right in front of it.

· · ·

Sometimes the universe creates little parallels in life. Driving by the Dunkin' Donuts near our house on the way home from the hospital I noticed a new drink advertised.

"Arnold Palmer Coolattas!" I said.

"I thought you'd like that, honey," said Nicole.

My new favorite thirst quencher that I had concocted on the fifteenth floor by combining iced tea and lemonade Crystal Light flavors was now in Slush Puppie form. Even though I was only allowed to drink sixteen ounces of liquid per day at that point, the inside of my mouth curled with anticipation of what it would taste like.

"After I get settled can you go out and get me one? Just a small?"

"Of course, Meesh."

It was everything I imagined it could be, the perfect split between lemonade, iced tea, and slush. I tried my best to savor it and drink it slowly, but the euphoric process of quenching my thirst won out.

It was good to be home again, back to doing everything myself. Somehow, I had gained a few pounds in the hospital, which brought me up to a hefty 107 pounds. I was back to managing my care by myself, with short appointments from visiting nurses, and of course my constant contact with Diane at the Brigham. I reveled in the fresh air of the backyard and the sense of well-being brought on by the oxycodone in four-hour intervals.

I made it twice as long this time, sixteen days, until my next trip back into the ER in early June. This time I had respiratory symptoms to go along with my fever of 102.8. But by the time I made it into the ER, the fever had gone down to 99.0 on its own. That was a good sign. It showed that it wasn't like last time when I'd been septic.

"They're going to keep me for observation," I told Nicole over the phone. "They need to get the test results back to prove that it's not another bloodstream infection. They're pretty sure it has something to do with my lungs this time around."

"Okay, well I'm glad you're feeling better at least," she said.

"How'd it go putting the boys down?" I asked.

"Oh, they were fine. Cooper misses you already."

Over the past few months, Nicole and I had been through everything together. She understood the nuances of my critical health condition and could tell that despite a few hiccups, I was improving. We're good in a crisis.

After hanging up with her, I called my dad and got the opposite response. He sounded groggy and tired, but as per usual he launched into his report of what he did that day.

"I went up to the New England Steakhouse in Mendon for lunch, I always like it there. I ordered..."

"Dad. Listen to me."

He stopped.

"I'm back in the hospital."

"Oh damn!" he said. "Damn. I thought you were doing so good." He was clearly upset. I'd made a mistake in calling him so late. He just couldn't comprehend everything, especially at night when he was tired. Like my mother, he was a worrier, especially when it came to me and my health. Now he wouldn't sleep. I should have waited until the morning to break the news to him. Unlike Nicole, my father could never understand the details, only the headlines. I was either progressing nicely or in imminent peril.

They had me on broad-spectrum IV antibiotics overnight, and after getting some test results from the doctors first thing in the morning and dealing with some leaks in the appliances, I texted Nicole.

"Well, good news, I have pneumonia! One of the tests they had me do where I spit phlegm into a cup proved it."

"Pneumonia? Jesus."

"No, that's what I've been hoping for! Seriously. We've been hoping that the infection is stemming from my lungs instead of my Hickman line. That means it's not a bloodstream infection. I'll be able to keep my Hickman line and I'll be able to still get TPN."

"I know that's good news. But what's the treatment for pneumonia?"

"Just one antibiotic. And they said I'll probably be able to go home tomorrow because I can get it as an outpatient even though it has to be administered via IV."

"Okay, that's great. Sorry, I don't mean to overreact. It's just that pneumonia sounds serious."

"I know, right? But in the grand scheme of everything I've been through, it's not. Plus, you're not in here with me getting all of the info like usual."

"That makes sense. Good news, Meesh."

They discharged me the next day.

36

SUMMER

THIRST CONTINUED TO BE THE MOST UNBEARABLE ASPECT of my situation. I got all of my hydration from infusions: three liters of TPN for nutrition, and an additional liter of IV fluid. All I was allowed orally was sixteen ounces a day, and that wasn't enough to keep me comfortable. Evenings were the worst. Maybe it was because I was only partway through my infusions, which started late afternoon, or maybe it was because my willpower to not drink had worn thin by then. I took a page from my playbook from being NPO in the hospital, when I would revel in the process of brushing my teeth at night, swishing the cold water in my mouth and spitting it into the pink kidney-shaped container. Just having the water in my mouth was almost as good as drinking.

So, I would spend my nights before going to bed in the kitchen, rinsing. I would fill a pint glass with ice water, savor it in my mouth, and then spit it into the sink. Mouthful after mouthful I would trick my body into thinking I was actually drinking, hoping that the primal urge would somehow turn itself off. Once the first glass was empty, I would turn back to the water and ice dispenser on the fridge door for another. Rinse and repeat. Each time, trying to satiate my thirst.

In the afternoons Nicole would leave work and come home to pick me up before she got the boys. We'd pick Redd up first at daycare and then Cooper at his preschool. Driving through town talking about our days was wonderful. It was a small slice of family time that made things feel normal.

On Redd's second birthday, he came out of the daycare center wearing a tall Cookie Monster crown. He was deep into his Sesame Street phase of being a toddler and I frosted a Super Grover cake for him, which gave me that familiar buzz of excitement I always get from making things, even in this small frosted form that I couldn't eat.

The following week I had an in-person appointment with Diane and Dr. Boyle.

"Well, things are looking good. I think we can advance your diet," Dr. Boyle said.

"Ah! That's great news," I said.

"Just stick to soft foods. Bread. Rice. Pasta. Cooked meats."

"Got it. What about drinking? Can I drink more?"

"Well, we need to take it slow there. What are you at now?"

"Sixteen ounces a day."

"Okay, let's try thirty-two ounces," he said.

Relieved, I left his office and headed for home. While I was more excited about being able to drink more, I hadn't eaten anything solid in ten weeks. I texted Nicole a little shopping list for her to pick up for me so I could eat dinner with her and the boys that night. I wasn't going near the bread, rice, and pasta that Dr. Boyle suggested because I had been steeped in a gluten-free and SCD diet mentality for so many years, and felt that stuff was potentially going to aggravate my stomach. But I was going all-in with the cooked meat. I had Nicole get some ground beef and some gluten-free BBQ sauce. And I had her get some bananas, something sweet for dessert.

After ten weeks of not eating, it felt amazing that night to use my teeth to chew the hamburger patty I grilled for myself.

Everything seemed to go okay with the meal because the numbers on my bathroom chart of I's and O's didn't differ much from the previous days. The next day I wanted to eat something I really craved. Indian food. I reasoned that chicken tikka masala was within the guidelines of what Dr. Boyle listed as soft food. Cooked chicken and rice, and tomato sauce. Maybe some naan bread to go along with it. Nicole arrived home that night and the kitchen became saturated with the smell of the Indian food as she opened the bags. I knew this was going to be good, but nothing could have prepared me for the flavor of that savory chicken after almost three months of nothing to eat.

One of the crazier things I did that summer was that I went to Cape Cod with my family. By that point, our house practically qualified as a remote hospital based on the amount of medical supplies we had. But, I figured, why couldn't I just pack everything up and move to the Gingerbread House in Truro and operate from there?

The morning we were about to leave, I was quiet. Even though this whole health crisis had given Nicole and me a stronger system of communication, I sometimes reverted to my old ways and withdrew when things went bad.

The struggles with keeping appliances on the wounds on my abdomen had grown increasingly more difficult in the past day. The skin in the area became more irritated, and on top of that, the perimeter of the whole thing changed shape in a gradual but deliberate way, like the tectonic plates of the Earth shifting undetected right beneath us.

With all of these factors swirling around in my head, I needed to break my silence. Despite everything we had been through, disappointments were still Nicole's Achilles heel. It would be upsetting to mess up our plans.

"Hey," I said, interrupting her from the packing frenzy that was happening in the living room, and the only thing keeping her mind off of me.

She looked up.

"I'm sorry, but I need help today. I need to see Diane."

"Oh. Is she definitely in?"

"I'm going to call at nine. If she's there, I know she'll see me."

"Well, what does that mean for the Cape?"

"I don't know. I guess I'll drive down tomorrow morning."

"By yourself? Why don't you have Steve give you a ride?"

"Maybe. I just need to find out about Diane first."

Nicole turned back to her task at hand with worry on her face, and I went back to the living room to call Diane. Fortunately, she was in the office, and just as I had hoped, she made time for me.

The appointment was long, over an hour. As usual, Diane and I had a great collaboration session as we dealt with the complexities of the science project on my abdomen.

"How have you been doing with drinking and eating?"

"Pretty good. I know I'm supposed to be just sipping liquids at this point, but my vice is the Arnold Palmer Coolatas at Dunkin' Donuts. They're amazing."

She laughed. "Well if that's all then I'd say you're doing okay. What about food?"

"I've been following Dr. Boyle's directions. Keeping it boring and fairly bland. It's been going well. I had Indian food one night, and that went okay. But yeah, mostly I'm having small meals with cooked meat as the main part."

"Wait, Indian food?"

"Yeah, chicken tikka masala? It's just chicken in a tomato sauce with rice. Technically it's..."

"You should not be eating Indian food, Brad. That's way too advanced for what your system can handle."

At that point, Dr. Boyle entered for a quick check-in. When he learned of the Indian food he was astonished.

"No more Indian food. Your belly is very delicate now. We can't have you eating anything that would risk making things worse."

"Okay, okay," I said. "I'm sorry. It went through fine though, I swear."

They were both shaking their heads at me. I wasn't going to win this argument.

Besides the food talk, the appointment was a success. We finished with a new solution and a plan for my week at the Cape. She wished me well and as usual, told me to keep the communication lines open.

By the time I got home the house was empty. Nicole and the boys were driving to Truro and I was feeling a bit less brave about making the three-hour trek all by myself in the morning. So I called Steve and we planned on having him pick me up at seven the next morning. I went to bed after I packed my entire mini-hospital in brown boxes on the living room rug.

That night, with Nicole and the boys out of the house, was one of the worst nights of the summer. I had been asleep for only an hour when the first leak happened. I scurried out to the living room and tore through the boxes to find what I needed. Nicole wasn't there to help me, so it took a full hour and a half. Exhausted, I hoisted my TPN backpack onto my shoulder, walked back down the hall to the bedroom, and collapsed into a fast sleep. Around 4 a.m., the second leak happened. Again, I returned to the living room for another hour-long appliance change. I began to theorize that sleeping horizontally was the issue, and decided to nap in the chair for the remaining hours before my brother's car would pull into the driveway.

Steve was a little taken aback when he saw me in that morning light. I must have looked like hell on almost no sleep. He loaded all of the boxes into his car, and we were off.

"I'm exhausted, I hardly slept last night," I said as I slumped down into his passenger seat with my TPN backpack still cranking away at my feet.

"That sucks," he said. "If you want to just sleep go right ahead."

I slept lightly and cautiously, wary that a leak might happen on the drive down. But the rest did me good, and by the time we passed the white Gingerbread House sign that still advertised "Fishermen Welcome," I was awake and happy to be in Truro again.

I'd had my TPN delivery that week sent to Truro, and Nicole already had everything stored in the fridge when I arrived. I sterilized and set up my supply table with everything I needed.

The first full day, Sunday, we all geared up and went to the beach. I wouldn't be swimming at all because of my Hickman line. There was no way to safely protect it from having the saltwater enter my bloodstream for a surefire bloodstream infection. Still, I went to the beach with everyone. It was a blisteringly hot and humid day. I could sense the adhesive on my stomach loosening in the heat. I stuck it out and had some dad time with Cooper flying a kite together.

The rest of the vacation I stayed home at the Gingerbread House while everyone went out to the beach or other activities. It felt great to be in a different location though. I spent a lot of time listening to podcasts and music in the shade of the weeping willows at the Gingerbread House.

37

HOME STRETCH

In mid-July, I had a really good appointment. My weight was up to 117 pounds, which was 14 more than my low point of 103. The steady influx of TPN was working.

"Well, good news on the horizon," Dr. Boyle said. "You're coming up on the six-month mark, which means you'll be clear for me to operate again." He went into an explanation of why six months between surgeries was important, but I had one question for him.

"So if that surgery goes well, then what will that mean?" I asked.

"Well with you I never know what things will look like until I get into the OR, even with all of the CT scans we've done. But if all goes well, you'll be back to normal with just the one colostomy."

"Really!" I said. This was the first time that the idea of getting past all of this became a reality.

"That's the goal, and it's crucial that I'm able to operate on you in a scheduled operation and not in a crisis like last time. There's still a risk of more fistulas, and possibly short bowel syndrome, which depends on how much I might have to remove this time."

We talked about pain management, and he prescribed a fentanyl patch to give me a steady hum of pain relief moving forward.

"And lay off the Indian food," he said as he left the office. "I still can't believe that one."

The science project continued to be the biggest issue, however, and Diane and I continued the appointment to attempt to innovate on new ways to pouch the fistulas and keep leaks to a minimum.

My surgery appointment was set for September 22. Two months away. But still, I was hopeful that Dr. Boyle could put me back to how I was before.

At the beginning of August, I returned to work for a brief period. This had been a moving target from the emergency surgery I had back in February. Initially, Dr. Boyle had me down for May, and that date kept moving out.

At one point I remember being on the phone with the company that provided my long-term disability insurance.

"Well Mr. Harris, with what you've been through we'd expect you to be out for the rest of the year," said the agent. "Maybe longer."

"Ha, no. I'm going back to work in August," I told the agent.

I had hoped to work right up until the surgery. It was nice to go back and be amongst normal healthy humans once again. I worked on some small, inconsequential projects like sizing photos for the company's new website, and a pitch for a new project. I worked half days, and by Friday I had once again spiked a fever and decided that the Brigham emergency room was where I needed to be once again.

All tests came back negative, and they sent me off with a new prescription for more antibiotics.

On Monday, I got ready for work by putting on a fresh set of appliances. My commute takes less than fifteen minutes. I pulled into the parking lot and stepped out of my Jeep and onto the sunny summer pavement. I hadn't even closed the door before I realized that the appliance was leaking.

I sat back in the front seat and deflated with a long sigh.

"Well, that's that," I said to myself. I drove back home, changed the appliance, and called my boss to tell him that it wasn't working and that I would be back probably in October after I'd recovered from my next surgery.

After that, I entered another dark period. Leaks happened every day and took two hours to change every time. I slept every night on a chair in the living room, attempting to keep my abdomen vertical.

I still walked every day. It was my way of fighting back. About a half-mile away was the Canton Junction Commuter Rail station, which had a monolithic structure of steel and concrete stairs for commuters to get to each track. That became my training ground in the middle of the day when there weren't many people there. I would climb the stairs to the top and down again, and every day I would add another set. By the time I got home, I would collapse on the couch and sleep. But little by little I was gaining more strength to go with my weight.

At my next appointment with Diane and Dr. Boyle in mid-August, they could immediately tell that things were worse. I'd grown accustomed to how unsightly my stomach looked, and when we removed the patchwork of adhesives and appliances even I was taken aback. The skin around my wounds had turned furiously red. One of Diane's colleagues, Mary, who was also an ostomy and wound-care nurse, was there at the appointment. She took a photo of my wound for their reference, or possibly some kind of hall of fame entry for their worst-ever cases. That photo lives on a computer somewhere in the Brigham, and I hope I never see it again.

Dr. Boyle came in to check on me and was also alarmed at how the wound had deteriorated in only a few weeks. Later that day, his admin person called me to tell me that my surgery date had been moved up to the first week of September, which was only three weeks away.

I set a timer on my phone for twenty days and checked it every day. The ultimate countdown. I struggled through those three weeks, rarely leaving the house except for walks. Diane and I remained in close contact, emailing every day, and talking on the phone every couple of days. To say my quality of life was low would be an understatement, but eventually, the surgery date came.

That morning, Nicole and I were standing at the main desk at Brigham and Women's surgical center when I felt the telltale sign of wetness on my abdomen. Here I was with the finish line finally in sight and I had another leak. We were surrounded by an enormous waiting room filled with the weary and worried. I approached the desk.

"Hi," I said to the receptionist in the most dreadful tone I could muster as I felt the slow run of output leaking down my leg. "So. I know that there are other people ahead of me, but I kind of really need to get to pre-op. I'm having an issue here. I think if you let them know it's me who's asking they'll understand."

"I'll see what I can do," the woman said noncommittally.

I turned to Nicole. "That's probably not going to work. I'm going to find a bathroom," I said as I scanned the room for the M/W sign.

Like a good Boy Scout, I had brought a bag of supplies with me in case this happened. In the bathroom, I made a makeshift seal with toilet paper and some of the adhesive supplies I'd brought.

After about an hour I was brought to pre-op where I could properly fix things. It was far from perfect, but good enough to get me to the operating room.

I was the most excited about getting rid of the G/J tube. I hadn't used it in a couple of weeks because I'd put on about twenty pounds from my low point, enough weight for the SMA syndrome to clear. No vomiting, no need for the G/J tube. Even when it wasn't hooked up to anything it stuck out like a finger from my stomach. It had served me well, but it was awkward and a bit painful. However, both the nurse and anesthesiologist said that removing it wasn't on the agenda for today.

Dr. Boyle arrived in his surgical scrubs. His plan was for me to go last on his schedule for the day.

"Hi Brad," he said. "Today's the big day."

"Yes," I said with a smile. "But, everyone seems to think that the G/J tube isn't coming out."

"No, not today. We'll be leaving that in for"—he paused—"oh, about another month or so for good measure. That's something we take out right in the office. It just kind of pops out." As he said this, he made a jerking motion with his arms like he was starting a lawnmower.

My eyes widened in fear, imagining how painful it would be to have him rip it out of me while I was wide awake. "Um, okay. If you say so," I said disappointedly.

I signed the consent form and passed the clipboard back to him.

"Okay," he said, smiling to both of us. "Now I have to go upstairs and prepare."

"What do you mean?" I said as Nicole gave him a knowing nod, dismissing him.

"He means mentally prepare, honey."

"Oh, yeah," I said. "I guess this is kind of a big deal."

Finally, the time came for me to get wheeled to surgery.

"Meesh," I said. "I love you."

"I love you, Brad," she said back, and leaned in for a kiss at about the same time the fentanyl hit my bloodstream.

In the operating room, I could feel my appliance leaking. Groggily I told the OR nurses about this, and they assured me that it was okay.

"Hmph," was all I could say. I relaxed into the table beneath the commotion of people getting me ready. The last thing I remember was thinking, "I made it. Finally."

Hours flew by in a flash like they always do. I awoke in post-op, and I could see Nicole's face hovering over me. I had the bitter surgical aftertaste everywhere in my body. I had just one question for her before I drifted back to sleep. It was a question that I had rehearsed to myself in the days leading up to surgery. In all of the complexities of my case, it was the lowest common denominator of words that would give me the only answer I needed.

"Is Dr. Boyle happy?" I said.

"Yes," she said. "He is."

And I fell back asleep.

Diane would relay a similar story in the days that followed. She said that the morning following my surgery, a typical Wednesday morning in the hospital, she got off the elevator on the fifteenth floor and saw something she had never seen before. Dr. Boyle was standing by her office door, his hands folded, waiting patiently for her to arrive.

"I fixed Brad," was all he said, with a smile.

It was true. For as broken as I had been, he had put me back together again. One ostomy, totally normal and manageable. Normal for me anyway.

My hospital stay was much more typical this time around. I had some pain management issues at first, but overall, all of the minor issues that arose just ended up resolving themselves. My white count was up one day, and the next day it went down on its own. A week later, as I got ready to be discharged, Dr. Boyle stopped by. After the usual exam, I asked him a couple of daring questions.

"So, how much intestine do I have left after all of this? Will I be able to stop the TPN soon?"

"The surgery went very well, and I think you're on the line of being able to eat a regular diet without any additional nutrition support."

"So, like how long until then, do you think?"

"It's hard to say, but we're in September now. I would say by the holidays you'll be back to eating on your own."

I didn't press the issue of exactly how much intestine I had left, which has always been sort of an amorphous measurement. When I would have surgery and intestines removed it was always reported back to me in the metric system, so X amount of centimeters. At this point, I had no idea what was left, or even what was the baseline for most people. Getting off TPN by the holidays sounded great though.

I made it home only eight days after surgery.

38

THE FALL

SOMETIMES IT'S WHEN I'M DOING INCREDIBLY WELL WHEN the worst things happen. The previous fall I had decided that it might help me to talk to a therapist. I interviewed three different people and decided that I connected the best with Kate, who had an office right in Canton. Despite my ability to deal with hardship, it felt good to talk to her about my chronic illness. She even came into the hospital at one point and we had an appointment with me lying in my hospital bed.

A few days after I was discharged, I was at an appointment with her, sitting on her couch and talking through the events of the past few weeks, when I felt wetness on my stomach. It's funny how accustomed I had grown to dealing with leaks, and yet now a wave of panic jolted my body. This should not have been happening. I hooked my thumb inside the waistband of my jeans to inspect what was going on.

"No," I said out loud. What should have been dry was wet. The wound that Dr. Boyle had completely closed up was leaking. My mind raced. Another fistula? How could this be?

"Are you okay?" Kate said, understanding that I was dealing with a physical issue. "Can I get you anything?"

"Um. Yes." I thought quickly about what she might have in her small office. "Can you get me some paper towels?"

I plugged up the leak with the paper towels she handed me and realized that my hour was just about up. Nicole would be waiting outside in the car by now, and I was going to have to explain this to her. I thanked Kate and headed for the parking lot.

"How did it go?"

"Terrible," I said. "Meesh, I have to get to the Brigham. I don't know how, but I think there's a fistula where the ileostomy was."

We went home where I still had leftover supplies. I pouched this new leak, cursing it. I called Diane and arranged for us to come in. It didn't seem possible after all I had been through, but this was the darkest day of all. It would mean that the surgery had not, in fact, been successful and I'd have more problems to deal with moving forward.

I was able to see Dr. Boyle first, who was skeptical about my over-the-phone explanation of what had happened. Surely, he dealt with patients misdiagnosing themselves on a regular basis. I unzipped my pants to reveal two appliances. My regular ostomy, which still donned a hospital-issue transparent pouch so he could see the color and contents, and the fistula pouch, also transparent, covering the exact spot where he had sealed the location of the ileostomy in surgery about two weeks earlier.

"See?" I said, almost to the two bags themselves. "The output is the same color." Just then, as if my body could sense Dr. Boyle's skepticism, my body produced identical output into both pouches simultaneously. I looked up to see the color drain out of Dr. Boyle's face.

"That can't be," he said quietly.

"I know, right? I can't believe it either."

Nicole and I relocated to a different exam room to see Diane. While this wasn't as bad as what had happened to me in February, or as challenging as trying to keep up with leaks all summer, it was beyond frustrating. This was insult and injury and defeat. Nicole was crying. Diane was crying. No one could believe this was happening.

But yet there I was, coaching everyone.

"Come on you guys, this isn't that bad. I'm still better off than how I was. We'll get through it."

That was the moment I realized the magnitude of what being on heavy opioids for the past seven months had done to me. I should be feeling the sadness and frustration they were feeling, but all I could feel was my warm Christmas spirit vibe.

My body is a mystery, sometimes to doctors and sometimes even to me. Dr. Boyle had me stop eating and drinking in an attempt to put the least amount of substance through that area. Over the next few days, the output in this new fistula changed colors and started to slow down. A few days later I saw Dr. Boyle, who said that he thought it was the color of lymph fluid.

As puzzling as this new fistula was, it gradually closed up on its own over the next few weeks.

When I reached the one-month mark post-surgery, I got the green light to have my G/J tube removed. I had been told by others that it hurts coming out. Other doctors would casually say this when they learned that I had a G/J tube. "Hurts coming out," is all they would say. Even one of my visiting nurses who was a cancer survivor had had one, and she said the same thing. In my head, I replayed the lawn-mower-starting gesture Dr. Boyle had mimed when I was in pre-op. The tube was uncomfortable lying still; yanking it out was going to be awful.

So, the Friday afternoon that I had the appointment scheduled for the G/J removal, I swallowed a double dose of oxycodone before venturing into the Brigham.

I was as prepared as I could be when the doctor entered the quiet exam room. Dr. Boyle wasn't available, so another doctor was covering.

"I'll be honest, I'm not looking forward to this. Everyone I've talked to says this is painful."

"Yes, I'm sorry about that," he said. "Most patients say that it hurts for only about thirty seconds. Think of how great it will be after it's done to get rid of this."

"That's true," I said.

"Well, let me explain how this works. To keep the tube in place, there is a reverse-umbrella attachment inside your stomach that keeps it positioned on the stomach wall, and prevents it from falling out. To remove it, I'm going to collapse the umbrella part, and then I'll count to three before I remove it."

I exhaled as he made the adjustments to collapse the umbrella.

"Ready?" he said.

I nodded.

He counted to three and pulled.

As expected, it hurt. But as he said, I felt better about a minute later. Getting dressed afterward, without the stump of the G/J tube sticking out of my abdomen, I felt just a bit more human.

Over that weekend, I spiked a fever. By Monday I was back in the Brigham ER with what they thought was another bloodstream infection. This time it was my Hickman line.

"I bet I know when it happened," I said to Nicole when she found me in the ER. "It was that nurse who was in training."

A few days earlier I had a visiting nurse appointment at home. Jeff, who was one of the best visiting nurses I'd had, brought a nurse in training along with him. He asked me if she could help.

"Hickman lines are pretty rare," he said, "so I'd like to show her the ins and outs."

"No problem," I said. I've always consented to have people learn from my situation whenever possible.

But almost instantly I knew that was a mistake. This woman seemed to have no experience as a nurse whatsoever. She seemed to struggle with alcohol wipes and flushes, let alone PICC and Hickman lines. At one point she held up a saline flush, which always has a small bubble of air in it. Knowing that the air shouldn't go into my bloodstream, she fumbled with angling the flush in different, unsuccessful ways.

"Tip it up," I said, knowing how to do this from several months' experience.

She followed my instruction and the air bubble shifted to the back of the syringe. Problem solved.

She continued awkwardly and unsure of herself, and Jeff instructed her as they got into the actual dressing change. I did not feel good about that visit.

Back in the ER, I was scathingly mad. The ER doctor said that my Hickman line would have to get pulled.

"Okay," I said, calming myself down. "I'm guessing that's something you can do right here? Like the PICC line?"

"Well, no, Hickmans are a little more complicated. The metabolic services team will have to do it. But the good news is we can put you on antibiotics and send you home."

"Oh really? I'm not staying here until my labs clear? That's great."

We left the ER and walked next door to the clinic side of the Brigham to get the Hickman line out.

"You don't have to stay for this," I said to Nicole.

"Okay Meesh, good luck. I'll see you at home."

A couple of residents met me at the clinic, and we found an empty exam room. The less experienced resident was going to perform the procedure while the more experienced resident more or less oversaw everything and took notes.

"How long is this going to take," I asked.

"That depends," said the junior resident. "How long have you had this line for?"

I hesitated. I'd had it for four months at that point. Was that a long time? What's going to happen if it was a long time? I just decided to tell him. "Four months."

"Aw, that's nothing," he assured me. "Some people have these for years. One woman we recently saw had hers for five years. When people have it that long, a lot of scar tissue can build up and it can take longer to get it out."

"Phew, okay, awesome," I said. "Let's do it."

"Yeah, the last one of these that I did took less than five minutes."

The Hickman line snaked over my collarbone and down about an inch and a half below my skin before it exited. They explained that they had to cut a couple of sutures under my skin that were securing the Hickman in place. In theory, after they did that it would simply slide right out.

They numbed me up with a few shots of lidocaine and began. Scissors slid up the opening into my chest, clipping away at the area. Apparently, I had quite a lot of scar tissue. The junior resident couldn't seem to get it loose, and after about twenty minutes of snipping, decided to have the other resident give it a try. Every few minutes I would be moaning so they'd give me more lidocaine. The more experienced resident couldn't get it. They called for the chief resident.

"You're just really scarred down," one said to me as we waited. "You've really just had this for four months?"

"Yup. My body is tricky though. I'm full of surprises."

We were getting to the point where they had used all of the numbing medication allowed for this procedure. The chief resident couldn't get it out, either.

"We're calling in the head of our department. She'll be able to get it, and then we'll get you out of here."

The woman who was head of the department knew just what to

do. She made an incision near my collarbone and freed up the line after cutting the last of the scar tissue.

What was supposed to be a short procedure had taken two full hours.

I drove myself home, and after I walked into the house Nicole said, "How'd it go?"

"I don't want to talk about it," was all I could say.

After Dr. Boyle had determined that the fistula wasn't putting out stool, I went back to eating and drinking. He advised me to eat mostly carbs for my diet. Again, this was pretty much the opposite of the gluten-free and high-protein mentality I'd been used to before this health crisis. Everything out there says that carbs are bad, especially for people with stomach issues.

My next appointment with him was a week after the Hickman removal. This trial period without TPN or additional IV fluids had not gone well. I was putting out far more than I was taking in, and I was dehydrated.

"Hi Brad, how's it going," he said as he entered the exam room.

"Ugh, down eleven pounds to 125," I said. "I was doing so well on the TPN."

"How's it been going with the eating though? Simple carbs, right? Bread. Pasta. Stuff like that."

"Well, actually, I try to stick to high-protein gluten-free things..."

"Look," he said firmly, "that's not what you need to be eating and I'm not interested in hearing any of your theories on nutrition. A patient in your situation needs a diet high in complex carbohydrates and no sugar. That's what the research says. That's the only way you'll get the calories you need."

Tough love again. If he was going to essentially prescribe an all-carb diet for me, I wasn't going to complain.

"You see, an interesting thing happens with people with your kind of anatomy. The large intestine somehow knows that you're lacking absorption of nutrients and pitches in to help. Instead of only absorbing water, it absorbs nutrients as well."

"Okay, I'm on board," I said. "Bread and pasta here I come."

"We're getting you another PICC line today, that's going to help to put the weight back on."

"Right, okay great. I have a whole new respect for TPN now."

In time, my dose of oxycodone was decreased. I wasn't in pain any longer, but I found that the process of getting off of the opioids came with something new and unexpected: depression. I had never truly known what depression felt like until those fall months. It wasn't that I was sad, I was just completely unmotivated to do anything. I would lie on the living room couch, staring around. I would listlessly gaze out the big bay window at the now leafless trees outside. There was this one branch that I would focus on that looked like a skeletal hand. In my head the branch was animated, beckoning me in a come-here gesture. What's the point of all of this? Why should I continue living? I could just waste away right here. Other scenarios entered my head that a father and husband should never think.

Around that time I returned to work, and that was good. Projects and deadlines would keep my mind occupied. But even with specific tasks, I felt empty. I wasn't sure I could do this.

Opioids had taught me one thing so far that year. A little chemical bump was good for me and my well-being. I had certainly exhausted everything else in my trials with chi gung, meditation, and other ways to initiate the relaxation response. So, over the summer, I had started taking a small dose of Prozac. I knew the opioids were going to be a short-term solution. Once my pain went away, so would the drugs.

Prozac would ideally keep me going long-term. The goal was to curb my sometimes-short temper and keep my overall well-being positive.

My therapist, Kate, wasn't a psychiatrist, so she couldn't prescribe drugs. So I began seeing a doctor for just that. Our appointments were usually short and ended in me getting another Prozac refill. When I saw him in November, however, I reported my depression.

"How much oxycodone are you taking?"

"I went from about 2.5 down to zero last week."

"Well, I think that's the problem," he said confidently. "Especially seeing as you've been on opioids for such a long time. You have to come off of them very, very slowly."

He wrote up a plan for tapering the oxycodone slowly over a few weeks, and thankfully I began to feel so much better. I couldn't believe how slowly I had to come off of them, but it worked. The depression vanished and after a few weeks, I was off of all opioids.

39

ALMOST KILLED ME

The holidays came and went, and my need for TPN was still going strong at a full seven days a week. With my weight at a robust 135 pounds, I was learning to love my nighttime supplement. I could never have held steady at 135 pounds before this health crisis, and a twelve-hour infusion at night was so much easier than the mental chaos of managing active Crohn's. The way I saw it, my digestive system was officially broken. TPN allowed me to get the calories and nutrients I needed by cutting out the middleman of my poorly performing intestines.

Without a need for surgical care and with the hope of getting more ideas on how to slow down my gut to better absorb nutrients, Dr. Boyle transferred my care to the metabolic services team. They would manage my TPN and my all-around nutrition moving forward.

Tricia, a dietician in metabolic services, was my first stop in the two appointments I had at the Brigham clinic that day. With her loud, carefree laugh, you couldn't help but be in a good mood around her, and I liked her instantly. She explained to me, for the first time, how much bowel I had left.

"Anyone with less than five feet of intestines," she explained, "and reliant on nutritional support, like TPN, has short bowel syndrome."

"And, how much do I have left?"

"Four feet," she said. "You have about one foot of large bowel and three of small bowel. We treat everyone with SBS differently because every patient has a different anatomy. Many have no large bowel, and some have more large bowel than small. So because of this every patient absorbs food differently and needs different supplements."

"Okay, but how much bowel does a normal healthy adult have?"

"About twenty-five feet."

"And I have four feet left," I said softly, knowing that Crohn's, of course, never goes away. There's always the risk that it will return and take more.

We went on to discuss my diet. I had listed off everything I had eaten in the past three days to give Tricia an idea of what I was eating. I was doing okay, but she had many more suggestions.

"You shouldn't be having any sugar, but you should be eating upwards of 4,000 calories a day in small meals."

"All salty carbs, like bread and pasta?"

"Pretty much, yes," she said.

"That's like a Michael Phelps level of eating though. I would have to be a professional eater to hit that number."

"Well, let's try and see how high you can get it."

She went on to talk about other aspects of SBS, like how water is bad for me. Drinking anything, in general, was bad. I just don't have enough runway left to absorb fluid, so everything I drink just flushes through my system.

"Have you tried oral rehydration solutions?"

"Um, no, what are those?"

She handed me a pocket-sized book all about SBS. "Here you go, this has all kinds of information and recipes. Oral rehydration solutions were designed for people in third-world countries who are dying of dehydration. They have an ideal ratio of sugar to salt to fluid that allows the intestines to rapidly absorb water. They taste very salty, and some patients struggle with drinking them. But you should give it a try. Ideally, this is what you should be drinking."

We went on to discuss all of the drugs I took to slow down my gut. Immodium. Metamucil. DTO. If a regular person took what I took they wouldn't go to the bathroom for a month, but none of it seemed to make any difference for me.

"There's also a new drug that's come out, which I'm sure you would be a candidate for. It's specially designed for short bowel patients. It's a shot every day in the morning, and what it does is it increases the absorption in the intestines that you still have. Some patients have even come off of TPN completely, which is the ultimate goal."

"I've kind of grown to love TPN though," I said. "I'm 135 pounds without even trying, which is pretty good for me. The way I see it, my digestive system is broken and this is a way to bypass it and get the nutrients right into my bloodstream."

"That's true," Tricia said with a hearty laugh, "but people can get complications from TPN. For example, it can be very taxing on your liver."

Still, here I was about fifteen pounds heavier than I was a year ago, and I continued to put weight on. I looked great and had my TPN routine down. I would hook up around 7:00 at night, and the twelve-hour infusion would be done in time for me to go to work in the morning.

I met with my new doctor, and he reviewed everything I had gone over with Tricia. I walked away with the small book about short bowel syndrome and felt a sense of optimism despite having a new disease to add to my resume.

I started Humira, another immunosuppressant like Remicade, except it was a biweekly shot I would give myself at home. Eight months later, I would start Gattex, the short bowel syndrome drug. Like my grandfather, I would give myself a shot every morning. It reduced my need for TPN, but I could never come off of it completely. Every night I would either do a TPN infusion or give myself a liter of IV fluid for hydration. My PICC line lasted for another year until I opted for a port in my chest. I was taught how to access and de-access the port at home by myself, which allows me to feel a little more human by being able to swim in the summer and on vacations with the boys. Nicole put together a table for all of my health care supplies in our bedroom for my TPN. It was a mini-nurses' station with bins for flushes, tubing, and port supplies. I hooked up to my infusion at night, disconnected in the morning, gave myself a shot of Gattex, and carried on my life as normally as I could.

My next appointment at the Brigham that day was with Diane.

"What a refreshing appointment this is going to be," I said to her as she got the room ready. "Just a regular appliance change today, nothing too exciting."

She started talking, ignoring my banter. "You know, Brad, Mary and I were talking about you this morning." Mary was one of the other ostomy and wound-care nurses that Diane worked with. These women were seasoned professionals at wound care, not only because they had been in that role for so long, but because the Brigham was a lightning rod for all of the worst cases.

"I told Mary that you were coming in today, and we started talking about you. We both agreed that you are the only person who could have survived what you went through."

Now she had my attention. This was the first time that anyone had said that to me.

"I've always known you to be an independent and hopeful patient. But you were so driven to get out of the hospital and home to that family of yours. To actually get home. That saved you. You taught your-self to do everything. Anyone else would have been sent to a rehab center for the summer, and have nurses take care of them. I'm not saying that rehabs aren't great for many patients with certain ailments, but it probably would have killed you. Rehabs just aren't as clean as hospitals. They're full of other people's germs. The weak condition your body was in when you left the hospital"—she paused—"you never would have made it. Your home, on the other hand, was a clean envi-ronment for your body to heal. And you were determined to get home to Nicole and those boys. That saved you. That's what Mary and I were talking about. Ninety-nine out of a hundred patients wouldn't have survived what you went through, Brad. But you were the one that did."

I sat quietly for a moment, taking in what Diane was saying. Though I had been teetering on the edge of bad things, no one had explicitly told me how lucky I was to survive. I had been in denial about being severely sick throughout the whole ordeal. I was just trying to get back to my regular life.

"Sure," I said, "but I also couldn't have gone home without you. You were always on-call for me. Email. Phone calls. Appointments when I needed them. There was that time that you gave me your home phone number, too."

"Well, maybe we make a good team. It's funny, at the beginning of this Dr. Boyle was skeptical about the communication issues, but I think you've changed his mind about technology."

"Well, that's Nicole with her spreadsheet of my I's and O's."

"Yes, and the photos of your wound that you would email."

"Yeah, I guess so."

We went through the rest of our appointment, which was pleas-antly uneventful. My life was pretty much back to normal, or normal for me. I was back at work full time and had a manageable stomach.

"Well, thank you for telling me about the conversation with

Mary," I said as we were wrapping up. "I think I needed to hear that perspective."

"You're welcome. Say hello to Nicole for me."

I made a two-month follow-up, put on my black puffer coat, and headed out of the office.

The lobby downstairs has always been bustling with life. A vast atrium of natural light shines down on doctors, nurses, and hospital staff. Patients and loved ones. You almost always see a new mother in a wheelchair with a newborn baby, waiting for the new father to bring the car around. Next to this new life is old life. A crowd of elderly patients paired with their middle-aged sons or daughters wait watchfully for the valet to pull up with their cars. People come in and out of the revolving doors, wait in line at the food stand, or commute from one end to the other. Next to the main door sits a grand piano, and sometimes they have a pianist playing it, laying down a soundtrack to it all. Today was one of those days.

A woman was playing a song that sounded familiar, but I couldn't place what it was. Beautiful though. I replayed Diane's story in my head. I shouldn't be here. No one had ever said that to me before. Not surviving wasn't ever a possibility.

I walked to the elevator bank for the parking garage and pushed the down arrow. As I waited, I turned around and watched the woman play the piano. The elevator was taking forever, and other people began to gather around me, waiting, but I was lost in the moment, listening to this woman play this song that I couldn't quite put my finger on. The song didn't matter, I told myself.

I've always wanted to learn to play the piano, similar to how I'd learned to play the guitar when I was in college. If ever there was a sign to start taking lessons, this was it. I just stood there, totally immersed, waiting for that elevator. Tears creeping into my eyes. I was not only alive, but thriving once again. I wasn't in the hospital anymore, I was home with Nicole and the boys. I was back at work among the healthy. I was back.

The doors finally slid open, and people filed in. As the elevator car pulled us down to the garage, away from the lobby, the sound of the piano diminished.

I've spent a lot of time over the years wondering what my life would be like if I didn't have this lemon of a belly. In my younger years, I would fantasize about a healthy body and imagine how free I would feel. What would that be like? Healthy people have no idea how good they have it, but I know they can't help it either.

Maybe I'm wrong to think that, though. Crohn's has quietly been teaching me all along. It's given me this wonderful thing that I never considered until after I'd endured my health crisis in 2014. It's taught me to appreciate my life. Most people live healthy lives for six or seven or eight decades before their health declines. My health timeline since age ten looked more like an EKG report. Peaks and valleys. Disease and remission. You can't appreciate one without the other. Remission is bliss the same way my fellow New Englanders enjoy the summertime. You enjoy those warm months partly because someday soon the leaves will change, and the air will become cold. It will be winter again, and the cycle will repeat. It's chronic, and just like Crohn's it never ends.

It's like that day in May when I got home from the hospital and I began appreciating the tiny parts of life, like washing my hands, and smelling food cooking, and feeling the sun beat down on my skin. There are small joys everywhere, all you have to do is slow down and pay attention.

Since then, moments at home with my family have become sacred. If things hadn't turned out this way, I wouldn't be here experiencing them. My heart warms every time the boys call me Dad. I go into their rooms at night and watch them breathe as they sleep and I'm thankful that they're healthy. I tell my family I love them all the time and I mean it. When Nicole hugs me I feel the same way. I'm constantly filled with joy for a life I'm grateful to still have.

And so, the day after I heard that piano playing in the lobby of the Brigham, I went into town and signed up for piano lessons. A new art form for the next leg of my race.

Like I said, I was back.

ACKNOWLEDGMENTS

In a way, this project began with an Acknowledgments section. I remember the exact moment after finishing Michael Ausiello's fantastic memoir titled *Spoiler Alert: The Hero Dies*. He began his acknowledgments by thanking his writing coach at WriteByNight. My index finger touched that phrase and I said out loud, "that's what I need." Having worked in marketing agencies for most of my career, nothing gets done without a deadline. WriteByNight gave me the framework I needed to write chapter after chapter.

To Resa Alboher, my writing coach at WriteByNight, for being the creative writing teacher I never had, the cheerleader for each chapter, and as it turned out a fellow veteran patient. To John Sibley Williams at WriteByNight for setting me up for success in the publishing world.

Thank you to my mother for letting me give the eulogy at my grandmother's funeral in 2001, which was the first piece of creative writing I've ever been proud of. To my grandfather who once told me that you could fill a book with the stories you amass in your lifetime. I did it, Gramp.

To everyone at Shire and Takeda who invited me to share my health journey as a patient speaker. Those talks shaped this book and made it clear that people connected with my story.

To Angel Micarelli and Sean Maher for reading drafts and giving notes and encouragement. To all of the friends, family members and healthcare professionals who read my manuscript and offered their support.

And special thanks to my wife Nicole for being the first fan of my writing, the Editor in Chief for this memoir, and just for being a real neat lady. You're my favorite, Meesh.

ABOUT THE AUTHOR

As a thirty-five year veteran of Crohn's disease, Brad Harris has inspired thousands by sharing stories of his health journey with audiences at Crohn's and Colitis Foundation of America events and private speaking engagements. He has lived in Massachusetts his whole life, where he currently resides with his wife Nicole, their two boys, and their mini schnauzer. At the publication of this book his Crohn's is still in remission.

For updates and author information please visit:
lemon-belly.com

Made in the USA
Las Vegas, NV
06 July 2022

51173449R00218